THE PRIMACY OF THE INDIVIDUAL IN PSYCHOANALYSIS IN GROUPS

Alexander Wolf, M.D.
Irwin L. Kutash, Ph.D.
Candice Nattland, Psy.D.

JASON ARONSON INC.
Northvale, New Jersey
London

Production Editor: Judith D. Cohen

This book is set in 11 point Palacio by Lind Graphics of Upper Saddle River, New Jersey, and printed and bound by Haddon Craftsmen of Scranton, Pennsylvania.

Library of Congress Cataloging-in-Publication Data

Wolf, Alexander, 1907-
    The primacy of the individual in psychoanalysis in groups /
Alexander Wolf, Irwin L. Kutash, Candice Nattland.
        p. cm.
    Includes bibliographical references and index.
    ISBN 0-87668-548-3
    1. Group psychotherapy. 2. Psychoanalysis. I. Kutash, Irwin L.
II. Nattland, Candice. III. Title.
    [DNLM: 1. Group Processes. 2. Psychoanalytic Therapy.
3. Psychotherapy, Group.   WM 430 W853pa]
RC488.W59 1991
616.89'152 — dc20
DNLM/DLC
for Library of Congress   90-14537

Manufactured in the United States of America. Jason Aronson Inc. offers books and cassettes. For information and catalog write to Jason Aronson Inc., 230 Livingston Street, Northvale, New Jersey 07647.

dedicated to those patients

who have found their authentic selves

in psychoanalysis in groups

Contents

PART III   APPLICATIONS

About the Authors

Alexander Wolf, M.D. is in the private practice of psychotherapy and psychoanalysis in New York City. He is Dean
Emeritus and Director of the Training Program in Analytic Group
Therapy at The Contemporary Center for Advanced Psychoanalytic Studies in New Jersey. He is also a senior supervisor,
training psychoanalyst, and faculty member of the Contemporary
Center for Advanced Psychoanalytic Studies and of the Postgraduate Center for Mental Health. For twenty-five years he was an
associate clinical professor of psychiatry at the New York Medical
College, and a training analyst, supervisor, and faculty member
in the psychoanalytic division there. He received his M.D. in 1932
from Cornell University. Dr. Wolf originated the practice of
psychoanalysis in groups in 1938. In 1957, he received the Adolph
Meyer award from the Association for Improvement in Mental
Health "for his contributions to psychoanalysis in groups," and in
1963 he received the first Wilfred C. Hulse Memorial Award from
the Eastern Group Psychotherapy Society for outstanding contributions to the practice of group therapy. Dr. Wolf received the
Distinguished Writer's Award of the New York Center for Psychoanalytic Training in 1985, and he is a distinguished fellow of
the American Group Psychotherapy Association.

Irwin L. Kutash, Ph.D., is in the private practice of psychotherapy and psychoanalysis in Livingston, New Jersey. He is the Dean of The Contemporary Center for Advanced Psychoanalytic Studies in New Jersey and Director of the Institute's Analytic Training Program in Adult Psychoanalysis and Psychotherapy, where he is a training psychoanalyst and senior supervisor. He is also a field supervisor at the Graduate School of Applied and Professional Psychology of Rutgers University. Dr. Kutash received his Ph.D. in clinical psychology in 1972 from the Institute of Advanced Psychological Studies of Adelphi University and holds a postdoctoral certificate in psychotherapy and psychoanalysis from the Postgraduate Center for Mental Health, where he received a ten-year service award in 1982. He also holds a diplomate in clinical psychology from the American Board of Professional Psychology.

Dr. Kutash served as president of the Society of Psychologists in Private Practice in New Jersey, as president of the New Jersey Academy of Psychology, and as a board member of the New Jersey Association for the Advancement of Psychology and of the New Jersey Psychological Association. Dr. Kutash is past president of the section on group psychotherapy of the psychotherapy division of the American Psychological Association. He received the Distinguished Writer's Award of the New York Center for Psychoanalytic Training in 1988.

Candice Nattland, Psy.D., is in the private practice of psychotherapy in Montclair, New Jersey. She received her Psy.D. in 1984 from The Graduate School of Applied and Professional Psychology, Rutgers University and her M.Ed. in 1978 from Bank Street College of Education. Dr. Nattland is a candidate for certification in psychotherapy and psychoanalysis at The Contemporary Center for Advanced Psychoanalytic Studies in New Jersey. She is the Membership Chairperson of the Division of Group Psychology and Group Psychotherapy of the American Psychological Association.

Foreword

The timing of the present volume with its emphasis on individuality could not be more germane. Individuality is currently being replaced by pop conformity on one end of the continuum and pseudo-individuality on the other. We see this manifest in the media, in the social, economic, political, and cultural aspects of our society, and we see it of course in the present theory and practice of psychotherapy. Talk shows on television, for example, are capable of taking a valuable, useful concept (i.e., co-dependency) and turning it into the word of the week. The idea of *victim* has been so exploited by the news media that it sometimes becomes difficult to know who or what a victim is. Young people today are afraid to marry amid dire warnings of divorce statistics, faltering economic trends, or an ecology on the verge of self-destruction. Years ago a person in the street carried with him the internal feeling of safety that if in trouble his neighbor a few yards away would protect and rescue him; today fear and isolation reign, with the anticipation that his neighbor will ignore him or actually exploit or hurt him. This is especially true in large urban areas where people are massed together.

In groups, people are also massed together. Does a group member need to fear that he or she will be ignored or emotionally

injured by a group-mate or herded into the group structure and
mores either overtly or subtly by the leader or leadership style?
Heinz Kohut, the great psychoanalytic pioneer and founder of
self psychology, told me in a private conversation about his fears
of group therapy. He grew up in a time when the Nazis were
gaining power, not only through military tactics, but through
psychological coercion and group bandwagoning. Kohut was
concerned about the possibility of a loss of individuality in group
and the possibility of social pressure coercing members like herds
of cattle. He was further concerned about possibility of the
charismatic leader using the group for his own power and
interests, which becomes even more dangerous when his unconscious is at play. Kohut, however, had no idea about the benefits
of group, never having been a leader or member of psychoanalytic group therapy.

Alexander Wolf is a master of group psychoanalysis par
excellence. He is the exemplary group leader as a clinician,
teacher, supervisor, theoretician, and writer. He is a man of
extraordinary humaneness, kindness, warmth, and brilliance.
His clarity of communication, stated simply yet profoundly, is
reflected in this current volume. One doesn't have to reach very
far to perceive how this reflects in his personage as group
psychoanalyst. I am not personally as well acquainted with the
other authors, but I know and fully respect Irwin L. Kutash's
psychoanalytic thinking regarding group therapy.

Alexander Wolf and his colleague Emmanuel K. Schwartz were
major pioneers and founders of psychoanalysis conducted in
groups. Their 1962 book, *Psychoanalysis in Groups*, is the bible of
group psychoanalysis and the primary textbook for training in
this area. Hundreds of articles, papers, and books have followed
since then. Schwartz's untimely death has not, fortunately for us,
diminished Wolf's unbelievable productivity. His recent collaboration with Irwin L. Kutash, whose psychoanalytic thinking
regarding group therapy is much respected throughout the
psychoanalytic community, further adds to the clear, creative and
comprehensive thinking and organization present in *The Primacy
of the Individual in Psychoanalysis in Groups*.

This current volume is valuable, virtually necessary, for both
novices and experienced group psychoanalysts. It touches on

almost every conceivable aspect of group psychoanalysis and it goes into great depth as well. It is a primer and a handbook, but it also carries a cogent, well-defined point of view. It is full of basic facts containing all of the how-to's and the thinking and reasoning behind them, but the authors never lose their focus and point of view regarding the crucial importance of maintaining the *individual* in the group. One can use this book to learn about group, to start a group, to conduct a group, to teach about group, or to further one's theoretical thinking. It contains everything a therapist would want to know plus a great deal more. It is clear, informative, comprehensive, and extremely well organized.

The authors concentrate on the submerged personality, which is essentially the condition in which the ego has been suppressed and there is a failing in the individual's expressiveness, uniqueness, and creativity. On page 254 Wolf and Kutash state "The submerged personality needs to hear his or her internal messages, with the therapist alongside, and not those of any dogmatic or despotic other." This defines empathic listening so that the emergence of the self can occur. There has been a recent surge in the field of group psychotherapy to push group process and group-as-a-whole thinking. No doubt there are accurate generalizations one can make regarding the course of group events, but the entire purpose of the group should be to facilitate individual growth and development—nothing more. The authors' pertinent refrain is that the whole is *less* than the sum of its parts. One can recount case after case of a leader making a group interpretation thereby inhibiting the analytic development of an individual. As the authors well point out, the dangers are of an individual's either submitting to a group norm, or rebelling against it, leading to discordant relating—both extremely negative outcomes. The aim of good group therapy should be to allow and promote the emergence of the deepest self, to have that self accepted and be made acceptable, and to use all that as the foundation of relating to oneself, others, and the world. The group arena is the optimal catalyst for the emergence of the self to occur. Of course the group has a process and personality of its own, but the constant emphasis on these aspects can and will obscure the individual.

The authors correctly point out the dangers of a false or

premature cohesion. Some examples might be "Today we should all be 'lovey-dovey' to each other" or a comment by a group leader to a group member, "Isn't it wonderful that today you were able to defer your own needs to help out Johnny; we are very intimate in here." This is a definite group pressure that can make it difficult for Mary, who may be having very unaffiliative feelings. The authors wisely discuss a "false group-ego." Winnicott of course considers this in his "false self" concept. The authors talk about the danger of burying a weak ego. They mention the risk of too much consensus and the concomitant pressures to conform.

I especially like their concept of group as creating a family with a new look. The authors clearly are attuned to attending to the insides and outsides of each family member. Their emphasis on group therapy as distinguished from individual therapy as an optimal means of resolving certain resistances also has great merit. In the chapter on "The Future," we see the ultimate optimism of the authors, and how difficult problems are solved in the group and translated to the individuals' outside lives. The emphasis on no gimmicks and the value of reason is particularly refreshing in today's sometimes chaotic and frightening world. This current volume will be a lasting and significant contribution to the theory and practice of group psychoanalysis and to its future directions and applications.

—Frederick Arensberg, Ph.D.

Preface

This book contains the basic principles of psychoanalysis in groups as developed by Alexander Wolf in the 1930s and updated to reflect the recent advances developed by the authors through the 1980s. It is also intended to challenge the group-as-a-whole approaches, which we feel are drowning the individual in homogeneity. The essential thesis of this book is that the individual ego is primary in or out of group.

The authors of this book are just as eager as the group-as-a-whole practitioners to create a climate in the therapeutic group that is supportive to the reconstructive treatment of the individual, but it has been our clinical experience that the most appropriate way to achieve this end is by sponsoring the individual growth of each member's creative ego. This does not mean that we conduct individual analysis in groups, but rather that we support interpersonal freedom of expression, of fantasy, association, thoughts, feelings, dreams, ideation, and the analysis and working through of transferences. This does not lead to narcissism but to the development of a realistic self-love and complementary appreciation of the expanding ego of the other.

The danger of trying to create a positive group climate by emphasizing group process or group-as-a-whole is that the psychoanalytic therapy of the individual tends to be neglected. But,

more importantly, emphasis on the group as-a-whole diegophre-
nogenically suppresses rather than promotes the emergence of
each member and produces submerged personality problems in
the participants with less freedom of choice for each patient. The
group-as-a-whole emphasis induces withdrawal by its deafness to
each member's difference with the group-as-a-whole or worse.
The individual is swallowed by the group, carried along by the
prevailing group process. The opposing mind retreats and suc-
cumbs or rebels. Group-as-a-whole is like the authoritarian dictatorship that professes to support the individual but in fact
mismanages and denies him freedom of expression. The bonds
imposed by group-as-a-whole produce a pseudocohesion
whereas such bonds can be loosened only by each valuing the
other's right to freedom of expression and candid opposition to
any group-as-a-whole tyranny. For it is only when the patient has
recovered, developed his own ego, that he is able to be friendly
enough to the other members to sponsor a complementary
process in them, complementary to his own or quite disparate.
Such a course allows each an individualized self that leads to a
genuine unity, not the pseudounity of catering to the group
process that tries to govern, control, restrain, and curtain him off.
The individual patient cannot unburden himself in an officially
imposed group process. He cannot in such an atmosphere come
up with his own responses and judgments. It is almost impossible
in a prevailing group-as-a-whole for him to see, hear, or think.

We have tried to make clear in this volume the importance of
recognizing how a group can be used to liberate each member's
creative ego, but that when misused it can impede the individual's struggle to liberate the self. It is our position that the gems
should not be lost in the tiara.

* * *

The majority of the material in this book is new or based on
revised and updated writings of Alexander Wolf and Irwin L.
Kutash with editing by Candice Nattland (see bibliography for
updated references). Chapter 3 is based on papers of Candice
Nattland and Chapter 9 is based on a work of Emanuel K.
Schwartz (deceased) and Alexander Wolf, with revision and
updating for this volume.

I

THE PRIMACY OF
THE INDIVIDUAL IN
THE GROUP

1

The Primacy of the Individual

There are forces at work within our society that contribute to preventing the development of autonomous egos, diminish our humanness, contribute to inhibition, and foster pseudohomogeneity. Examples include the crowding out of individual initiative, limitation of choices, over-mediaization, automation with its assembly-line mentality, and breaking down of family structure. For more ample coverage of the link between modern-day stresses and personality, see Kutash and Schlesinger (1980). It is clear that excessive individuation more and more is considered an illness in a heavily populated, group-oriented society. These same tendencies need to be resisted in therapy groups. The authors have observed automated groups, those in which group themes limited individual choices and in which transferences were ignored as if familial influence could be neglected. In other words, a person drowning in the homogeneity of modern-day society may find himself in a group, being videotaped and tape-recorded, expected to shift quickly to group values and to follow the externally imposed pace of group instead of evolving and unfolding as individual ego growth is fostered.

If the contention that present-day society is submerging the individual in homogeneity is accepted, it is not surprising, then, that a generation of group therapists raised in such a society should fashion group therapy approaches that can do the same thing. Therapy designed to cure a person from the ills of a sick family or sick society ought not to rely on joint group mood or consensus to influence and cure a sick member. The exploration and working through of the intrapsychic unconscious pathology of each individual member remains the most difficult but most valid goal of treatment. The group simply provides a more economical treatment setting, affords one the opportunity to develop relationships with peers as well as authority figures, and allows both intrapsychic and interpersonal processes to occur and brother-sister as well as mother-father transferences to develop and be analyzed.

In 1938, Alexander Wolf began psychoanalytic treatment in a group setting. In 1940, five groups of patients were in treatment, and now, over 50 years later, groups, being open-ended, are still being eagerly sought out and utilized. Psychoanalysis in groups, however, has been relegated by some of today's group-as-a-whole therapists to an historic role. This is unfortunate because this type of treatment, as shall be illustrated, is more relevant today than ever for some very important individual and societal reasons, most importantly because psychoanalysis in groups stresses individual differences and individuality as opposed to group process "healing." Individuality can lead to greater group cohesiveness than efforts toward homogeneity, since a person needs to appreciate himself before he can truly appreciate others.

The thrust of psychoanalysis in groups is that the creative growth of the individual ego is primary. Group psychotherapy is a misnomer for a technique that, while conducted in a group, is designed to aid the individual. It is the treatment of ailing individuals in a group setting, not treatment of ailing groups. Only individuals have egos, internalized object relations, introjected parents, or, for that matter, intrapsychic dynamics.

There are some group therapists who, when applying the theories of Bion, Ezriel, Foulkes, Scheidlinger, or Erickson, deny the distinction between individual and social psychology and see psychopathology in the network of the interaction as opposed to the individual or as an intrapsychic disturbance. The loss of the individual in the group, in the Gestalt, in group concept, in the group-as-a-whole, is a rejection of intrapsychic psychopathology and health. It is a nondiscriminatory effacement of the individual to the point where he may vanish in fusion with the group. These practitioners profess to therapeutize a group and ignore the primary obligation of psychoanalysis—treating the individual, either on a one-to-one basis or in the interactive contact of a group. They abandon the exploration of personal psychodynamics, suggesting we trust the group rather than the individual, a thing rather than a person, the mass rather than the man. Their beginning assumption, that group process is the transposition of individual intrapsychic states into group-level conflict states, is flawed. Not accepting this means believing that all that is built on it does not follow. Scheidlinger's (1980) statements such as, "to belong to . . . a group also implies a more or less transitory giving up of some aspect of the individual's self to the group-as-a-group" (p. 220) or "in the individual's sense of belonging, in his feeling so at one with the perceived group entity . . . it is theoretically not possible to speak of an ego identity apart from group identity" (p. 220), in our eyes, show the group when misused can put into play within itself the forces in present-day society that are endeavoring to squelch individuality.

Group therapists should help build nonnarcissistic egos in patients by working through each individual's tendency to submit to the group process, a tendency that we see as pathology in the patient or an inappropriate emphasis on the part of the therapist. Scheidlinger does go on to suggest that every item of group behavior be viewed as the behavior of individual personalities in a special process of social and emotional interaction. This advances the thinking of the earlier group dynamicists closer to where psychoanalysis in groups began in 1938. We are glad the circle is coming back toward our fundamental belief: the individual ego is primary in or out of group.

Group-as-a-whole approaches utilizing such techniques as consensual validation can exert strong influences on group members toward conformity or uniformity of thinking, feeling, and behavior. The acceptance of group uniformity can only manifestly satisfy the needs of those who have always felt different and isolated and frustrates the more basic need for independent egos.

This conflict between individuation and the need for a sense of inclusion is engendered by group approaches with group goals as opposed to group approaches with the aim of fostering individuality and a sense of differentiated identity. In the latter approach, each person discovers his own goals, which prove mutually beneficial to complementary difference. The primary purpose of psychoanalysis in groups is psychoanalysis of the individual within a group. The group leader must protect the members with weaker egos from the danger of incorporation by the group-as-a-whole for successful psychoanalysis within the group. We do not ignore the usefulness of wholesome commonalities, but imposing group-as-a-whole interpretations too artificially can submerge the individual ego. That one interpretation can fit eight individual egos is absurdly impossible.

The Talmud advises that if someone says you are drunk, you can shrug your shoulders. If two persons say you are drunk, stop and listen. But if three say you are drunk, lie down. These and similar stories have been used to illustrate the powerful positive influence of consensual validation that can occur in a group setting. The authors would see this as an illustration as well of a danger in the group process. What if these people say the individual is drunk and he is not? The weak ego is further buried. A more valuable experience may occur when an individual correctly tells other group members that they are mistaken and when the individual is in touch with his internal experience and has the strength to withstand the consensus and even the leader's opinion. The group, rather than suppressing the ego, at times with a short-term behavioral gain, has provided the laboratory for the individual to acquire ego strength. This has been observed by one of us (see Wolf 1980) to be a quality of creativity: freedom from the tyranny of the homogenized consensus. In some cases, a group can be a composite of eight weak egos supporting each other to survive but unfortunately not to grow. This has been termed *malequilibrium* in group by one of us (Kutash 1980) and will be discussed further in Part II.

An example of group atmosphere in which individuality is cherished over consensus is illustrated in the following case. A group member was offered a new job in another state and asked the group what to do. Each member in his own way told him to trust himself, not to listen to parents, bosses, or even the group but to discover what *he* wanted to do, separate from complying or rebelling against others. This patient then analyzed the situation independent of his struggle with introjected parents and moved forward on his road to recovery. This encouraged the others to trust their own egos. The group atmosphere was such that the members did not feel compelled to arrive at a consensus that might have overwhelmed the individual ego involved.

E. James Anthony (1971) wrote that just as "the superego is soluble in alcohol, it's also soluble—as LeBon, McDougall and Freud pointed out—in the ecstasies occasioned by close group interaction. But there is always a hangover when reality once again asserts itself" (p. 29). To this we would add the further warning: the ego may be equally vulnerable. The weaker the ego, the more suppressed it is in homogeneous group responses. While acknowledging that, at best, there are some positives in homogeneous group responses, and although it is valuable when patients relate to each other positively and support one another's weak egos, such mental sustenance should not be confused with psychoanalytic treatment. Furthermore, in some group-as-a-whole approaches lies potential for ego damage when the leader does not analyze peer pressure. Psychoanalysis in groups makes the claim that the whole is less than the sum of the parts but only because the parts are so very precious. In the rare event that the manifest affect of the group members is similar, this can be comforting to patients but does not replace analyzing the latent differences in what this external mood represents. This can happen in the first session of a new group, for example, when anxiety is the most manifest symptom.

Wherever there is weakness of the ego, whether in the schizophrenic, the borderline, the submerged personality (Wolf and Kutash 1991), the psychopath, the impulsive patient, or the hypnotic subject, there is a tendency to be swept along by the other or the seeming other homogenized as the group. Perhaps this is true in cults or gangland phenomena where the members act out the aggressive and irrational demands of the leaders. To the degree to which a person has ego strength he will be able to value his own perceptions, judgment, and constructive uniqueness, and pursue his own line against the domination of other egos. To the extent the therapist emphasizes the group-as-a-whole formulation he underlines the *we* of the group, he fosters submerged ego problems. By denying personal aspirations, ego resources are weakened, and submerged personality pathology is cultivated.

If, in the therapeutic group, the patients move toward the expression of themes, the therapist is overvaluing homogeneity and denying individual differences. It is in the nature of human beings to be diverse as nature is diverse. Allowing a group theme to prevail is not unlike the situation in some pathogenic families where the child must conform to the parental demands, values, and ways of behaving. Such a point of view does not fit the analytic conception of individually differentiated psychodynamics and psychopathology.

The therapist working with patients in groups might then inquire, what is the correct therapeutic handling of group-as-a-whole manifestations such as themes? We would respond that if the therapist sees a group trend or theme developing, he ought to test it by exploring the patients individual by individual, to see whether he has been deceived by manifest conformity and missed the latent diversity. If the therapist will regard such themes as manifest and explore each individual's latent reactions, he will be able to penetrate the manifest content, generally resistive. To encourage the theme is to encourage the resistance, homogeneity, conformity, pathology, and the denial of individual differences. It emphasizes a closed rather than an open environment, an illusion of cohesion rather than the reality of cooperation, an overly-controlled climate rather than a liberating one. By analyzing the individual in interaction with other individuals in the presence of still others, including the therapist, the analyst fosters morale, cohesion, constructive heterogeneity, and complementarity of values, in short, the primacy of the individual.

2

Kinds of Groups

Group therapy began at the turn of the century, but its psychoanalytic form appeared in the 1930s in a period of economic depression that promoted a variety of collective endeavors. During World War II, the need for treatment was so great that group therapy spread rapidly. Since then, many kinds of treatment in groups have been developed.

INDIVIDUAL AND GROUP THERAPY: A CONTRAST

The therapist who treats patients individually is inclined to dismiss the group method as if it cannot be a deeply reconstructive technique. He tends also to be more concealed and less subjectively involved with the patient than group members and the group leader are. As a result, the patient treated individually may become less active, more withdrawn, insulated, and fixed on his subjective psychic processes rather than on his relations with others. The therapist of individuals may challenge the notion that his commitments, qualities, and preferences elicit particular reactions in the patient. The group therapist, however, learns from his group experience that his values, his characteristics, and his choices, like those of other group members, provoke specific responses in each patient.

The individual therapist does not have the opportunity in the one-to-one relationship to get a many-sided view of the patient. He cannot see the protean reactions incited by the group members. He does not actually see the patient's responses to people outside the consulting room on whom he projects his original family. Nor does he see the patient's wholesome reactions in his coping mechanisms in the group. As a result, the therapist may misperceive his patient as more or less limited and more or less adequate than he is in fact. In the group, each member is called upon to render emotional sustenance or understanding on occasion to a needy other. This is a role unavailable to him in individual therapy. His behavior in the group displays an unrevealed aspect of his personality, a discerning, knowledgeable, and helpful quality, hitherto undisclosed. This facet in him promotes group solidarity, group cohesion, and is multilaterally ego building. This health-giving interrelatedness among the members is not at hand in individual treatment.

In one-to-one therapy, the patient is generally handicapped in attempts to assert himself in the face of the over-invested therapist. Group members, however, support one another in coping with the authority-laden group leader. The individual therapist can more readily govern one member at a time than he can a number of them gathered together. They support each other to ventilate thoughts and feelings about him less easily expressed when with him alone.

NOVEL DIMENSIONS PROVIDED BY THE GROUP

Several new vistas open up in the course of experiencing group therapy. These are provided by the structure of the group and are not available to the individual therapist and his patient.

One of them is the presence of *authorities and peers* in the group. These are both real and transferential. The therapist, for example, is an accountable expert and a projected parent. Patients experience one another as peers in fact and transferential elders and peers in fantasy.

Another dimension provided by the group is the phenomenon of *multiple reactivities,* in which the members respond to the leader and to one another in normal and distorted ways. They misperceive each other in transferences, identifications, and so forth. Multiple stimulation engages the withdrawn and silent members. Not infrequently, patients will try compulsively to fulfill each other's archaic needs. At such times, it becomes necessary for the leader to analyze the inappropriateness of such engagements.

A third dimension provided by the group is *intrapsychic and interpersonal communication.* The intrapsychic experience emphasizes insight into oneself and ends in personal integration. Individual treatment is often more of an intrapsychic revelation and struggle. Group therapy is more of an interpersonal enlightenment and exertion. But, carefully led, each can in the main overcome the limitations of its setting. In one-to-one therapy, treatment generally moves from the intrapsychic to the interpersonal: in group therapy, from the interpersonal to the intrapsychic.

Fourth is the dimension of *forced interaction.* Most patients hesitate to show themselves in the presence of others. They find it difficult, particularly when they feel pressure is being exerted for the sake of a collective goal. But members will not generally let others sit silently for too long before insisting that they contribute. More active members will insist that those who do not speak at least explain why interacting in the group is so difficult for them. The insistence by peers that everyone contribute can chip away at a patient's refusal to speak especially when silence represents a resistance.

Fifth is the dimension of *shifting attention,* which challenges and helps to work through the anticipation of the member without siblings that he alone is entitled to the group's consideration. The group makes him face the reality that others exist too, require being heard, and deserve some attention. It may be the patient who was favored or unfavored in the nuclear family who tries in the therapeutic group to shut out his projected siblings. This stratagem is less obvious in individual therapy, in which there is little need to compete for the therapist's attention. In the group, the center of observation moves from one member to another. No one totally appropriates the therapist's and the group's observation. The shifting attention gives each patient a chance to consider the disclosures suggested to him. Others appreciate a respite from being the subject of inquiry. Still others resistively try to escape such examination in order to preserve their illness and not face the anxiety evoked by the struggle to change.

Sixth is the dimension of *alternating roles*. Each member both seeks to be helped and offers help. He is server and served. He ministers to and is dependent upon. He gives and receives. His roles are expanded, multiplied by new kinds of expectations, experiences, and activities. This moment he is trying to make sense of what others are saying. Before long they are trying to fathom him. Just before he was responding impromptu. Now he is reflectively examining what was at this moment offered to him as a segment of insight.

ANALYTIC AND NONANALYTIC GROUP THERAPY: A COMPARISON

There are relative but not absolute differences between analytic and nonanalytic group therapy. The nonanalytic group therapist is more likely to deal with the group-as-a-whole and to make group interpretations, whereas the analyst in groups is more regardful of the subjective unconscious motivation of each member. The nonanalytic group therapist is more committed to the here-and-now, but the group analyst is just as alive to the there-and-then, its unwelcome perseverance, and the meaning of its resolution. The nonanalytic group therapist tends to form homogeneous groups and to treat the members like a homogenized patient, whereas the group analyst leans to the formation of heterogeneous groups and to providing the unique treatment each patient requires. The nonanalytic group therapist searches for uniformity among the members so that accommodation, compliance, and submission are the results of treatment, whereas the group analyst looks for diversity among them, so that perceptivity in depth, personal differences, and individual privilege are some of the therapeutic gains. The nonanalytic group therapist concentrates on the overt conduct of the patient, whereas the group analyst attends to the hidden, the subjective, the unconscious. As a consequence, the nonanalytic group therapist elicits less anxiety, whereas the analyst of a group of patients evokes more.

In nonanalytic group therapy, the patient often reproduces his surrender to the nuclear family's demand that he capitulate to overprotective command, that he suppress his ego once more, and that he remain undifferentiated from his neighbors. In contrast, analysis in a group enables the patient to understand how he relinquished his ego to a dominating parent in the past and how to resist doing so to the parental surrogate in the group in the present. The analytic group encourages the flowering, the emergence of his repressed ego, his unique resources, his singular and distinguishing differences.

INDIVIDUAL, INTERPERSONAL, AND GROUP-AS-A-WHOLE APPROACHES: A CONTRAST

These three models can be conceptualized as follows:

Model: Group-as-a-Whole
Agent of Change: attention to group qua group phenomena; individuals change by applying total group process comments to themselves.
Use of Individual Dynamics: ignored (Bion) or relegated to a secondary role (Foulkes).

Model: Interpersonal Process
Agent of Change: attention to interpersonal phenomena; individuals change by exposure to curative factors developed within the group context.
Use of Dynamics: group dynamics and individual dynamics interpreted.

Model: Psychoanalysis in Groups

Agent of Change: attention to intrapsychic phenomena; individuals change by becoming aware of their unconscious wishes,
fears.

Use of Dynamics: Individual dynamics emphasized; group dynamics are recognized but are addressed only when they
become impediments to individual ego growth.

Therapists working in a group-as-a-whole model believe that
the major or only task is to make interventions at the total group
process level. Bion (1959) hypothesized that the group functions
as either a work group or as one of three basic assumption
groups, that is, fight/flight, pairing, or dependent. He believed
that group process existed because individual intrapsychic conflict transposed into group-level conflict states. Bion's interpretations to group members were in terms of how the individual
related to the group. He assumed that each individual would
benefit from mass group process interpretations because they
could find some degree of relevance in these statements. They
could extract from what was said about the group and apply it to
themselves. This model proposes to help individuals by focusing,
not on individuals, but on the group as though the group had a
life of its own. It is unclear how treating a group might help
individuals in the group learn to differentiate themselves from the
group.

The basic difference between psychoanalysis in groups and
group-as-a-whole approaches has been termed a difference between dyadic psychoanalytic techniques and group-specific factors techniques. This is not the case. Psychoanalysis in groups is
an interactive technique involving eight to ten individuals with a
leader as a facilitator. Group-as-a-whole approaches are often
dyadic, or an interaction between a leader and a projectively
homogenized "group ego." The true difference is that the indi-
vidual-within-the-group approach focuses on understanding intrapsychic dynamic patterns, with group interaction used to
facilitate insights leading to more wholesome ego development
and interpersonal relations. Group-as-a-whole approaches focus
on interactive patterns within the matrix of a group, believing in
their generalizability to a more fulfilling outside life. The ap-

proach of psychoanalysis in groups leads both to more pain and more pleasure in one's life outside the group as a person comes to know and appreciate himself and others as individuals, whereas the latter facilitates more comfort while decreasing the possibility of these emotional peaks and valleys. The choice becomes philosophical as well as judgmental. Does therapy aim to help the person be himself or fit in as its priority? If these are the choices in emphasis, the patient should be aware of them before treatment begins.

Furthermore, a sharp distinction needs to be made between the therapist's recognition of group trends, the enrichment of his knowledge of the group as a group, and his activity as a therapist for patients who constitute the group. There are various kinds of groups, therapy groups and groups of a nontherapeutic nature. One may then use the group in order to study group process or to accomplish other purposes such as education. Or one may use the group therapeutically. If we focus our attention on group-as-a-whole processes, we cannot also at the same time easily attend diagnosis, psychopathology, individual psychodynamics, dream analysis, resistance, transference and countertransference reactions, provocative roles, multiple reactivities, and other relevant parameters. Concentration on group process can become a way of anthropomorphizing the group, while rationalizing that treatment equates with the elaboration of group-as-a-whole process.

The therapist is involved in a process of leveling when he expects a group to function as if it were a uniform group. Such obscuring of disparity applied to the family group would repudiate the reality of the difference between parent and child, between older and younger child, between girls and boys, between father and mother. Although the family may seem to function as a unit, it is unreal to view it as if it were constituted of mirror images within the family structure. These unlikenesses are rejected in the implication that there is a basic family dynamic, a family unity, which contains within it no place for independent motivation, personal history, variance in one's own reactions even to the same family traditions, structure, and heritage. The second child is not entering the same family as the first child or the third child. With each birth, the family becomes a new unit, in which a new fragment of history is added and a new generalized structure is developed. Each succeeding child must deal with the family as a changing family; its structure changes as distinguishable children are added to it.

A review of the literature and clinical experience demonstrates that there is no evidence that exclusive attention to the group-as-a-whole approach is useful to the understanding and treatment of the patient in a group setting. A positive group climate or group equilibrium (Kutash 1984) can be therapeutic, but what promotes individual ego development is the psychoanalytic treatment occurring within that climate. A group climate is the result of the interaction of unique individuals with their individual dynamics, but attending to group process is either doing a disservice to the individual egos involved or a projected group-as-a-whole transference by the therapist. The individual is the baby, group process at best is the bath water, cleansing for some, drowning to others, but healing to none. Healing takes more than cleansing the wound or defining the injury. Reconstructive analysis requires the treatment of the individual's psychopathology, not a group-as-a-whole dynamic or the therapist's projection of a dynamic upon the group.

An illustration of the approach of psychoanalysis in groups as contrasted with group-as-a-whole approaches follows (Nattland 1983, 1990).

On the night of the interaction to be analyzed, three members are absent and two members arrive late. This sequence of interactions was selected because it involves only three members and one leader. From the point of view of psychoanalysis in groups, even simple interactions involving few members rapidly tend to become complex.

A, a 55-year-old man seeking therapy for his bouts of depression that, according to his report, usually follow the breakup of brief extramarital affairs, begins to discuss the tactical aspects of leaving his wife. Since joining the group several weeks earlier, A has dominated each session with repetitive talk about his affairs and his depressions. He has resisted any attempt by group members to examine his behavior. B, a woman who compulsively offers support and advice, asks for details. A says he feels guilty and worried that he may become seriously depressed after moving out of the house. B tells A she is glad he is moving out on his wife because he "has been in turmoil for so long." She continues by giving him a great deal of support. Then she expresses her feeling that A has not yet dealt with the anger and jealousy he feels for a woman with whom he had been having an affair. A ignores this comment. The leader points out that A has ignored B's last statement. A snaps at the leader and B admits that she, too, "skirts around issues." The leader persists in trying to get A to examine why he doesn't listen to others. A becomes increasingly angry and tries to close the topic by sarcastically retorting, "I'm glad I know I don't listen." A short silence occurs. C, the third member present, a woman often frightened by intense emotion, has been silent throughout this interaction.

A therapist with a group-as-a-whole orientation might describe this interaction as characteristic of a basic assumption *fight/flight* group. The protagonist, A, is fleeing from B and alternately fleeing and fighting the leader's questions, which are designed to encourage him to reflect on his behavior. C has fled from the group by remaining silent. Other members have fled by being physically absent.

The therapist with an interpersonal process orientation might view this same interaction as an example of A confronting the leader and maneuvering to solidify his position in the group sociogram.

A therapist using a psychoanalysis-in-groups model would focus on each individual and allow other members to do the same in order to uncover unconscious elements of each individual's behavior as it becomes manifest in interpersonal interaction. The hypotheses that might run through a therapist's mind will be explored here in greater detail than in the preceding two models. Of course, the decision to actually interpret any of these in the group setting would be influenced by a complex array of factors.

A simplified illustration of psychoanalysis in groups with its multiple reactivities, multiple transferences, and neurotic distortions, and its attention to unconscious elements of each individual's behavior follows.

A was viewed by C as her irritating and overbearing father because of A's initial talkativeness and repetitiveness in the group. At the same time, A was seen as the giving, caring father always wished for by B. B experienced A's talkativeness as his attempt to connect with her out of concern and love. *B* hungered for this kind of contact and this appeared to underpin her compulsive advice and support-giving. *A* initially merged all the individuals in the group and felt as if the group were his overpowering mother whom he had to ward off by talking. When he eventually worked this through and became less overbearing, he began to relate to members of the group as individuals. Then each group member found himself examining *A*'s growth in terms of his own transference to him. *B*, for example, had to resolve how she could feel love and concern from someone who wasn't even relating to her individually, only as part of a group.

The task of the therapist conducting psychoanalysis-in-groups is to (1) allow each member to become self-reflective about the transference distortions he exhibits interpersonally, (2) to allow group members to respond to each other in their characteristically distorted manner, (3) allow group members as they reveal themselves to reflect and confront others on how and why they respond the way in which they do, and (4) interpret, when appropriate, the unconscious motivations behind specific interactions.

3

The Individual in the Group

$\mathbf{P}$henomena occur at all levels in a group. There is the potential for group-as-a-whole, group dynamic, and interpersonal events to occur simultaneously and in isolation. There is also an intrapsychic concomitant for each individual member of the group for every event in the group. For the purposes of this discussion, group is defined as from two to eight patients who agree to meet together with their therapist for a regularly scheduled session each week. The duration of the session is generally 90 minutes. The purpose of the group will determine both the level at which the therapist works and the kinds of interpretations that will be made. Educational groups and supportive therapy groups most often remain at the level of manifest content. Any group designed for the therapy of individual members must encompass all levels of group functioning with the ultimate work done at the intrapsychic level. This is because the individual and not the group seeks treatment. Groups do not exist in the way individuals do. Consciousness lies inside the skin of the individual, not inside abstract boundaries of a group. Groups cannot be conscious, only individuals. As an individual, a person can participate in an interpersonal dyad or a group dynamic or even turn himself over to a group-as-a-whole process. While interpretations at rare times must be made at these other levels, ultimately a person must come to know himself in terms of himself alone, and this requires interpretation at the intrapsychic level. Then the patient comes to understand his internal objects and their power.

Freud first spoke of the loss of the individual in the crowd in *Group Psychology and the Analysis of the Ego.* Kernberg (1980) explains the process whereby an individual can lose a part of himself in the group. "The projection of the ego ideal onto the idealized leader eliminates individual moral constraints as well as the higher functions of self-criticism and responsibility that are so importantly mediated by the super-ego" (p. 212). Thus, the individual in the group is exposed to a pull toward identity loss.

Group phenomena, when ascendant, can be disruptive to individuals seeking to learn about themselves. And yet, paradoxically, within the group an opportunity is provided for self-study that can, at times, surpass that provided by the individual therapy setting alone. The therapist must be constantly alert to group process and group-as-a-whole interactions or drifts in order to bring about the safe and appropriate environment for the individual to do his ever more intense intrapsychic work. The therapist must guard against identity losses or diffusions in the group in order to secure the ground for clear functioning interpersonally and intrapsychically. It would be inappropriate for a patient to reveal and explore himself at an intimate level without having first tested the leader and the group members over an extended time to determine whether the situation was free from injurious group process or group-as-a-whole motivations.

Kernberg (1980) points out that the regressive pull in groups is enormous and even normally highly mature people must be able to tolerate the isolation of standing alone to withstand the regressive pull group contains. Kernberg explains the regressive features of the small group in terms of internalized object relations that predate object constancy and the consolidation of the ego, superego, and id. "Group processes pose a basic threat to personal identity, linked to a proclivity in group situations for the activation of primitive object relations, primitive defensive operations and primitive aggression with predominantly pregenital features" (p. 212).

Some group therapists, by attending only to group-level phenomena and thus ignoring the unique internalized object relations of the individuals, intensify the regressive pull of the group. In attempting to cope with this, members can merge together. This masquerades as cohesiveness in some groups but is in fact a loss of the individuals' ego functions.

An example will illustrate the complex array of forces at work within a group and how group-as-a-whole interpretations, even in a well-functioning group of mature individuals, can be misapplied, in this case by a patient in the group to serve her own defensive purposes. This example also illustrates the complicated interplay between the individual and group forces and how individual group members and the therapist must remain centered within themselves for the group to remain a therapeutic experience.

The group was approximately 3 years old with six members. Over the course of many months, the therapist and group were observing and commenting on one aspect of one member's way of relating to the others in the group, which was experienced by each of them as her inability to take in what was being said to her by any of them, especially when the patient experienced the comments as a criticism. She admitted that this phenomenon occurred in her outside relationships as well, leaving her isolated and afraid that she would never have a satisfying intimate relationship. She was reluctant to explore this, but it began to predominate her interactions in group and therefore became unavoidable. Members repeatedly experienced it, reacted to it, explored their reactions to it, and began to demand that she do the same. Eventually everyone in the group insisted that she look at the particular way she refused to take what was being said seriously. Of course, each of the group members experienced what the patient was doing to him in his own way determined by his own internal object relations; however, each member could also see that the patient was ignoring other members as well as him. At one point, the patient made a group-as-a-whole interpretation that all the members had merged together and were scapegoating her because the therapist had a distorted countertransference reaction to her and had manipulated the group members into attacking her. Thus, in one sweep, she diminished each of the group members and the therapist as being incapable of independent thought and accused each member of losing himself to the group-as-a-whole dynamic of fleeing from the real issue, which she called the therapist's manipulation of the members into scapegoating her.

Certainly this is a possibility, especially in groups in which individuality is not valued and the therapist encourages group members to pressure one member to accept his interpretation about an issue. This is not what was occurring in this group, however. The genetic history, symptomatology, behavior in group, and behavior reported by the patient outside the group all supported the interpretation made by the therapist and various group members that this patient had distorted the occurrences in group to protect herself from examining an especially painful area of her life. At her accusation, each member consulted himself as honestly and scrupulously as possible for any evidence that there might be elements of truth in it. All of the group members felt they were reacting truthfully and individually even though they all happened to agree about what the one member was doing. There was enough good faith and cohesion in the group to allow this potentially divisive issue to resolve itself with every member growing during the process. The one member, after repeated confrontations by the therapist and individual members in the here-and-now each time she employed her strategy of ignoring comments, as well as her self-exploration of relationships outside the group, was eventually able to look at her behavior and analyze this persistent narcissistic defense. In addition, each individual member was forced to deal with the issue in terms of its impact on him. Over many months of work, one patient explored his fear of being overcome by a powerful force, another to deal with the anger about the enormous amount of time devoted to the patient; another member faced the frustration and sadness of having a parent who acted in similar ways.

To summarize from this example, the battle for the individual in therapy, be it in a group or in an individual setting, must be won in the field of the individual's own consciousness. The battle takes place in a field in which other levels of forces are operating. Thus, group-as-a-whole, group process, and interpersonal events occur, and these other levels cannot be ignored. Although the data they provide can be vital to the process, ultimately their pull must be dissipated to allow work at the individual level, because it is only there that internal change occurs.

According to Kernberg, Bion's basic-assumption groups constitute the basis for group reactions that *potentially* exist at all times, but are particularly activated when the task structure *work group* breaks down. This generally occurs to avoid aggression in the group. Thus, rather than experience aggression that can be constructive assertion and should not be connoted to mean simply hurtful or attacking behavior, individuals become lost, from themselves, within the group. It is the therapist's role to identify this process, as it is occurring, in an effort to unhook the group members from operating within the malevolent basic assumption and resume the work group task, which in group therapy is the analysis of the transferential material that emerges in the interactions in the group. This is the raw data of the group members' internal object relationships. In a well-functioning group of relatively mature individuals, despite the regressive pull of group forces as described above, these basic assumption states do not occur with frequency or regularity. When they do occur, they do not endure long because the state becomes the focus of attention and analysis.

An example follows that illustrates how a whole group interpretation served to unhook a group from acting out within what might be seen as a Bion flight/fight assumption. In doing so, the therapist refocuses the group on its task, a work group is re-formed, and the work proceeds. This example is taken from the same group as was discussed in the previous example. At one point, a new member was added. Each member expressed his ambivalence about the group's expansion and also his anger at the therapist for adding a new member. Members examined their anger at the therapist and discovered a variety of wishes and needs behind the anger. One member wanted the therapist to herself and hated the idea of sharing him with another member. Another member was furious at the therapist for selecting such a young person to enter the group for fear that he wouldn't be as sophisticated as the others. One member realized that, while initially angry for the disruption a new member might cause, she actually welcomed the addition, especially since the young man would provide an opportunity to explore new material stirred by his unique presence. When the new member was added to the group, each member found a great deal of fault with him. One felt he was not as old or as mature as the other members. Another that he was too quiet. Another that he was not serious enough. He withstood the members' criticisms calmly. After several weeks, the new member suggested that the group members change the way they normally entered the office at the start of the session to a way that would make it easier for the therapist to begin. He was attacked by every group member for his suggestion, accused of trying to be needlessly or even sycophantically helpful to the therapist and he was invited to examine his motives. The therapist asked each member to look at why this new member's suggestion was so provocative to them. He interpreted that the members were displacing their anger over the expansion of the group onto the safer target of the member himself rather than feel angry with the therapist. Each member examined the hypothesis and agreed in different ways and to different extents that it appeared to fit. The group-as-a-whole interpretation jolted the members from their unproductive acting out and turned them back to the task of understanding why they each might do this. One member talked of how she felt proud of being part of a senior group and felt diminished by such a young member. Another member recognized that she had transferred onto the new member a younger sibling of whom she felt envious. What turned the situation from a false assumption group-as-a-whole phenomenon into a moment of insight was the therapist's openness to a new idea without prejudice. By considering the minor procedural change proposed by a new member, he was modeling how the other members should consider raw data such as feedback on themselves. Once the therapist was clear on his take about the situation, he proposed to the group that they were acting from other motives than those they presented, that they should examine again their own motivations for questioning the new member's suggestion. The fancy explanations they were offering as to the new member's motivations might hide their own real motivation, which, it turned out, was anger at the therapist for bringing in a new member who seemed so like a baby and who threatened to be a drag on the group's good functioning. This is an excellent reason to be angry at a therapist potentially, but what the members did not do was to give the new member a chance to prove himself. Rather, they jumped on the opportunity to distort what he was doing.

While the group-as-a-whole interpretation was necessary to unhook the members from their unproductive battering of the new member, the pay dirt of therapy does not lie there but in what ensued after the work group re-formed, that is the exploration and understanding of the intrapsychic material that lay behind the behavior of each individual. The group-as-a-whole interpretation was not sufficient to accomplish this, but it was a necessary step in refocusing the members. In the long life of this group, these group-as-a-whole interpretations were seldom necessary, but, on the few occasions when they were used, the individual members had lost themselves to the regressive pull of the group and needed to be refocused.

When a therapist misinterprets or misapplies an interpretation from a group-as-a-whole perspective, particularly if there is no allowance in the group to challenge this and explore individual reactions, the results are confusing to the individual and divisive to the group's cohesiveness. The following example illustrates this.

A group of mental health professionals in postgraduate psychoanalytic training were meeting in a transference–countertransference supervision group. The class had been conducted as a group since the first meeting. After a presentation by one of the more seasoned clinicians in the group, the teacher/therapist interpreted the group's silence from a group-as-a-whole framework. He interpreted that the patient's pathology had affected each of the students in the same way that the presenter had been affected: the group was silent because they were frustrated just as the presenter had been frustrated in her attempt to be this patient's therapist. The teacher commented on the feeling of deadness and defeat in the room. One student objected and noted that she had several reactions to the case, including annoyance that the presenter repeatedly commented throughout her presentation that it was inadequate, in spite of the fact that the presentation was an excellent one. This comment was met with silence, which the teacher interpreted as group support for his original interpretation.

The dissenting student spoke no further nor did any other student, and the feeling of flatness in the room continued.

In this case, the group-as-a-whole interpretation appeared to have stifled movement in the group. At least one person felt it didn't apply, and this should have been explored, at the very least to ascertain how the others felt.

The task of the therapist who conducts psychoanalytic therapy in a group setting is complex and requires sophistication. The therapist must be thoroughly grounded in the functioning of the individual psyche and knowledgeable about the forces that may occur in groups as the individuals submit to the regressive forces inherent in the group situation. In fact, it is because of this that group therapy allows a person to explore himself in a different way than occurs reliably in individual psychoanalytic psychotherapy. The primary task is to analyze an individual's functioning as manifested in the interpersonal interactions that occur in the group setting. These interactions reflect the transferential relationships that develop based on the internal object relations of each group member. The multiple transferences that develop in the group as manifested in the repeated interactions observed by the therapist and group members provide the raw data to be analyzed. Data generated in the group setting can be even more persuasive and revealing than that produced in the individual setting because of the multiple transferences and reactivities in the group.

Groups in which group-as-a-whole phenomena occur frequently are groups in which intrapsychic material is not valued. Groups in which the therapist misinterprets group-as-a-whole phenomena frequently run the risk of becoming groups in which individuals comply mindlessly with a force they believe to be greater and outside of themselves. This kind of group does not enhance the development of the individual. Groups should not be conducted so that the individual becomes a good compliant group member. The goal of group therapy is not to create a good group, but to help the individuals alleviate the pain caused by their inner conflicts.

In groups in which the individual is not valued, when therapists ignore the intrapsychic dynamics of the group members, the patients learn to lump themselves together and begin to speak as though they are not unique. Members speak about themselves in general, applying platitudes and rules to their behavior.

The loss of individual identity and the misapplication of group-process dynamics is illustrated in the somewhat extreme example that follows.

A group of ten patients was being observed through a one-way mirror for supervision purposes. The observation group formed a group of its own. It consisted of eight graduate students and a supervisor. The patient group met daily as part of a partial hospitalization program. Among the adult members were two older adolescent boys. The group had been talking about loneliness for several sessions, but no one spoke of his own personal experience of it. No one dared to differentiate himself from the group; everyone remained at the safe level of complaining about an issue in general. At one point, an older woman with a history of hospitalizations for manic episodes stood and walked toward one of the adolescent boys who had begun to talk about being alone at the holidays. His body movement strongly suggested that he felt frightened by her approach. The therapist stated that the members would have to restrict themselves to communicating in words. The woman returned to her seat and stated that she wanted to hug the young man to make him feel better. The therapist asked the boy to articulate his feelings, but he said he was too embarrassed to do so. The group ended.

In the follow-up supervisory session, the supervisor faulted the therapist for interfering with the development of group cohesion. He felt it would have been therapeutic for the two members to embrace. The therapist felt the primary issue was how each of the group members, especially the two involved in the action, experienced what was happening at the moment. The boy felt frightened about the physical advance of the female patient much older than himself. The female patient, in the following session, talked about how she often felt taken advantage of by men. These seemed to be the first truly personal reactions articulated by any of the members. Here was the beginning of members working at the individual level.

Therapists working exclusively from a group-process frame of reference can submerge individual reactions in the name of cohesiveness. Even when everyone in a group agrees, every member agrees for his own individual reason, unless the members have relinquished their egos, merged with the others and lost themselves. In that case, the group is no longer therapeutic. Cohesiveness does not mean that members agree nor that individuals are no longer free to express their differences or confront one another with their different perceptions and understandings. A truly cohesive group develops when the individuals in the group have been allowed to become more differentiated from their internal objects so that they have the opportunity to know themselves and the capacity to stand alone if they choose to do so.

II

CLINICAL PRACTICE

4

Basic Principles

Psychoanalysis has had to endure many transitions during its evolution. We believe that Freud himself was farsighted enough to know that certain changes in form and techniques would have to be made as society changed. One of the good things about psychoanalysis is that in many instances it has been able to adapt to cultural change so that it could make some contribution to the society in which it operated. Where it has not, where it has remained rigid or flown off into irrationality, psychoanalysis has become the butt of humorists and a scapegoat for the bitter, the skeptical, and the disillusioned.

There are those who behave and write as if Freud were responsible for all the ills of the present world. There are those who take the equally unreasonable position that if one would just psychoanalyze everyone in the world, there would be no problems, no wars, no famines, no disasters—natural or manmade. And there are those diehards who would tell you that to strike out one word of Freudian text or change one iota of original analytic dogma would be tantamount to treason, if not heresy.

Although we are not the kind of people to run away from a good fight, we believe many of these battles are unworthy of us. To take extreme positions for one form of treatment as against or

31

totally excluding any other, and to hold that extreme position at all costs, does a disservice to patient, therapist, and discipline alike. We are content to be connected with a behavioral field that is flexible enough to meet the challenges presented by our rapidly changing society. This society is moving more and more toward group orientations, which presents a particular dilemma for modern man. His struggle to adjust to complex organizational demands and yet retain some measure of his individuality and his agony as he finds himself enmeshed in increasingly threatening clashes between Goliaths are bound to have their effects on the emotional problems presented in therapy today. And, with such massive group pressures, where the individual feels more and more confused, anxious, helpless, and hopeless, it seems to us only natural that the therapist should propose and the patient accept group therapy as one logical means of dealing with personal problems as placed against the new reality of group demands.

We need to remember that Freud and his original followers developed their one-on-one psychoanalytic techniques at a time when the individual still saw himself as the hub of the universe. Today, we in psychoanalysis in groups still consider the individual as the center of treatment, but we also feel that the group is a realistic, pertinent setting for the resolution of those personal problems in the context of our society today.

The conflicts of the human condition—life and death, good and evil, success and failure, love and hate, male and female, work and play, conformity and individuality—are, alas, eternal. But history has proven that the circumstances of each new age highlight one or another of these conflicts, creating distortion in all of them and so affecting the values and behavior of the individual. We live in an age in which widely differing ideologies are confronting each other. Their ultimate clash might mean catastrophe for all of us. During the present standoff, the pressures toward conformity have become so overwhelming that the individual has become submerged and, to some extent, dehumanized (see Wolf and Kutash 1991).

Psychoanalysis in groups is just a drop in the bucket against this trend, but we believe it can be one of the last strongholds where the uniqueness of the individual can be preserved. At least our experience with psychoanalysis in groups has shown us that, in successful treatment, as each individual interacts more constructively with his fellow group members, his fears of individual and group pressures both inside and outside the group are lessened. And, as this constructive process continues, each individual in the group increases his capacity for positive fulfillment, personal responsibility, and more humanized and creative adaptations.

Over five decades in the practice of psychoanalysis in groups has influenced our views on psychoanalytic theory and practice and brought about modifications of our individual analytic techniques.

The therapeutic group more easily challenges the therapist in a way the individual patient has greater difficulty in doing. The group promotes the expression of free association and affect toward patients and the therapist. The individual patient's caution in exposing attitudes and affect directed toward the therapist tends to feed his grandiosity and sense of omnipotence, a dangerous hazard for the individual therapist. The knowledge of the isolated patient's reserve has led us in individual analysis to encourage the patient more strongly to present all his mixed thoughts, associations, fantasies, dreams, and feelings about others in his life and about the therapist.

One of the ways group members develop better egos is derived from their alternative roles of helper and helped. It is almost impossible for the patient in individual analysis to be the helper. But aware of the value of this experience in psychoanalysis in groups, we have spoken to patients in individual analysis about the value to them of helping in treatment by valuing others' dreams, others' associations, others' interpretations, as very useful to us in facilitating noncompulsive helpfulness.

Psychoanalysis in groups has made us more aware of our own transferences and countertransferences, largely through listening to patients' perceptions of us, their criticisms and corrective suggestions. While a part of their observations was distorted and transferential, another part was always appropriate to some degree. So the practice of group therapy has led us to be more self-examining and self-critical in both group and individual analysis, more attentive and mindful of what each patient has to say to us, not only in terms of his distortions but in terms of his valid estimate of our behavior.

Psychoanalysis in groups with its greater activity has enabled us to understand better the psychology of the ego and given fresh directions to our practice of individual analysis. The observation of patients' social behavior has impressed us with their need for activity, for ego activity, not just ego support. In individual treatment, therefore, we ask the patient to take action, not just talk, think, or feel but do. We ask him what he plans to do in reality with this or that insight. The analyst is often a poor example, just sitting, thinking, and feeling. He, too, needs to do more, to take appropriate action, make appropriate interventions without acting out.

Psychoanalysis in groups has led us to question the necessity of total frustration of the patient's archaic needs. Freud questioned the wisdom of such absolutism without the benefit of experience in group therapy. An analyst, practiced in psychoanalysis in groups, took a patient's hand in a group situation, because not to have done so would have been a traumatic repetition of her father's silence and rejection of her. The therapist could have taken the same action in individual treatment. Here then a gratification of an archaic longing was seen as an immediate therapeutic necessity. But the analyst needs to be discriminating. One of us (A.W.) would not, for example, take the hand of an asthmatic patient with whom he worked because her aim in pleading for this was to control the therapist.

The aggressive evaluation and criticism of one another that goes on in group therapy is in part an acting out but also a genuine, relevant estimate of each other that is very insightful. Its critical quality demands of the observed and the observer a movement and change toward a more realistic adaptation. It has taught us to be less neutral in our role as analysts. It has made us more challenging than we used to be. We are not neutral with regard to the patient's pathology. We do not accept his resistance, his distortions. We keep questioning his commitment to out-moded ways of thinking, feeling, and acting. We do not accept his rationalizations. We pursue his latent motivations more actively. We are equally assertive in promoting the necessity for him to be as questioning and challenging with regard to everything we say and do.

Group experience has demonstrated to us the value of the presence of peers in the horizontal vector. In the individual analytic setting, only the vertical vector is present, and peer relationships are usually not experienced. Accordingly, the patient works through his relationship with authority, the mother and father invested on the therapist in the hierarchical vector. Sibling relationships tend to be neglected. Therefore, in individual treatment we are much more alert to the patient's relationship to his siblings and his peers beyond his dyadic involvement with the therapist. This means that we pay more attention to his contacts with his fellows apart from his oedipal and preoedipal engagement with the therapist. This leads to a working through of his vertical relationship with the therapist and to freedom from an overly long regression.

The need to attenuate the hierarchical vector, to remove the patient from his parents and their surrogates in or out of the therapeutic milieu, is facilitated by putting the patient in a therapeutic group of peers. In individual analysis, when the patient has worked through his oedipal and preoedipal transferences, the therapist is experienced more in the horizontal vector as a peer, a dyad in which sibling relationships emerge and are worked through. Members in a group, in addition to providing a range of opportunity for stimulation of sibling transferences, also offer stimulation for the development of parental transferences. Patients frequently make parental transferences to another member of the group.

Psychoanalysis in groups has led to a more refined understanding of family life, of how the patient invests members of a group with counterparts of mother, father, and siblings, and of how he relates to a stranger to the family in the group member who is not so invested. This experience has led us more and more in individual analysis to explore the patients' relationships not only with his primal and current families but with his professional and work associates, colleagues, friends, and enemies alike, as well as strangers.

Our group experience has taught us to be less the parent who induces preoedipal regression and more the authority and peer who gives and takes, who will not incorporate or be incorporated, who pursues the security of the patient's primary trust in us to the end that he develops his own autonomy.

All group therapies share three fundamental ingredients: (1) a group therapist and at least two patients, (2) multiple interaction among the group members, and (3) limits on what takes place. Psychoanalysis in groups, one form of group therapy that was pioneered by Wolf in 1938, shares these three parameters (see Wolf 1949, 1950). There is, however, an additional ingredient basic to psychoanalysis in groups: the exploration and working through of intrapsychic unconscious processes.

THE THERAPEUTIC GROUP

In order to practice group psychotherapy, the therapist must have a group. One therapist and one patient do not make a group. A therapeutic group demands at least three people, two of them patients and the third a therapist. There is no psychotherapy without a therapist, and there is no therapeutic group if two of the members are therapists and the third is a patient; this is a group setting, but the treatment is individual. Two patients and one therapist or a number of patients and one or two therapists provide structurally for the simultaneous presence of hierarchical and peer vectors. The therapist fills the need for a responsible authority figure. Two or more patients afford an opportunity for peer relatedness.

The presence of authority in the person of the therapist and of peers in the persons of patient group members provides for an interplay of vertical and horizontal interactions that elicits parental and sibling transferences. The distortions projected onto the peers are generally diluted versions of more intense projections onto the therapist. The claim is sometimes made that these dilutions interfere with the emergence of intense transferences to the therapist and, therefore, promote resistance. It seems, however, that, where transferences to peers as parental figures are worked through, the patient sooner or later is confronted with his projections onto the therapist. Having worked through, if only in part, the less-threatening aspects of parental transferences onto his peers, the patient is able to more easily face the authority of the parent invested in the therapist. There are occasions when a peer, because of his particular character structure, will elicit a more threatening transference than the therapist, but this kind of distortion is diluted by reality. The peer is, in fact, only a peer and, therefore, more devoid of parental authority than he seemed at first.

In the therapeutic group, the focus of attention moves from one patient to another. This is the principle of shifting attention. No one patient has the exclusive attention of the therapist. The more patients there are, the greater is the diffusion of attention from the therapist as well as from the patients. For many, this shifting attention gives them time to assimilate and work through whatever insights they have obtained. For others, it represents some freedom from continuous scrutiny, which in individual treatment can be experienced as immobilizing. For still others, it becomes a form of resistance, a way of avoiding examination of their intrapsychic distortions.

Shifting attention can be a means of working through the demand that one be the only child in the family, a problem that is sometimes not adequately challenged in the dyadic therapeutic relationship. Group therapy, with its insistence that there are others besides the self, provides a medium for working through the irrational transferential demand that no one else be heard.

Another consequence of group structure is the phenomenon of alternating roles. Each patient is propelled by the presence of others to listen, to try to understand them. New kinds of activity, feelings, or responsiveness are induced. A patient would not necessarily experience these reactions if he were the therapist's only patient. In the group, each person listens, gives counsel, tries to understand, reacts, feels empathic, becomes annoyed, and elicits reasonable and irrational responses. He seeks help and offers help. He experiences interaction on a peer level, an experience that is not available to him alone with a therapist. In individual treatment, the difference in status and activity between patient and therapist is so marked, and the roles of helper and helped are so clearly defined, that a patient has less chance to alter both his role and his activity. As soon as other patients enter the treatment structure, the role limits and dimensions are enlarged by new kinds of activities.

LIMITS

One of the characteristics of emotional disorder is the pursuit of limitlessness. The patient often tries to overcome his anxiety in an inappropriate way. The search for absolutes or for immortality is one such irrational aim and is related to the irrational hope for omnipotence. Treatment needs to be limited in duration, in number of sessions in a week, in the length of each session, in activity, and in participation. The therapist's and the patient's agreement to limit themselves is a commitment to reality. The ingredient of limits is essential for all forms of therapy.

Group Size

Eight to ten members are considered the ideal number for psychoanalysis in groups. Believing that most families consist of between three and eight members, with the majority today four or five, a group of eight to ten provides transferential room for the nuclear family, as well as some extrafamilial significant others. With fewer than eight members, there is often not enough interpersonal provocation and activity, leading to dead spots in spontaneous interaction. With more than ten, it is difficult for patient and group therapist alike to keep up with what is happening. However, some individuals feel lost even in a group as small as eight, because they were neglected in a family that may have numbered as few as three; an experience in a group setting where the leader can assure them a prominent role can provide a new constructive experience.

Several people who had previously found themselves over- whelmed in large groups were placed in a group with three or four individuals, a minigroup (Kutash 1988). The smaller size of the group was never mentioned as the reason for the invitation to these groups. These patients found themselves participating more and feeling a unique freedom. They were at last in a setting without overpowering mother, father, or sibling figures; simultaneously, they did not feel lost in the crowd. At a later date, additional members were added, including less passive potential transferential mothers or fathers. At this point, their egos were more secure from their previous experience with the leader as good parent. They felt his respect for their participation and the regard for their siblings who were not perceived as overpowering or parental favorites. The larger group then became the arena for their future growth.

Time

Group meetings are most effective if they last between 1½ and 2½ hours. Just as the regular session should be limited in time, so should the alternate meeting. Although a group may have an alternate session that lasts longer than usual, the members inevitably resist unduly prolonged sessions.

Moreover, it makes sense to limit the length of time a patient remains in any given group. If he does not appear to make some progress in 6–12 months, continuing in that same group seems to be of doubtful value. A time limit should be placed also on his remaining in his particular group for more than 4 years. Beyond this time, some patients seem to deteriorate in their capacity for cooperative endeavor with the same group of participants. Such members might be referred elsewhere for treatment.

Activity

Sometimes the analyst in groups is too permissive of patient activity. He needs to take a stand against sexual relations and physical aggression among group members. A monopolist may, for example, dominate a group with insistent demands that he always be heard at the expense of the others. Or a masochist, by assuming the position of scapegoat, may repeatedly invite group members' aggression.

Families

Psychoanalysis in groups should be limited to patients initially unknown to each other. Such a view excludes family members, as well as married couples, from analytic groups. It is not appropriate to make parents and children or husbands and wives aware of one another's unconscious processes. There are too many potentials for mutual destructiveness in such exposures. It is, however, possible to do group therapy with families and married couples when the therapist plays some interpretive, supportive, guiding, and mediating role.

Most married couples get along without full awareness of the details of their history or of one another's unconscious processes. The exposure of these details might threaten the stability of a marriage. For most couples, the less they know about the significance of one another's dreams, the better the marriage. It is a rare couple, but there are a few, who, the more they know about one another in terms of unconscious processes, the better they get along. These unusual married couples may do well in psychoanalysis together.

Kinds of Patients

Limits need to be imposed on the introduction of certain kinds of patients to psychoanalytic groups. Not everyone is suitable for such therapy. Severe alcoholics who cannot come to meetings sober need to be excluded, as do drug addicts who come to sessions under the influence of drugs, seriously handicapped stutterers, the mentally retarded, epileptics, hallucinating psychotics, the actively deluded, suicidal and homicidal patients, the psychopathic, cardiac patients who develop pain under emotional stress, adolescents less than 18, the very seriously depressed, and the hypermanic. Such patients can be better treated in individual therapy. If they improve, they may become suitable candidates for psychoanalysis in groups.

The Therapist

The analyst must also impose limits on himself. He should be available to patients for the whole of their appointed time. He should neither keep them waiting to start a session nor see them beyond the time of the regular meeting. He needs to deny himself sexual and aggressive acting out with patients. At the sessions, the analyst may not be disturbed himself, unable to concentrate, intoxicated, drugged, hallucinating, delusional, very depressed, or suicidal. He must have undergone psychoanalytic training and have been an analysand in individual therapy and in group.

Whether he admits it or not, every therapist has a point of view, a philosophy—a therapeutic personality. Regardless of any assumed manner determined by theory or technique, his underlying commitment and his behavior are revealed to the patient. His position with regard to the human condition shows itself in the appearance of his consulting room, the clutter or neatness of his desktop, the kind of wardrobe he has, the paintings on his walls, the color and light in his office, the quality and volume of his speech, and how and whether he responds to phone calls during sessions. The patient experiences him in what he selects to analyze and in what he seems to neglect, in whether he engages vital or trivial issues, in whether his attitude is welcoming or rejecting at first meeting, and in whether his greeting is warm or distant. The therapist indicates his approach to life by his hopefulness or cynicism, and by whether he attends the patient's association or pursues his own fantasies. His preferences are demonstrated in whether he asks the patient to use the couch or the chair, whether he prefers to see the patient alone or in a group, and whether he asks to see members of the patient's family or not. Every therapist betrays to his patient his sense of what he believes is relevant and irrelevant. He exposes himself and his values to the patient not only by the content of what he says but also by how he says it, and by the way he behaves.

EXPLORATION OF LATENT MATERIAL

Group therapy that introduces psychoanalytic means is concerned not only with the manifest, but with understanding the latent in patient interaction and function. The analyst takes the lead in the search for unconscious processes by promoting free association, the analysis of dreams, resistance, and transference. The search for unconscious motivation and processes leads patients away from the here-and-now and into the there-and-then, into historical determinants. Group therapy is converted into psychoanalysis only when this element—the investigation of intrapsychic material—is introduced.

Under such circumstances, the other parameters take on new depth and meaning. Hierarchical and horizontal vectors cease to be merely current experiences with authority and peers, but instead acquire parental and sibling transferential qualities that are reexperienced; conscious plans are then introduced to work through these distortions.

The intercommunication characteristic of multiple reactivities is no longer promoted simply for cohesive socialization, which admittedly has its psychotherapeutic benefits. Interaction is also used to proceed from the interpersonal to the intrapsychic, from the manifest to the latent. The pursuit of the intrapsychic in the interpersonal stresses self-knowledge that can lead to personal integration. This personal integration can lead to more wholesome social integration. Nonanalytic group therapy frequently imposes a more superficial social interaction that can disregard the personal psychodiagnostics of the individual.

In nonanalytic group therapy, the patient may either be well served or victimized by the principle of shifting attention. The patient overly concentrated on may welcome a respite from group examination. Still another member may find himself too frequently bypassed. Little, if any, time is spent in a study of each member's psychodynamics in provoking the response he gets and the latent nature of these reactions. The contrast when psychoanalytic means are introduced is striking. The patient who is focused on may be masochistically provoking whatever latent sadism exists in other members. Manifestly, he is a monopolist, but on a deeper level he may be trying to exclude his younger siblings from getting parental attention. He may be demanding attention in an oral-incorporative way, or he could be receiving such attention because of his narcissism, his exhibitionism, or his phallic overbearance. There are multiple possibilities. The bypassed member may be latently the good child quietly waiting his turn—hurt, disappointed, and enraged at being neglected. He may be frightening to the other patients, who vaguely sense in his silence an enormous hostility they are afraid of tapping. Here, too, the bypassed patient, like the monopolistic one, may have any one of a series of unconscious determinants that require exploration in depth.

In group psychotherapy, with the principle of alternating roles, members are sometimes asking for help, sometimes giving it. In psychoanalysis in groups, some members use the role of helper as a way of resisting treatment. The same is true of those who are always helplessly demanding. The analytic group searches for the historical determinants that have imposed this particular repetition compulsion in order to work it through.

The analyst in groups introduces an activity not generally available in other group therapies: he interprets the nature of the unconscious processes in the interaction among the patients and between the patients and the therapist. The patients in time learn how to understand the latent meaning of their contributions and make significant interpretations as well; their impressions are sometimes appropriate, sometimes not. Unconscious material is worked out and worked through. The patient develops insight, which helps him to understand his disability. He is thereby able, with the support of the analyst and the other patients, to struggle to resolve his difficulties.

The nonanalytic group psychotherapist may use many of the means of the analyst. But unless he emphasizes an exploration of latent content, he is not practicing psychoanalysis in groups. The analyst in groups does not limit himself exclusively to the search for unconscious manifestations. If he entirely neglects manifest behavior, he is practicing individual analysis in a group setting. Analysis in a group requires attention to horizontal and peer vectors, to multiple reactivities and to unconscious processes, with special emphasis on the last. But individual similarities, manifest behavior, and group dynamics are neither neglected nor denied.

HOMOGENEITY AND HETEROGENEITY

The group analyst tries to form a heterogeneous group. Although he is aware of likenesses in the members, he is alert to the

differences and singularity in each. He is awake to each patient's
need and right to differ from the group. For there is something
unwholesome in the tenacious inseparability of a nonanalytic,
homogeneous group that too frequently rejects the new applicant
as an outlandish intruder. The group analyst sees restorative
quality in the complementarity and mutuality of difference, in
men and women struggling together more effectively just because
of their constructively responsive and challenging reciprocity.
The group analyst regards the likeness of the members of
nonanalytic therapeutic groups as only manifestly homogeneous,
therefore pseudohomogeneous, as fundamentally segregating
and insulating.

It is impossible to organize an absolutely homogeneous or
heterogeneous group. Patients are both similar and different, and
their diversity creates some heterogeneity while their likeness
establishes some homogeneity. The therapist does not gather
together adults, adolescents, and children in the same group. He
assembles them in groups of approximately the same age: children, adolescents, or adults. He does not place his more sophisticated patients with the slow-witted or the psychopath with the
accountable. As the group therapist makes allowances for the
human need for some homogeneity, as successful treatment goes
on, patients become more disparate.

If the therapist fosters uniformity, he attenuates the depth of
treatment. Members who make progress in the group ask for
dissimilarity and contrasting others in new patients. Such a
petition is a sign that the therapist is effectively engaging his
patients in the treatment process. The more the leader and the
members explore the latent material and penetrate resistance,
recall early personal history, experience the associated repressed
affect, and understand unconscious motivation, the more wholesome personal distinctions, nonconformity, and heterogeneity
appear in the group. A sound group therapeutic approach
enhances the originality of each and thereby makes the group
more diversified. Each member becomes increasingly distinctive
with a particular history, development, and a more flexible way of
behaving. The patients become more reactive to each other as
they recover their own egos. A trial ensues in which each member
tries to comprehend and accept the originally alien other.

All therapeutic groups have relative degrees of homogeneity and heterogeneity. Nonanalytic group therapies tend to sponsor homogeneity. A group therapist may select patients with similarities: a shared psychovisceral symptom, a common diagnostic category, a similar chief complaint. The psychoanalyst in groups tries to provide more diversity in organizing his groups. Although he acknowledges certain similarities among patients, he is alert to each patient's uniqueness and is sensitive to each member's right to be different. He sees homogeneity as insular, isolated, snobbish, and antisocial, for there is psychopathology in the formation and cohesion of a homogeneous group that too often rejects the stranger as deviant.

If there are several homosexuals in the group, for example, the analyst is not only aware of their manifest similarities but alert to the differences in historical development that led to the underlying psychopathology. Given a group of alcoholics or obese patients, the analyst is cautious about making an interpretation that assumes his observation is equally insightful for all members. Rather, he sees the end product of homosexuality, alcoholism, or obesity as having divergent origins and different bases for its persistence, despite similarities in operational forms.

Since treatment, in large part, constitutes analysis of transference, it is advantageous to place the patient in a group setting in which he can project father, mother, and siblings as well. This can best be accomplished by a heterogeneous group. Furthermore, heterogeneous groups reflect a microcosm of society, and they tend to reproduce the family. Since the family probably ushered in the patient's neurosis, it is the logical agency for checking it. Despite the fact that, at first, many patients do not cope successfully with dissimilar character structures, the battle can best be won where it was apparently lost. In psychoanalysis in groups, the early precipitation and recognition of multiple transferences are facilitated by the presence of numbers of provocative familial figures in the persons of the various members. The presence of both sexes incite and sharpen projection.

When group members and the analyst, even in the most homogeneous group, examine each other deeply, they find that each person is different from his neighbor in his history, his development, and his psychodynamics. A working out and working through takes place that makes each patient more interesting to the next. A regard for one another in difference becomes more appealing than the superficial pseudocollusion of similarity and identification. Divergence in healthy resources for gratifying and realistic involvement—not just differences in pathology—can be the basis for mutual interest and acceptance. The novelty that stirs the membership to try to understand and accept their differences represents a reciprocity based on contrast. While the members study one another in depth, they nevertheless discover and grant each other areas of commonality.

In psychoanalysis in groups, the exploration of intrapsychic processes enables the patient to understand in greater detail the nature of his submission to members of the nuclear family and members of his current group. He is encouraged to find his way out, to recover his repressed ego. The psychoanalytic group sponsors his individuation, his nonconformity, and the recovery of his lost self.

Once having assembled a heterogeneous group, however, the battle is not yet won. Homogeneous structure or heterogeneous structure can be a consequence of the position taken by the therapist. He may believe that mental health comes from individual concession to the group. Under these circumstances, it is not the group that strives for such homogeneity, it is the therapist. For the group, given its head, even if it is originally relatively homogeneous, achieves a more wholesome heterogeneity. It's the therapist's drive for homogeneity that is the significant force. The imposition of a make-believe unity is a projection of the therapist. When the therapist turns the group as a whole into an earlier familial figure of his own, it may be termed the leader's group-as-a-whole transference.

The treatment of diverse patients as if they were identical helps the therapist to evade the necessity for the differentiated therapy of each one. It is quite possible that he is looking for an abbreviated form of group therapy. He may expect that the group, its climate, or its dynamics will somehow heal the patient with less need on the therapist's part to intervene. He may, like the patient, hope to evade conflicts or the struggle to resolve distortions of patients at cross purposes. By ignoring this disparity or leveling them in similarity, he can be relieved of the differentiated necessity to work through their divergent problems. Some therapists fear subjecting the patient to alien experience, as if they would protect him from the new and unknown.

He may misjudge singularity as compulsive nonconformity, and uniqueness as pathological deviation. He may try to render his group homogeneously irrational with a view to establishing a therapeutic psychosis. Here the aim is to obscure the difference between patient and therapist.

An unconscious objective in homogenizing a group may be the therapist's need to manipulate it. A group can be more readily dealt with if it is made coalescent, if it is of one mind, as if this were possible, or if the individual members have been conditioned to follow. The homogeneous group may be used by the therapist to bludgeon the patient to conform to the consensual view. The group can be more adroitly handled in the mass than in the man. But if the patient is to be lost in the group, his irrationality must be stimulated, encouraged, and intensified. For he will resist his immersion in homogeneity with whatever sound reserves are still available to him.

One homogeneous aim is infallibility. In this view, the therapist can be positive if the group's tenor is unquestioned. Homogeneity then has the quality of massive conformism. It creates new problems by encouraging infectious parapraxes. The nature of psychoanalytic practice requires that we question the motivations of patients and our own as well. Otherwise, we are homogeneous with their resistance. When the right to question patients and for them to question and disagree with one another and the therapist is disavowed, we are forced to accept homogeneity and illusory assurance.

A pitfall the group therapist needs to guard against is the formation, in the therapeutic group, of a clique of elite patients who underline the analyst's values or manage to establish a homogeneous bias to which they demand the remaining members conform. There is a danger here of the group's becoming noxiously homogeneous, for example, in its insistence that the only acceptable material for expression must be affect loaded; or in the rule that no experience of a patient outside the group is relevant; or in the dictum that historical data are immaterial and that only the here-and-now counts; or in the attitude that dreams are of little consequence—and a bore besides; or in the position that this or that new member is not bright enough, not up to the group's level. With such a development, the therapist must analyze, as thoroughly as possible, the psychodynamics of each patient parity to this autocratically harmonizing influence until the multiple individual and divergent aspirations in the group recover. Otherwise, he caters exclusively to the majority and neglects the needs of individual patients.

What often passes for concurrence in the group is itself the expression not so much of constructive cohesion as it is of submerged pathology (Wolf and Kutash 1991). The pseudoegos are so characteristic of our time that many patients passively follow the more assertive leaders, lending to the group the appearance of cohesion. This manifest accordance, so liable to be sponsored by the therapist as a salutary group climate, needs to be analyzed, as it shows itself in each dominant–submissive relationship. Each group may have one or two members whose personalities strongly sway the others. They are frequently the most verbal and active but are not necessarily reparative in their insensitivity to others. In order to support submerged egos, the therapist must not be misled by an appearance of uniformity and to analyze any compulsive passivity or leadership. Individuality can lead to greater group cohesiveness than efforts toward homogeneity, since a person needs to appreciate himself before he can truly appreciate others.

The therapist discriminates between patients in order to discover their different illnesses and to be able, for each, to work through the specific way to enlist their cooperation and help them resolve their disorder. By this discriminating means, the therapist gives each member particular insight, so that patients do not expect the analyst to approach them in a homogeneous way. Sometimes a therapist is disconcerted by patients' objections that he does not treat one member like another. When the leader is sure that patients are heterogeneous and need to be treated differently, he ceases to feel disturbed by such complaints, and he soon discovers that patients stop insisting on identical treatments from him and instead appreciate his distinguishing their respective needs.

What is the role of the therapist in the face of a developing homogeneity, a common dynamic, a shared motif in his group? It is the analyst's function to accept and understand the manifest, but also to penetrate the resistive, generalized facade to each patient's concealed, unconscious, and differentiated interest.

It is important for the therapist to value multiformity, to appreciate diverse thoughts and feelings, and to demonstrate to his patients the productive import to each heterogeneous organization. For, as group members discover the worth of parity in difference, they permit and encourage appropriate dissimilarity in others. Then the patients themselves cultivate a climate of mutual examination that is cordial to unlikeness. The receptivity toward divergence encourages each to unfold his particularity, which in turn enriches the group experience of all. The group's interest in the discordant view fosters a medium of friendly candor in which the patient can expose himself and have more choice in determining destiny. A patient is helped more by learning to cherish his differences or individuality than to be comforted by his sameness or conformity.

MULTIPLE INTERACTION IN PSYCHOANALYSIS IN GROUPS

Here again, the structural situation encourages group members to respond to one another. Patients become involved with each other as well as with the therapist. In nonanalytic group therapy, the interaction is largely phenomenological and deals with manifest content. Here-and-now responses take precedence over an examination of historical determinants. There is preoccupation with group-as-a-whole dynamics: cohesion, what the group is feeling or doing, group themes, and climate. Special topics may be discussed, and patients protest if a member tries to divert the group from a prevailing subject. Group roles, group rituals, group traditions, and a group history emerge in the course of interaction. To some extent, these phenomena determine the ways in which patients and therapists behave over a period of time.

In the multiple interaction that prevails in group therapy, a homogeneity tends to develop in which group members join or submit to whatever theme, climate, or tone is set by a dominant member. On the other hand, attention may suddenly shift from one theme or member to another without an in-depth examination of how or why this phenomenon occurred. Patients counsel or advise one another and suggest alternative solutions to each other's current dilemmas. There is more emphasis on what the group is or is not doing than on the individual. When the therapist encourages the group to function in this way, it remains homogeneous and nonanalytic. Group members under such influence identify with one another, rather than differentiate themselves. The result is that the group becomes more cohesive as "treatment" emphasizes the likenesses among patients. Group conventions take precedence over individual differences, and patients conform to group rules. Personal exception is rejected and unrewarded.

MULTIPLE REACTIVITIES IN PSYCHOANALYSIS IN GROUPS

Multiple reactivity, a characteristic of group therapy, is given fuller play in a heterogeneous group than in a homogeneous one. It is not present in the dyad except to the extent that the therapist is able to evoke diversified reactions. It is available indirectly in the dyad when the patient talks of his responses to persons outside the treatment milieu. But then the therapist is required to see through the analysand's subjective distortions in his accounts of events outside the consulting room. In the group, the analyst is a direct observer of how the patient reacts to others in a multiplicity of situations. Through the variety of their provocations, the group members evoke a larger picture of the patient's disorder. At the same time, they call for a more inclusive reconstruction in the face of a greater variety of appropriate and inappropriate expectations.

The patient in a group has an opportunity to take part in an invaluable exercise not available in the dyad. He becomes aware that all people do not necessarily react as he does to the same provocation. He finds that, when he feels one way, others feel differently; when he wants to share a feeling, another person wants to retire in self-examination; when he is feeling warm, the object of his empathy is about to castigate him for his offensiveness during a previous encounter. But he does not learn that there is never any complementarity of interaction. He learns, in fact, that there are as many mutually responsive interactions as there are antagonistic ones.

MULTIPLE TRANSFERENCES IN PSYCHOANALYSIS IN GROUPS

The analytic group speedily and successively furnishes the patient with a number of evocative stand-ins who excite multiple transferences more readily than the analyst alone. Each group member invests every other member with a variety of transferences in the course of every group session. In dyadic treatment, such a variety of misperceptions of the analyst does not occur in a given therapeutic hour. The fluctuating distortions in the group follow from the multiple interaction in which the relationships among members change from time to time. Transference is more inflexible in dyadic analysis. Similar shifting of transferences to the analyst may be seen in one-to-one treatment only if the patient is very unstable.

Some patients homogenize the whole group into a single transferential figure. This coalescence is a phenomenon that, of course, does not occur in individual treatment, at least not in the treatment setting. When it occurs in the group, the members are misperceived as one parent and the analyst as the other. Very likely, similar distortions are made in social situations, but the individual analysand is generally not aware of this. The distortions can be dealt with in the group, since the difficulty becomes manifest. The patients must be urged to react to the other members as individuals, to distinguish one patient from the other, to look for differences in them and to see them in reality.

Sibling Transferences

In dyadic analysis, parental transference is usually the prevailing distortion. Transferences to siblings tend to be disregarded or casually discussed as being less noxious, because they do not as a rule manifest themselves in the same deeply felt way. In the analytic group, the presence of peers provides the stimulation for the evocation of sibling transferences, and they can be more readily seen, examined, and resolved. The availability of peers provides the opportunity to work out and work through problems with members of the family beyond the parents. Group members are not always perceived as familial surrogates, but, because this distortion is generally a recurrent finding, it needs to be looked for.

Parental Transferences to Peers

Transferences to peers may have a parental as well as a sibling quality. The investment of copatients with mother and father distortions is usually experienced as less formidable than when the therapist is perceived as a symbolic parent. Because the peers are also perceived in reality as less authority laden than the analyst, the parental transferences to them are less intense and more easily resolved. Some patients who assume aggressive or dominanting roles may elicit strong parental transferences, but even here the awareness of their relative equality in reality as peers reduces the distortive predisposition. The preliminary experiencing and working through of mother and father distortions invested in peers makes it easier to resolve the same distortion when patients begin to undertake, as a later experience, the resolution of the more difficult parental transferences to the analyst seen in the hierarchical vector.

Transferences to the Therapist

In the group setting, the transferences to the therapist are more fixed than those made to co-patients. Transferences are more stable with relation to the analyst because his role is more consistent than that of the patient, who plays multiple roles and elicits, therefore, a multiplicity of transferences. In dyadic analysis, transferences to persons other than the therapist are only approximately or inaccurately understood because the analyst is dependent on the patient's filtered reports of interpersonal exchanges. In the group, these same transferences are present within the treatment setup. Transference to the therapist is less attended at first because patients find it easier to work out whatever distortions they make with peers seen in the hierarchical vector than with the reinforced authority of the analyst. In dyadic treatment as well, if the analyst first works out and resolves transferences toward persons in the patient's life outside the consulting room, it then becomes less difficult to work through transference to the therapist. If the strategy is transposed – if the analyst tries to work out and work through transference to him as an introductory procedure – he usually encounters greater resistance.

Countertransference

No analyst is totally free of transference or countertransference involvement. To the degree it is present, the therapist experiences trials and crises in his struggle to understand the patient and see him objectively. In the group, the analyst's inappropriate behavior is more quickly seen by patients, who demand more germane responses from him. As a result, there is protection against the misperceptions of the analyst. A patient alone with a such a therapist has no co-patient allies to support him in confirming his belief that the analyst is distorting reality.

Occasionally, the therapist's countertransferential difficulty takes the form of compulsively trying to induce a transference neurosis in the patient. By so binding the patient to him in a symbiotic tie, he may in some instances remove the patient from productive and invigorating relations with his peers. The analytic group tends to counteract such exploitation.

Analysis of Transference

Transference in group analysis is dealt with somewhat differently than in individual analysis. In dyadic treatment, the analysis of transference tends to be one of the major functions of the therapist. The patient often plays a lesser part in this activity. In the group, however, patients call attention to each other's misperceptions and make proposals for more realistic alternative ways of functioning.

This willingness among group members to consider and admit to their multilateral distortions refines and enriches the insight into the multilateral nature of transference. The provocative nature of each member in eliciting the transference of each patient is observed more clearly in the group than in dyadic analysis, where the therapist is more reluctant to admit to his inciting role. This denial cannot be so readily maintained in the group in the face of a number of patients concertedly pointing out how his behavior provoked particular patient response.

In the group, transferences are generally interpreted as bilateral and trilateral. In individual analysis, they are generally analyzed as emanating only from the patient. The therapist is supposed not to transfer or countertransfer, which is an illusion.

In dyadic analysis, the rigidity of transference generally exceeds its duration in the group. Its persistence in individual treatment is promoted by the one-on-one situation and the separation from peers, thereby inducing a sometimes persistent and prolonged transference neurosis or psychosis. In the group, patients are invested with mother surrogate and father surrogate distortions, but, because they are also seen in reality in the horizontal vector and because they can move so freely in reacting subjectively from one patient to another, their transferential misperceptions are less virulent, more moderate, more yielding, and more readily relinquished for reasonable alternatives. Quantitatively and qualitatively, patient-to-patient transference is different from that of patient-to-analyst.

SUMMARY

Psychoanalysis in groups attempts to integrate and bring into concordance the intrapsychic and the interpersonal. In the group, the interpersonal interactions are closely observed at the time of their occurrence. The attendance of a number of analysands in a heterogeneous mix affords the concurrent presence of hierarchical and peer vectors.

In the group, the patient may withdraw unless the analyst promotes interaction and requires attendance at alternate meetings. However, it is more difficult for the patient to resist participation entirely because other group members demand action, reaction, and interaction. As a consequence, all the relationships of the members are magnified and amplified. Multiple interactions, multiple reactivities, and multiple transferences encourage the exchange among patients and are followed by analysis of intrapsychic material. A genuine cohesion is possible after the liberation of the suppressed ego in each patient and the working through of his individual resistances and transferences.

5

Group Composition

It is helpful in understanding people and particularly in forming groups to see which of four general categories that were coined by Kutash (1968, 1988a) best describes the qualities of a person's self awareness and the accompanying ability to relate feelings to others or the quality of their communication output.

First, there are some people who are predominately *consciously open*. These are the people who are in touch with their feelings and express them openly.

Second, there are some people who are predominately *consciously closed*. These are the people who are in touch with their feelings but will not express their feelings to others.

Third, there are some people who are predominately *unconsciously open*. These are the people who are not in touch with their feelings, but their feelings are obvious to those around them, such as the patient who characteristically says "I'm not angry" and believes it.

Fourth, there are some people who are predominately *unconsciously closed*. These are the people who are not in touch with their feelings, and they are a mystery to those around them as well.

A group should not be weighted with people from any of the

last three categories if it is to be effective. Consciously open people can be most helpful to each other and can provide the consensus necessary to reach the group members in the last three categories. We want to stress that everyone, at times, fits each of the categories above and always combines them to some extent, but in general, people will fit in one of these best. We hope you will keep this in mind in the analysis to follow as well.

Communication is, of course, a two-way street, and people must understand others and their feelings as well as being self-aware. These four categories describe the quality of a person's awareness of others' feelings or the quality of their communication input.

First, there is the type of person who is predominately *consciously receptive.* These are people who can understand and respond to all levels of communication.

Second, there is the type of person who is predominately *consciously rejective.* These are the people who can understand but refuse to respond to others.

Third, there is the type of person who is predominately *unconsciously receptive.* These are the people who may respond to the feeling of others, who, for example, respond to the distress of others without consciously even being aware that anything is wrong.

Fourth, there is the type of person who is predominately *unconsciously rejective.* These are the people who do not understand or respond to others, since they are not even aware of what is being communicated, who, for example, at best understand only the superficial in what is said.

Here, again, a group should not be weighted with people from category three or four if it is to be effective. Receptive people have the most potential to help others and, when in the consensual majority, can even influence rejective people.

The picture so far sketched is, of course, a vast simplification. To size up people and put together effective groups, the communication output categories and communication input categories must be combined in all their sixteen combinations to do some justice to the complexity of possible personality types and interpersonal vectors. Now, if you combine the quality of a person's self awareness with the quality of his understanding of others, you have a handy way of sizing up a potential group member and some of his strengths and shortcomings. Here then are the combinations and a few examples of the personality types they include.

The *consciously open, consciously receptive* person is one who is both in touch with his own feelings and willing to express them and in touch with those expressed by others. This is the ideal model for a group leader and describes a well-adjusted person. Someone who is consciously open may express his feelings but be inappropriate or inaccurate—for example, the hysteric—in expressing them. However, also being consciously receptive provides the feedback necessary to make the expression of feelings appropriate and accurate.

The *consciously open, consciously rejective* person is one who is in touch with his feelings and willing to express them but refuses to receive the real communications of others. An example would be the narcissist who talks only about himself and chooses not to listen.

The *consciously open, unconsciously receptive* person is one who is in touch with and willing to express his feelings and is intuitively in touch with the feelings of others. They are people who may outwardly disagree with what you say but what you tell them is actually sinking in. They are the people who may suddenly show therapeutic gain, and people may falsely think they had a "spontaneous recovery."

The *consciously open, unconsciously rejective* person is one who is in touch with his own feelings and willing to express them but is incapable of understanding the feelings of others. An example would be the person who thinks he is the only sensitive person in the world who suffers because he cannot recognize feelings in others.

The *consciously closed, consciously receptive* person is one who is in touch with his feelings, is unwilling to express them to others, but can understand the feelings of others. An example would be the patient who sits there quietly, but you can tell he understands all that is happening. This could range from an introvert to a catatonic schizophrenic. The receptive aspect makes improvement likely.

The *consciously closed, consciously rejective* person is one who is in touch with his feelings but will not express his feelings to others and at the same time will not listen to or accept what others express. If such a person does this out of wariness or suspicion of others, he may be paranoid-schizophrenic.

The *consciously closed, unconsciously receptive* person is one who is in touch with his feelings and won't express them to others and outside his awareness receives the communicated feelings of others. He may open up in a group, since he can be reached unconsciously initially.

· The *consciously closed, unconsciously rejective* person is one who is in touch with his feelings, won't declare them to others, and is oblivious to what is going on in others or what they communicate. This combination invariably leads to distorted feelings and in the extreme would describe an individual out of touch with reality or a psychotic.

The *unconsciously open, consciously receptive* person is one whom everyone can see right through. He cannot understand himself while being able to understand others. An example would be the bright, sensitive adolescent who is undergoing an identity crisis and is trying to find himself. Outwardly he rebels, not inwardly.

The *unconsciously open, consciously rejective* person does not understand himself and chooses not to tune in on others. You can read this person like a book, but he can't understand himself and won't bother with you.

The *unconsciously open, unconsciously receptive* person is one whom everyone understands, although he doesn't understand himself. What you say to him, while outwardly appearing not to sink in, actually has an unconscious effect, which can lead to change.

The *unconsciously open, unconsciously rejective* person is one who is not in touch with himself or others and can't help himself, since this is out of his awareness. He can be understood by others, however, but will be very hard to reach. This type is a big challenge for a group leader.

The *unconsciously closed, consciously receptive* person is unaware of his feelings so he can't express them, but is able to understand the expression of feelings by others. He is open, therefore, to re-education and can be helpful to others.

The *unconsciously closed, consciously rejective* person is unaware of his feelings and therefore can't express them, and he refuses to tune in to what others say or feel. He is cut off from his feelings and isolates himself. This could describe the schizoid personality or simple schizophrenic.

The *unconsciously closed, unconsciously receptive* person is unaware of his feelings but, outside of his awareness, is able to understand and profit from what others say.

The *unconsciously closed, unconsciously rejective* person is unaware of his feelings and cannot receive what others say or feel. He is a mystery to himself and others and the world is a mystery to him. An example would be a psychotic out of touch with reality.

With these character sketches in mind, the formation of a group and its interaction can, we hope, be more readily understood. A good group needs combinations of people who can help each other, and a good group leader can serve as a catalyst for this to occur.

DISEQUILIBRIUM, EQUILIBRIUM, AND MALEQUILIBRIUM IN GROUPS

The interpersonal environment of the contemporary group can fall into a generally destructive balance or pattern of interaction, and, perhaps most insidious, a generally comfortable but stultifying balance or pattern of interaction. These three group situations have been termed group disequilibrium, group equilibrium, and group malequilibrium (Kutash 1980). Group disequilibrium takes the form of a transferential, pathogenic, uncomfortable, re-created family with a new look; group malequilibrium takes the form of a pathogenic but comfortable family.

Group Disequilibrium

Just as an individual may re-create his pathogenic family, there is the ever-present danger that the group, functioning as a re-created family, may become pathogenic as a family. Without adroit management, some groups end up this way. The therapist must watch for the elaboration of self-sufficient, inbred, and incestuous trends that bind members together as neurotically as in the original family.

A recovering patient, for example, may be attacked as unready for discharge by a compulsively overprotective member who is parentally antagonistic. If a man and a woman gravitate toward one another with erotic interest, they may be invested with father and mother roles, and other patients may react to them with detached respect, voyeuristic and aggressive interest, or moralistic disapproval that corresponds to earlier ambivalent curiosity and condemnation with regard to intimacy between the parents.

Occasionally, a member or two will exhibit some reluctance to permit a patient who has recovered to leave the group. They demonstrate the same kind of envy or jealousy earlier directed toward a sibling or parent, and feel the family group or parental therapist is favoring the cured member, which his performance does not deserve.

Another unfavorable situation that may arise in a group is the development of intense neurotic resistance, accompanied by hostile bilateral transferences, and the formation of allies in groups of two or three, leaving some individuals isolated except for a relatively warm relationship to the analyst. Sometimes even this association becomes strained, because the patient blames the therapist for his having been exposed to such a trying antagonistic environment. Such forms of resistance need to be analyzed; otherwise, the group may fall apart. Attendance may become low and demoralize those present. The therapist, while taking an analytic view of absenteeism, confronts those who stay away repeatedly with attempts to understand their flight. He explores transferences that force aggressors into belligerent roles, and points out their illusory character. He is equally vigilant with regard to projective devices that impel the compulsively withdrawn to retreat further or to submit to the domination of other members. He seeks to uncover the causes for resistance to participation on deeper levels, pointing out explicitly the destructive character of particular defenses and encouraging free emotional ventilation.

All else failing, the analyst may be obliged to remove a patient here and there, one at a time, at varying intervals, introducing each retired member into a more constructive group. Such a crisis can usually be avoided by not organizing a group with a majority of strongly sadomasochistic patients, or with consciously or unconsciously closed and rejective patients. Too many such members in the same milieu provide an unfavorable climate for the evocation of the positive resources that need to be expressed if the group is to proceed efficiently.

Group Equilibrium

Group equilibrium is achieved when the group constructively re-creates the family but with a new look. By cultivating a permissive atmosphere in which mutual tolerance and regard can flourish, the earlier prohibitive character of the original family is projected with less intensity and is more easily dispersed. Furthermore, the general acceptance and sense of belonging that follow make it possible to achieve a similarly easy transition to correspondingly untroubled social relations beyond the confines of the group. The other patients, out of their numbers, provide more familial surrogates for transference evocation. Each member comes to the realization of the extent to which he re-creates his own childhood family in every social setting, and of the extent to which he invests others with inappropriate familial substitute qualities. The number of participants also clarifies the variety and multiplicity of central and penumbral transferences. Whereas in individual analysis the therapist tries to see clearly what perceptual distortions the patient makes of outer reality and what internal factors contribute to his social disfigurement, the analyst is often misled, because he does not see the patient in action. In psychoanalysis in groups, the therapist is also interested in what is happening at the moment, so that the patient's unconscious warping of fact can be observed in motion. He can then be confronted with his projective trends and the inciting role he plays in precipitating the environmental disturbance he resents so much.

An illustration of how a group helped an individual to see his misperceptions of the present as if it were the past is offered to show the usefulness of psychoanalysis in groups for this purpose, and to show how group equilibrium can emerge from group disequilibrium.

> A group member was transferentially viewed by one younger male member of the group as an immovable controlling figure (his father). A second younger male group member also viewed him as very controlling and irritating but also experienced a positive feeling that he would like to help him to feel free to be less controlling (feelings he felt for his father). A younger female group member saw the person as manipulative and subtly controlling (this was like both her parents). A fourth group member saw him as talking down to her and treating her as if she were unintelligent (again like her parents); yet a fifth group member saw him as a warm good father (the father she never had). When the first four members described their impressions, all began to express their feelings to this member, who was the recipient of so many transferences. They told him how he should behave; as a group, they thus became transferentially his mother, who always controlled him and told him how to act. He vehemently resisted their efforts. Only after each father transference was explored one by one and the group came to see the defensive nature of this man's controlling behavior—warding off his mother, while his transferences to the group were clarified—did progress for many group members occur. Many individuals came to see how they related to present-day figures as people from their past.

The group setting thus facilitates the emergence and acceptance of insight by confronting each member with his disparate investments of other patients and the therapist. When a patient joins a group, he finds that each patient, unconsciously warps his perception of the therapist and of the other patients as well. He begins to question the reality of his view of people in the group; and, as he discovers and studies his transferences, he also becomes aware of his provocative role.

Resistance seems to melt easily in this potentiating, catalytic atmosphere of mutual revelation in the group. The necessity of exposing oneself to another person without a corresponding disclosure by the therapist makes some patients self-conscious; however, each member is stimulated by the partial but always increasing self-revelation of another to expose more and more of himself. The discovery that the next person not only comes to no harm in showing himself but wins social approval besides, encourages one to uncover as well. The general feeling of shared divestment in a benevolent atmosphere enables a patient to show himself more freely. This experience is confirmed by the psychic climate of an ongoing group, and, after 3 or 4 months, each new member becomes part of the operation.

Another constructive advantage offered by a group is that in equilibrium it removes the patient from the danger of prolonged dependence on the therapist. In the isolation of private treatment, the analyst can encourage the patient to pursue his deepest personal longings. It may turn out that these aspirations are egocentric and that indulging them leads to detached, antisocial self-assertion. The gratification of his particular yearnings can amount to being allowed to exploit familial substitutes for neurotically satisfying ends. Humoring these impulses is bound to bring the patient into provocative, neurotic conflict with his associates, who will not tolerate such infantile actions. The group encourages reliance of one person on the next and more quickly demands and gets an abandonment of prolonged, possessive, and parasitic attachment that excludes the possibility of mature kinship.

Finally, one of the most valuable aspects of psychoanalysis in groups that are in equilibrium is that it facilitates giving up the ideal of having a relationship with the single-parent analyst. Instead of offering the questionable shelter of a private relationship to one omniscient ego ideal, it presents the patient with a group of persons in whose common effort he can join. Whereas the basis of a private relationship may well be evasive of social reality and tend to create an aura of isolation, the group serves in just the opposite way. Instead of enhancing the average patient's tendencies to neurotic isolation and his anarchic wish to act out his pathology, psychoanalysis in groups may help him realize his full potential as a social being. This is an added bridge to the establishment of healthy social relationships outside of analysis. Rather than strengthening the egocentric idea—typified in the neurotic's mind by the notion of the omnipotent analysis—psychoanalysis in groups helps to resolve the false antithesis of the individual versus the group by giving a patient a conscious experience that his fulfillment can be realized in a social or interpersonal setting without losing his individuality.

Group Malequilibrium

Group malequilibrium occurs when group members are all comfortable with each other but do not in any way challenge each other's defenses. The group itself is an unhealthy or stultifying balance. Conflict-laden topics are avoided, and everyone, in an unconscious deal, avoids stressful but potentially growth-inducing material. An example of a patient in such a group is the patient whose love for the emotional climate of the group borders on the ecstatic. He revels in the luxury of what he considers an absolutely honest relationship. He is in a family whose projections, having become at last analyzable and understandable, no longer alarm or hurt him. The danger in his case is that he runs from real life to the fabricated safety of an unreal laboratory. He finds the group warmer and safer than most associations on the outside. He needs to be instructed on how to carry the affective closeness he has consummated in the group to larger segments of society, beyond the confines of his fellow members.

This last is a common objection to working in concert with other patients. How can one transpose the good fellowship of the group to areas outside it? Group analytic technique offers the patient a means of making conscious those trends that stand in the way of his vigorous affective contact with others, whether loving or hating—hating, because there are some psychopathic influences in the world that can appropriately be hated.

The following case is also illustrative of malequilibrium in a group. A woman patient was placed in a group and arrived at her first meeting with a long cigarette holder and a very theatrical air and dress. After attending the session, she told the therapist, "This is not my kind of people; haven't you a group of people who have more in common with me?" The therapist, who was seeing a number of artists and theater people, was about to start a new group. He invited this woman and several other patients who seemed compatible into the group. Everyone immediately hit it off, laughed, joked, and had a marvelous time. No one talked about themselves, their feelings, associations, or their dreams. The group was eventually disbanded and its members placed into more heterogeneous groups, in which the cultivation of the group came through the promotion of differentiated, complementary and uncomplementary, agnostic and anti-agnostic, conflictual and nonconflictual personalities. People, through their growing individuality, learned—through differ-ences in realistic perception and unrealistic misperception—to appreciate one another's mutually proffered gifts of vision and the treasures of each other's perceptions.

6

Issues in Group Development

CLOSED VERSUS OPEN-ENDED GROUPS

Many schemes have emerged to describe phases of group development since the group process surge began. Some of these include: Bennis and Shepard (1956) who included a dependence and an interdependence phase taking the group from initial preoccupation with power relationships and leader authority to a concern with intimacy among peers; Martin and Hill (1957) who in six phases saw the group evolving from *autistic* to a more mature phase of interpersonal relatedness and individualization; Bion (1959) who described three kinds of basic assumption groups; Day (1967) who found groups passed through stages of fantasied familiarity, transient victimization, exaggerated perfect unity, and finally individualization; and Kissen (1976) who also included these ingredients.

An early example of anxiety over the new experience of being in a group, a stage that includes a dependence–independence conflict and a struggle for power or fight–flight stage, was mentioned by Bion (1959). A stage of group system formation or *condenser phenomenon*, was described by Foulkes and Anthony

(1957), a period of polarization or division, and finally a reuniting or reintegrating, culminating in termination.

Psychoanalysis in groups, however, is a totally open-ended approach unlike a laboratory or time-limited group. People join and leave as they are ready, not as part of a whole group readiness phenomenon. If the individual in any way goes through the stages in groups, by the nature of his individuality, these stages will occur for each person at different times, based on when he joined, how strong his ego was to begin with and his personal rate of progress. Furthermore, as in psychoanalysis per se, these phases of therapy are based on individual dynamics, ego strength, and individual rate of growth. It is like the analogy often given a patient at the beginning of treatment when he asks how long it will take: "If someone asked me how long it would take him to get to any location in the city, I would tell him, it depends on where you want to go and how fast a walker you are." For an entire group to go through therapy at one pace, some would have to walk too fast for others, some too slow, and where they all end up would have to be a compromise.

In psychoanalysis in groups, the group is self perpetuating. Although there is a transplanting of patients, the groups do not entirely disband as a rule. Patients may join and leave.

GROUP DYNAMICS

There are some positives in homogeneous group responses. Co-patients are often helpful to one another, sustaining in critical situations, compassionate, insightful, and empathic. In spite of variations in their history and character, they frequently identify with and feel for each other. To the degree that this takes place, members are constructively homogeneous, and the group leader can endorse such wholesome mutual support and positive inter-action. It does not seem technically possible, however, to incorporate into treatment the idea that, when patients love one another, there is a good reparative result. The therapist cannot in treatment create an atmosphere of love. To try to do so would deny the possibility of technical intervention determined by insight into psychodynamics. It is valuable when patients relate to each other positively and support one another's weakened egos, but such mutual sustenance should not be confused with psychoanalytic treatment.

Whenever a patient has ego weakness, he is inclined to deny his own perceptions, judgment, choices, wishes, and aspirations and to yield to those of the other. Sometimes this other assumes gigantic proportions, especially when it is the homogeneous group dynamic pressure of co-patients. To the extent that a patient has good ego strength, he has the capacity to respect his own ego resources and pursue his own inclinations in the face of the group-as-a-whole domination. To the degree that the group leader supports the group process position, he imposes on the individual ego a submerged problem—a dual pseudo-ego problem. In doing this, he limits personal development, weakens ego resources, and cultivates submerged pathology.

Health does not come from submission to group fiat. And healthy cohesion does not depend on a denial of individuality and wholesale acceptance of group standard. It should not be necessary to submerge one's ego in order to be accepted by a group. Any treatment based on submission to an authoritarian group is dictatorial. Reconstructive change is not achieved by capitulation to a dominating group but by careful analytic work. The patient cannot appropriately avoid conflict by obediently conforming to the common point of view.

The psychoanalyst is, therefore, opposed to routine group-as-a-whole interpretations, which do injury to already submerged egos. If the therapist does not recognize individual variations and does not promote each patient's autonomy, if he chooses to make group process observations, he guides the members toward a homogeneity in pathology instead of toward the more wholesome possibility of interactive diversity. He prevents group members from attaining the independence and freedom that are the goals of good treatment. An analyst who endorses group consensus fosters submergence by not promoting the privilege of each patient to differ with the majority. In so doing, he allows an authoritarian group to dominate the individual. Such a group therapist is satisfied with the emergence of group themes. The psychoanalyst is not content with this. He goes beyond the manifest conformity to get to the latent individual uniqueness of each patient.

DEMAND FOR PARTICIPATION

Another example of oppressive group pressure occurs when the whole group demands the participation of a silent or withdrawn member. Although such authority directed at a detached patient may, in fact, lead to his engagement, it seems to be an especially nonanalytic means to penetrate resistance. Are there not analytic devices more appropriate than aggressive group demand? Might not an occasional patient take flight in the face of such mass pressure?

Such a group demand seems dedicated to pressing members to do something. If it appears so, very likely several aggressive patients are leading the pack while the others are submissively following.

Even if the group demand that a member give up his resistance works under the influence of the united power of the group, the precedent seems dangerous. The idea has too many overtones of brainwashing, or forcing an individual to yield to group demand. The effect may well be de-egotizing and may lead to pseudoego pathology.

THERAPEUTIC VALUE OF GROUP-AS-A-WHOLE INTERVENTIONS

The leader's or the group's preoccupation with the group-as-a-whole is not psychoanalytically therapeutic. The group processor tends to neglect psychoanalytic confrontations and individual insights for observations about what the group-as-a-group is doing. He may neglect the individual's unconscious psychodynamics and psychopathology.

The leader who is repetitively engaged in pursuing group process tends to homogenize the group, to treat it as a whole. In doing this, the therapist may be motivated by anxiety in coping with a triad or a multivariable condition. He may be more secure in creating the illusion that he is in a dyad. In the dyad, he may be immersed in the illusory security of a relationship with his mother, a transference of his own. Or, he may be in a homosexual relationship with the group homogenized as a symbolic father. He may be excluding one parent or the other or disregarding a sibling with whom he is in rivalry.

The group-as-a-whole therapist tends to use group terms and concepts and to use phrases like *group ego, group id, group superego, group mind, collective unconscious, collective consciousness, group resistance,* and *group transference.* All these terms are distortions on the part of the leader.

A group may be reparative or destructive, but this is a matter of chance and must be distinguished from psychoanalytic therapy, which is a series of technical interventions, such as making the unconscious conscious, working through resistance, and transference.

An emphasis on group process is anti-analytic, a distraction from analytic work, because it focuses primarily on the group rather than on the patient. Interpretations of group process phenomena in therapy do not treat the patient. No means has yet been devised to psychoanalyze a group. The individual is not analytically reconstructed by mystical interventions dedicated to treating the group-as-a-whole, despite the ingenuity of Ezriel, for example.

The group process view is a mystique because it claims to heal by group cohesion and group atmosphere rather than through the individualized and expert attention and intervention by the analyst. The group is invested with a magically healing power it does not possess. It has no inherent benevolent influence that enables it to apply its magical authority. Such a belief in the group is sorcery, incantation. Group-as-a-whole therapists overvalue cohesion and climate, and they undervalue analysis.

Their dedication to the group leads to a denial of each member's individuality and differences. They tend to promote a pathological homogeneity, rather than interactive and complementary heterogeneity. They would influence the patient by group pressure rather than by understanding. This is repressive-inspirational rather than psychoanalytic. In their view, the manifest is seen as the individual patient's, and the latent is regarded as the group's activity as a whole. This is, of course, a reversal of the analytic view, in which the group's activity would be conceived of as the manifestation and the patient's unconscious contribution to the group's activity as the latent.

SPEAKING FREELY IN THE GROUP

Psychotherapists of individual patients are often doubtful about whether group members can speak freely, not only because of the presence of others but because there are so many interruptions of unpremeditated speech. But even in individual treatment the patient's spontaneous expressions have to be limited by the length of the session, suspended to allow the therapist to intervene at intervals and controlled in order not to permit the ego to be overwhelmed by unconscious material. His freely expressed associations need to be studied with discrimination. The group therapist's anxiety regarding interference with each member's free flow of speech may be interpreted as his preferring to practice one-to-one treatment in the group setting. Interruptions by one another may render one patient's fancy or dream intelligible but may also be utilized to grasp the meaning of and explain the fracturing interruptions of the other patients in a variety of interpretations. The therapist's perception of a patient interaction as obstructive interferes with reasonable mutual understanding. It fosters individual therapy in the group and promotes a rivalry to impede and surpass each other, a competition to court the regard of the leader.

The therapist encourages patients to express their thoughts, feelings, and responses to each other, urging them all to be in therapy rather than one after the other. He copes with presented associations as mutual and interactive, so that reciprocity is enhanced. In this way, the spontaneous fancies of all the members deepen rather than diminish. In a therapeutic group, a member in his uncensored speech is required to conduct himself with *some* consciousness of the rights and feelings of the other patients. This presumption of awareness of each other is ego building. Totally unmeasured freedom to say whatever one pleases without such consciousness may lead to more severe mental disorder.

HEALTHY AND UNHEALTHY ACTIVITY IN THE GROUP THERAPIES

Pathological activity is more easily disclosed in the group than in one-to-one treatment and can, consequently, be more readily explored and worked through. Members who disclose very personal matters to each other apart from group meetings with promises not to bare them to the group are acting out a resistance. Consequently, patients are prompted to unmask each other at group sessions. They are encouraged to bring each other's evasions to light before the entire group.

In the group therapies, there is much more animation, exertion, and movement than in individual treatment. The movement may be felicitous or it may be inappropriate. A good part of the behavior is not pathological but a healthful result of hearty interpersonal responsiveness in the group. One does not encounter merely animosity and contention there but vivacious exhibition of kindness, consideration, and sympathy as well. When abnormal behavior takes place, it is in part the result of intense affective mutual stimulation. If the therapist maintains his leading position as the observing commentator on the meaning of acting out, it can thereby generally be controlled. When such offers of insight are unsuccessful in restraining acting on transference, the leader may, all other means brought to naught, be compelled to proscribe it. The exercise of the prohibition usually offers such freedom from tension associated with acting out that group members are generally grateful for the external restraint.

Practice in the group therapies has established that there is no need for anxiety about pathological behavior. If members can comport themselves during the larger part of the day without the therapist, they can be trusted to maintain the same reasonable discipline with regard to acting out. Even if the therapist does not circumscribe it, the patients themselves soon limit it. If they appear incapable of controlling themselves, they appeal to the therapist to lead them to more self regulation. Thus, the acted-out pathology gets the analyst's attention but also the critical responses of a number of other members whose observations are insightful. In this respect, the patient has the advantage of being stimulated and observed by multiple resources not available to him in the dyad. Thus, the diversity made available by group members may be used to enrich whatever the patient presents, whether fantasy, dreams, conflict, or external problem. In the group, there may be less focusing than in analytic dyads but more stimulation to a wider canvas of psychopathological and healthy reactivity.

ISOLATION VERSUS SOCIALIZATION

Isolation and socialization are consequences as well as sources of intrapersonal and interpersonal dynamics. A good many individually but inadequately analyzed patients are poorly adjusted in their relations with groups of people. After extensive individual treatment, they sometimes find themselves to be more lonely and unsocialized than before. They may then seek out a group therapist to help them resolve their withdrawal and to promote their socialization. Previously committed to intrapersonal preoccupation, they may be propelled into ever more disengagement. The analyst in groups is aware that patients may socialize in mutually destructive ways that are resistive and acting out. He guards against such abuse of socialization by analyzing these operations and supporting limits and understanding.

Healthy, reasonable objective members undertake to undercut acting out. So, too, are the sustaining qualities in a variety of sound ego functions. Other elements of control are derived from the projection of rational judgment onto the leader and on group members, respect for the therapist as a reasonable restraining authority, the longing to be counseled by custom and common usage, by what is right and not wrong, by what is just, not unjust, by prescription and a sense of duty. A discouragement to acting on transference is that it will, as group meetings go on, be revealed. Finally, self-restoring necessities, sound influences in the group and the therapist lead the patients to set barriers to their acting out.

INDIVIDUAL VERSUS GROUP STIMULI

The members of a group provide the patient with more stimuli than does the analyst alone in the dyadic relationship. The analyst is also the focus of more stimulation in the group than in one-to-one treatment. This situation poses a problem. Do these multiple stimuli produce more diversion, more shifting of attention, and less careful examination of each patient than he might receive in individual treatment? It is quite possible. The answer depends in part on the competence, skill, and leadership of the therapist.

In a group, each patient receives not only interpretation from the various group members but also the wholesome qualities of social intercourse.

The feeling of abandonment is more vividly experienced by the patient when he is placed in an analytic group. In individual treatment, he has the therapist all to himself, at least in fantasy, and in reality the illusion is fostered by isolating one patient from the next. A group member repeatedly talks of his sadness, anger, or sense of isolation when the therapist or a meaningful co-patient seems to prefer another member. Because the therapist is less available, because he is not exclusively possessed, the feeling of being isolated recurs more frequently in the group. Therefore, the analyst can more easily pursue the interpersonal dynamics that led to the real and unreal sense of isolation. He can also explore the genetic determinants that led to the intrapsychic dynamics that now keep the patient in isolation. And the patient has group members with whom he can work toward a more gratifying socialization.

It is always enlightening to the analyst to find how often the problem of isolation presents itself when a patient moves from individual analysis to treatment in a group. The therapist may have been unaware of the extent to which this was a problem.

The previous dyadic setting, in which the patient had the analyst to himself, prevented the emergence of this difficulty. The experience in a group vividly promotes the appearance of a sense of isolation for all to see. The patient sets himself apart by reproducing in repetition-compulsion his refusal to participate, or by reproducing his competition with a parent or sibling who is favored by another familial figure whose appreciation or affection he wants.

Traditionally, socialization is regarded as a resistive maneuver, and it may become so. This need not be so as long as socialization is examined and analyzed for its resistive components. Socialization is a phenomenon that occurs to some extent in all group therapy. In psychoanalysis in groups, however, the issue of whether socialization is obstructing the analytic process or making it more manageable needs to be explored. It seems that socialization has a humanizing and a restorative value. But social intercourse may enable patients to resist the search for latent mainsprings. Therefore, the analyst needs to be alert for the way in which patients use the alternate sessions, the post-session, clique formations, and subgroup dating.

HIERARCHICAL AND PEER VECTORS

The phenomenon of transference in psychoanalysis in groups can be made more intelligible if one understands that the group provides for the simultaneous presence of peer and hierarchical relationships. By supplying a lateral vector as well as the vertical vector found in dyadic analysis, psychoanalysis in groups provides that patient with the freedom to relate to peers. These horizontal relationships may be facile or awkward, depending on each member's history. One common dilemma with sibling surrogates involves rivalry.

In dyadic treatment, the vertical dimension prevails, with the analyst seen as a parent surrogate. In the power-invested one-to-one climate, it may not be easy for the analysand to convey what he would like to say. In a group, the access of peers in some measure shrinks the ominous influence of the leader, and interaction among the members is usually freer. However, the opposite may occur. The analyst may be easier to talk to than the co-patients. A patient may coalesce the members into a single parental surrogate figure so that even patients are misperceived as being in the vertical vector.

If the analyst is dogmatic, the peers support each other judiciously and injudiciously in defying his predominance. For some of the patients, this support is salutary; for others, it is obsessive. In any event, it challenges the analyst, who is thereby less able to dominate the membership of the group.

Effective treatment leads to a sense of equality between patient and analyst. But actual parity cannot be achieved in dyadic analysis. It can, on the other hand, be accomplished with one's peers in a group setting. The achievement of a sense of equality in the group enlarges the hope and the feasibility of parity between analysand and analyst. In dyadic treatment, in which the patient is always being assisted by the analyst, a healthy sense of equality in difference is difficult to achieve. Fortunately, only a few dyadic therapists regard the patient as infantile and helpless and see themselves as models—dead certain and infallible. In the act of practicing psychoanalysis in groups, the therapist rejects such assumptions about his patients and himself. He sees wholesome potentials and sources of help among group members. He does not see himself as the only source of assistance, insight, innovation, and inducement to healthful change.

The dyadic therapist's all-knowing position tends to sponsor illusion. Because he is the only other person available to the patient, the latter is dependent on the analyst's views. The analysand has only the therapist's associations for testing reality. Group members, however, provide multiple others to define the nature of reality and unreality.

EQUALITY, FREEDOM, AND HOSTILITY

Whenever there is superiority and inferiority among persons, with limited independence for the inferior, enmity and hatred can be anticipated. Disaffection occurs when impartial opportunity is not available. The vertical character of dyadic treatment denies the analysand's feeling of parity. If the analyst stresses the analysand's disorder, the patient more than ever feels disparate, inadequate.

Parity, independence, and freedom are more readily experienced in the group. There, patients have more room to ventilate less acute anger, more empathy, more compassion, and more realistically positive affect than in the dyad, in which angry and warm feelings are most commonly dependent, child-like, and distorted—that is, one-sided.

On occasion, however, members of groups are inappropriately harsh and cruel with one another. Good treatment must not entail trial and punishment. The adherents of such a principle, whether patients or therapists, have residual unresolved sadomasochistic difficulties. The aggressor is acting out a negative transference, and his prey a compliant one. When this phenomenon takes place in a group, the therapist must analyze the bilateral distortions early to save the participants from damaging one another. Tolerance and compassion cannot develop during prolonged mutual attack. They grow only in a more wholesome atmosphere. Repetitive anger does not lead to mutual regard unless a member has never been allowed to express negative feelings. But if he is encouraged to ventilate his hostility, he will later be obliged to redeem himself, before other patients will trust his good will. Malice is usually met with resentment, open or concealed. The group analyst needs to be watchful for ways and means to deal with the disorder of hate.

RETALIATION AND FULFILLMENT

In the psychoanalytic group, there is more to both transferential and realistic expectations. It is the analyst's function to analyze the mutually hurtful character of bilaterally fulfilling archaic needs and to promote the gratification of more realistic requirements. The illusory exemption from retribution and the frustration of anticipated expectation that theoretically prevail in dyadic analysis may not always be a salutary influence. The analyst's need to overprotect a patient from his peers has something to do with his concern that they will damage each other. Patients, in fact, turn out to be not so hurtful. They demonstrate their healthy resources and their potential for growth in the decent and tolerant ways they treat each other.

There is an inclination in some quarters to regard the interaction between patients as just as significant and valuable as that between analyst and patient. Interaction among group members is generally less intense. In dyadic and group analysis, the authority of the leader is both real and illusory. To regard the leadership of the therapist in the dyad as an illusion and the authority of co-patients as genuine, or the opposite, is to misconstrue the quality of leadership in the dyadic and group setting.

Psychoanalysis in groups is effective because, in part, it does not deny the participant his freedom to examine his many-faceted affect about genuine and illusory hierarchical figures and peers. He had more of a chance in a group to retort and to gratify himself in fact and in fantasy in both the peer and hierarchical vectors. These gratifications, both wholesome and sick, in which he is supporter and supported, heard and hearing among his fellows, have an important place in group analysis.

ACTIVITY AND PASSIVITY OF THE ANALYST

There is dissimilarity in the functioning of the analyst in the two settings. In the group, patients turn more to each other for affective interaction, for understanding, for confrontation and insight. In the dyad, the analysand has only the analyst to look to for such responses, but the analyst reacts in these ways only when in his clinical judgment they are indicated. As a result, the therapist in a group can generally be more of an uninvolved and reasonable onlooker as interaction goes on about him. In the dyad, where every response is turned on him, he is expected by the patient to become more engaged than he may think appropriate. Here it is more arduous for the analyst to sustain a detached, reasonable, and regardful stance. The reverse may be true for those therapists who become more insulated and detached in dyadic sessions, and more affectively and inappropriately engaged in group meetings.

In dyadic treatment, the therapist may be obliged to be more animated, to cultivate the interaction that is inherent in a group. The group analyst may reduce his exertions because the group members foster the interaction.

Therapists, like their patients, choose to function in one setting or the other because they are able in one more than in the other to be more passive or active. An analyst may be more stirred, more quickened, more incited in one milieu and more immobilized, almost paralyzed, in the other. But one needs to explore the reality, the unreality, and the relationship to treatment goals of particular activity and passivity. In dyadic analysis, the analysand is generally more active and the therapist more passive. But if the patient is passive, it may be necessary for the analyst to become active. The very passive neutrality of orthodox analysis may require revision in the face of clinical experience with group analysis, in which forced interaction has shown itself to be productive. The dyadic analyst may find that, if he penetrates resistance more actively by provocation and by encouraging interaction, he will expediate treatment.

ANGER AT THE THERAPIST

Occasionally, co-patients support one another in expressing negative feelings toward the therapist. This type of support is extremely productive for those members who are not likely to assert themselves when alone with the analyst. An alliance enables them to do so until they have sufficient ego strength to stand up to the therapist alone. This group dynamic may be encouraged in general, but it seems inappropriate for each patient to experience anger at the group leader at the same time. Nor does it seem at all likely that each member is in that phase of transference relationship when the expression of negative feelings is indicated.

DISPLACEMENT

Group members frequently displace affect onto one another as a means of evading their responses to the analyst. This displacement is both expedient and resistive. An individual analysand may describe his attitude toward a person outside the treatment room, when, in fact, he is reporting how he feels about the analyst. In the group, a member may in the same way be responding to a fellow patient or to all his co-patients as stand-ins for the therapist. There is greater likelihood of secreting displacement in dyadic analysis because the inciting cause that leads to such proxy formation is often not discernible.

SUPPORT

A patient experiences a greater sense of security in a group because there is a probability there of finding co-patients who encourage his healthy or disturbed aspirations. The analysand in a dyad is usually less sure of getting support for his strivings when he is dependent on only one other person.

Relief and assistance are necessary requirements in all treatment. They are means by which the faltering resources of a patient may be promoted. By having his positive potentials encouraged, the analysand is stirred to show his disorder, his pathology, his gradually recalled history, and his suppressed feelings. The analyst's support is circumscribed because it is derived from the hierarchical position and because it is offered in kind, in degree, in quality and quantity that he believes to be relevant and required. He may deny offering this relief in the concern that it may deepen the patient's symbiosis.

In the group, sustenance is derived from other patients as well as from the analyst. The helpful function of co-patients is particularly apparent at the alternate meeting. Members often reveal problems there for the first time. Then only through the support of fellow patients is the exposed material presented at the regular session with the analyst. Some members need to be encouraged by the analyst in the dyad before they are able to reveal a difficult history of problems in the group. There are more chances of finding greater and various kinds of support in the dyad or the group in multiple therapeutic settings. The patients and the analyst offer different kinds of help. Co-patients' support is more spontaneous, more impulsive, and more compulsive. The analyst's is more purposeful, more useful, and more discriminatingly applied.

Indeed, the most moving experience in the group is not the comfort offered to the ailing but the attainment of fulfillment in reality, the triumph over the neurotic adaptation, the conscious alternative choice over the obsessive one. It is a moment that comes when the previously estranged group members accept and enjoy one another, when they treat each other like human beings, instead of brutes.

ACCOUNTABILITY

The patient in individual analysis is generally not held accountable for his wildest fantasies of love and hate, of sexuality or homicide. The analyst fosters this illusion to enable the patient to speak freely and regress with the assurance of support and without the fear of retaliation. No such security in illusion is available in the group. Expressed fantasies, dreams, thoughts, and feelings are met with all sorts of emotional reactions: fear, anger, rivalry, hostility, rage, anxiety, sensuality, and so forth. This responsiveness makes each member aware that, although he is always free to say what comes to mind and heart, he is accountable for what he says and does.

There is, therefore, more at stake in speaking up in the group. It becomes more hazardous, for there are always consequences. The wonder is that patients nevertheless do speak up. They always have allies, frequently the very members to whom they are being reactive. This setup is much more reality oriented than is the individual setting, in which the benignity of the analyst sponsors the illusion of nonaccountability.

In a way, it is dangerously irresponsible for the therapist to permit this kind of illusion to go on for too long without limiting it, without showing the patient the consequences of his thoughts and feelings, especially if he tends to express them or act them out beyond the consulting room. The analyst's leniency, permissiveness, and forbearance cannot be limitless. Group members quite appropriately hold each other responsible. This is salutary, for it seems to be more realistic to do so. At the same time, group members are enormously tolerant in the recognition of the value of regression as long as it is in the service of the ego. The nonisolatedness of the interaction in a group, when compared with the dyadic setting, supports the need to be aware of the other, the necessity to maintain communication. If treatment deprives a patient of awareness of the consequences of his expressions, it denies him orientation, a place among his fellows, an ego. Whatever he says becomes a whisper lost in the wind, and he becomes equally uncertain of his place.

Group analysis also cultivates a sense of social responsibility among patients. This is one of its values. The conditions that the dyadic therapist demands of the analysand relate mostly to paying a fee, not physically hurting the analyst, and not damaging his furniture and books. The largely tolerant stance of the analyst occasionally institutes or maintains in the analysand a frustrating inclination to take favor as his due and to complain if it is not always as immediately available as a pacifier. If the analyst does not frustrate and analyzes this inappropriate antici-pation, the exploitative patient's abrasive and inordinate claims for support are intensified. In the group, no member can maintain such exemption from obligation without protest from others. This protest is wholesome. The demanding, dependent patient is required to react with increasing resourcefulness, autonomy, and responsibility if he hopes to develop better relations with others. This pressure to relinquish the dependent tie to a parent surro-gate is a valuable influence in resolving a persistent transference neurosis.

THE ALTERNATE MEETING

Many group therapists reject the alternate meeting. They see it largely as encouraging the patients to act out. There may be greater opportunity for acting out when alternate meetings are made available, but alternate sessions are not proposed for the purpose of acting out, nor are patients encouraged to act out. They are, in fact, urged not to do so. Attempts are made to analyze imminent acting out. When it takes place, it is analyzed in order to interrupt it. All else failing, it is forbidden.

The alternate meeting has important advantages. One of these is spontaneous mutual support among members of the group, an advantage that appeared quite naturally in the earliest post-sessions. At these meetings, thoughts, feelings, and activities emerged that were different from those at regular sessions. By comparing and contrasting behavior at regular and alternate meetings, therapists found quantitative and qualitative differences in the two settings and were able to examine these differences productively.

Only the therapist is sufficiently trained to conduct the systematic intervention of treatment. Patients are not expected to be therapists to one another. If they try to assume such inappropriate roles, they are in resistance. They are generally incapable of making skilled observations required of the therapist. Therefore, treatment in this sense does not go on at the alternate meeting. Patients may attempt to conduct themselves as therapists for one another, but such behavior is usually rejected and resisted. They tend to interact spontaneously. They do not know one another's diagnosis, and they are unaware of what stage of treatment each member is in. The therapist has a plan in mind for the treatment of each member. The patients do not.

The therapist at regular meetings demands that the patients do analytic work. Patients also offer each other insight at alternate sessions, but there the pursuit of mutual understanding and insight is not so intense or concentrated. Patients in the alternate meetings experience one another as trying to be helpful. This diffused helpfulness is experienced in the regular meeting as well. But under the therapist's influence there is an effort to work more analytically in his presence. He is the primary source of insight and of pressure to give up archaic means. He induces them to apply themselves more vigorously to the tasks of getting well.

If the analyst tries to use a patient as a co-therapist, he is misusing the patient in countertransference. Whenever the analyst so misuses a group member, the patient may be induced to play this role at alternate meetings as well. But being a co-therapist should be neither his role nor his responsibility. He is in treatment to get well, not to become a therapist. The analyst has no objection to the members being helpful to one another. They do, in fact, repeatedly offer one another useful support and understanding. But whenever a patient compulsively tries to exercise the role of co-therapist, he is in resistance to his more realistic position as patient. Nevertheless, patients often turn to one another for emotional sustenance in anxiety and depression. When the analyst is unavailable—on vacation, for example— patients are obliged, as at the alternate meeting, to turn to one another for understanding, maintenance, and relief. Such assistance is useful and often insightful. Even at regular meetings, patients offer one another interpretations. The analyst welcomes such expositions as long as they are not pursued compulsively as a way of resisting analysis.

CONTROL

Psychoanalysis in a group would become untenable and dissolve if every member were emboldened to act impulsively on every flash of feeling or thought. The group limits acting out that endangers the mutual effort to resist the gratification of archaic longings. And it is necessary to limit certain activities to meet the needs for some social order in the group.

Impulsivity and compulsivity require a study of just how, when, and where his insufficiency or excess of inhibition developed. If few controls were imposed on a patient by his nuclear family, he may choose an individual analyst in the hope that the surrogate parent may likewise exercise little discipline. If the inducement to acting out took place with nonfamilial figures outside the home, he may choose an individual analyst in the wish of finding a parental substitute who will limit his impulsivity, his pathological repetition. If the peers in the nuclear family insufficiently controlled him, he may seek in group therapy peers who will help to limit him.

ACTING AND ACTING OUT

Because of his training, the analyst is not likely to act out. There are occasions, however, when he is predisposed by his own or a patient's disequilibrium to act out. If this happens, he loses his reasonable, examining, discerning, and objective role. In the group, he is required, even forced, to retain a regardful and watchful role because the patients sustain one another with refuges in reality. They maintain one another in resisting the inappropriateness of the therapist's acting out.

The members of every therapeutic group sooner or later set bounds on their acting out. Prime movers for this restraint are the wholesome, realistic aspirations in each patient and the prophylactic factors in various ego functions. Another mainspring inheres in the projection of influential power, of living by the rules and order of what is right and wrong, of superego values, which act to curb irrational behavior. The analyst, his attendance at regular meetings, and his vaguely felt presence at alternate sessions or afterward all exert a limiting influence as well. The members are aware that their activity will sooner or later be revealed. Apprehension over such an outcome is also a factor in controlling acting out.

Certainly, there is less activity in the dyad than in the group. The essential point is not whether there is more or less activity in one setting than in the other. As long as there are patients in therapy, there will be acting out. The issue rather seems to be that the therapist is alarmed at the prospect of acting out taking place among his patients. In the dyad, acting out is prevented by the analyst, but the patient may act out outside the analytic chamber without the therapist's knowledge for some time. Acting out in the group is more easily exposed and discovered, and it can be more readily worked through.

In psychoanalysis in groups, there is more activity of all kinds than in individual analysis. There is more expression of warmth, affection, helpfulness, anger, aggression, hostility. The analyst is obliged to interrupt an interaction from time to time by offering interpretations, insight, and analysis. On occasion, when analysis fails in its object to limit acting out, he may have to forbid it. At the outset, patients may object to the analyst's denying them in this way and to the imposition of control, but in time the interdiction offers them so much relief from anxiety that they show their appreciation for the limits that are set. A good deal of activity, however, is not acting out at all but a healthy consequence of wholesome group interaction. Acting out in group is, in part, a result of intensely affective mutual stimulation. If the therapist persists in his interpretive analysis of what is going on, acting out can be controlled.

SELF-IMPOSED LIMITS TO ACTING OUT

If the therapist does not intervene or interrupt acting out, even of the most dramatic kinds, group members sooner or later set their own limits. In the most seriously disturbed acting-out groups, the members inevitably turn to the analyst and ask him to help them set limits. Ultimately, there is always such frustration between members who act out that the parties to it inevitably turn to the other patients and to the analyst for control and insight. Patients who act out at alternate sessions sooner or later turn to the analyst, asking him to set limits and to seek greater understanding of the nature of their behavior.

ACTION GROUPS

In the last fifty years, group therapy has led to movement from lying on the couch to being seated in a circle. And in more recent years there has been a leap into vigorous action. There is an increasingly anarchic rejection of reasonableness and reality. Whereas psychoanalysis has always sought a controlled, systematic regression in the service of the ego, the disciplines of action promote irrational feeling, acting out, and assault on order—all in the name of love. Such destructive activity is a call for infantilism, for regression without thought, in the name of freedom from the bourgeois values of the establishment. This kind of activity is a repudiation of all that years of careful analysis have taught—the necessity for dispassionate study of the patient. It makes a virtue of his illness. It puts pseudo-love and its destructiveness above therapeutic reconstruction. It tells people to embrace one another without understanding. It says people can understand nothing. Therefore, they must give up as hopeless their historical aim of knowing one another. All they can do is act—act blindly but feelingly. This unthinking activity is destructive not only of the other but of the self.

What followers of the group-therapy-as-feelingful-action seem not to grasp is that, if feelingful action is the magic road to recovery, there is no further necessity for scrupulous training. Already, the group therapy movement is heavily weighted with dianeticists, scientologists, activists, zenists, and affectivists, who mindlessly lead loving and fighting groups into psychotic acting out. These leaders do not wish to be burdened by what they regard as the formalized disabilities of learning. It is easier to act swiftly and ruthlessly without the handicap of second thoughts or even first ones. What a patient needs, however, is thoughtful consideration. He turns to the analyst for insight, not rebellious exercises. There is serious danger that the group therapy movement will be taken over by the revolutionary know-nothingism of the affect-action promoters, for whom "id is beautiful."

CONCLUSIONS

The assumption by some dyadic analysts that psychoanalysis in groups cannot be effective because patients are too unaware of each other's realistic necessities and lack the capacity to grasp and deal with their archaic needs is not confirmed by clinical experience. On the contrary, analysands attain in groups an unusual facility for multilateral examination, for insight, and for mutually enhancing conduct.

In a group, no single member becomes the focus of analytic attention to the exclusion of the others. Consideration by the members and the leader moves from one patient to the next so that cyclic oscillation of activity and rest, disinhibition and restitution, take place. No member is obliged to engage in only one kind of activity or to play an assigned, homogeneous role. In the analytic dyad, it is difficult to change his repertoire, for he is always in the position of being helped by a helper. In psychoanalysis in groups, he is expected and even required to play a multiplicity of emancipating roles.

Therapists who emphasize group process and group-as-a-whole dynamics, as well as those who emphasize the psychoanalytic treatment of the individual in interaction and his intrapsychic life, wish to create a climate that supports the progressive evolution of each patient in a therapeutic group. The current emphasis on group process and group-as-a-whole dynamics not only fosters resistance, but also creates a submerged impact on every member and provides a pseudo-cohesion. Health follows only after the liberation of the suppressed ego in each patient and the working through of his individual resistances and transferences. An appropriate regard for each other can follow only after a member has realistic regard for himself. With the emphasis on the primacy of the individual in psychoanalysis in groups, it is, therefore, not the aim to lead the group into chaos of every man for himself. Psychoanalysis in groups is an approach that emphasizes harmony growing out of disharmony, reciprocity out of antagonism, ego growth through persistent emphasis on supporting the suppressed ego, self respect and respect for others in the course of the struggle, appreciation of differences, and a sense of mutual regard as treatment goes on. Indeed, psychoanalysis in groups, with its emphasis on protecting and promoting the wholesome uniqueness of the individual, is perhaps more relevant in contemporary society than it ever has been.

7

Resolution of Patients' Psychopathology

DATA

In dyadic analysis, the material for study is provided as a sequel to the actual event—that is, it is furnished out of recollection of experience. The only original and verifiable data that are experienced are provided in the patient's responses to the analyst. In the group, the stuff of analysis is available not only in terms of historical recollection but also on the basis of interaction with co-patients. The accent in the group is on multilateral interaction, which is then enlisted for understanding the unconscious urges and motives that generated it. The engaged group members join in an exploration and analysis of the shared experience. In dyadic analysis, an interaction outside the treatment room can be comprehended only by hindsight. In the group, the participants can be seen in action, direct observation can be made of how the episode began, and a detailed study can be made of the motives of the provocateur as well as those of the reactor. Group members tend to object to overlong, repeated stories, whether historical or current in nature. In the therapeutic dyad, an obsessive concern with the analyst can also turn into an insulating, symbiotic, and illusory experience.

SELECTION OF MATERIAL

In any setting, access to underlying psychodynamics and psycho-pathology is always incomplete, and the emphasis is chosen by the therapist. In dyadic analysis, the choices are directed by the character of the actual or subjective anxiety the patient experiences with the analyst, the analysand's capacity to trust the therapist, and his relative certainty of nonreprisal. In group analysis, the selection of material is defined by the patient's security that he will not be seriously hurt by the other members or the therapist, and to the extent that he can look for assistance and relief from them. What the patient consciously and unconsciously exposes may differ from dyadic to regular to alternate meeting. His choice depends on the nature of the material, the kind of patient he is, the makeup of the group, and the attitudes of his co-patients and of the leader.

In any form of psychotherapy, the totality of a patient's responses is not available. It is not selective of the therapist to be occupied with catching each and every response the patient makes. It is grandiose to have to be all-knowing and aware of the slightest detail. Treatment is discriminating, selective, choosing to pay attention to some processes and phenomena, and rejecting or analyzing others as resistive. In dyadic analysis, for example, the analyst may choose the patient's transference to him for study, or he may scrutinize among the patient's free associations those elements that illuminate his realistic circumstances outside the treatment room. But the therapist is in a position to explore only those reactions and recollections the analysand presents. In the group situation, a wider range of material is presented for direct observation. The analyst may choose to scrutinize whatever transferential response or defensive operation he believes is appropriate to work with at a certain time. He exercises his judgment in opting to examine this or that maneuver at the heart of things, one of the interconnecting elements that may explain the historically derived current behavior. He pays less regard to a multitude of other patient reactions; if he did not, he would fail to function effectively as an analyst. If he attends to everything, he is swamped and misses the core in a mass of less relevant data. He has to be selective. He has to choose for examination the list of things that fits each analysand, depending on his phase of evolution and growth.

GENETIC AND CURRENT MATERIAL

Interaction among patients followed by free association often leads to the recollection of significant genetic material. Either interaction spontaneously generates free association, or the analyst promotes it. By this means, history is made available in the group, unless the analyst or the resistive patient rejects it for an exclusive here-and-now experience. At times, the therapist may have to initiate the process of cultivating an interest in free association to early derivatives and their history, making clear the relevance of the past to its repetition in the present. If the analyst evades this responsibility, the patients will also do so and become more resistively involved in the here-and-now expressions of affect, thought, and behavior.

In dyadic analysis, preoccupation with current events in the patient's life outside of the therapeutic milieu is resistive. In the dyad, the interaction is largely in terms of transference and the emerging transference neurosis. In the group, current events in and outside of therapy play an integral part in analysis. The impromptu thought and feeling, the extemporaneous, and the present occasion are subject to examination and are explored for understanding. In the dyad, even in responses to the analyst, the preoccupation is with history, partly on theoretical grounds, and partly because the therapist believes he cannot or should not interact.

REPETITIVE PATTERNS AND FLEXIBILITY

Repetitive patterns may become apparent in dyadic analysis before they do in group. This is true in part because the analyst tends to be more experienced as a single parental surrogate. Therefore, the repetitive transferential distortion manifests itself more obviously in dyadic analysis. But transferences also emerge in the group. They appear, however, in more variety because more transferential figures are available from the outset. Because of their multiplicity, it may seem, at first, more difficult to designate the various transferences in the group. As a result, the impression may be that the patient has less rigidity than was at first thought. But the fact is that in the group he is exposing a larger variety of transference reactions. As treatment goes on, the inflexibility of these transferences becomes clearer.

In dyadic analysis, the patient is not required to make many flexible adaptations to the changing expectations of persons. The individual analyst does not usually make the multiple demands for health that members of the group do. Of course, they also have irrational expectations of mutual adjustment to one another's pathology.

Dyadic analysis tends to expedite the development of transference. One-to-one treatment promotes the evocation of repetitive patterns with the idea that an unvarying relationship between the patient and the therapist is essential to ultimate change. Diversified responses tend to be regarded as resistive to the repetition of transference and its final resolution. The individual therapist sees the constancy, regularity, and routine of characteristic distortion as the essential basis for therapeutic intervention.

The dyadic analyst, therefore, is doubtful about the value of psychoanalysis in a group, since uniformity of response seems not to occur, and group patients appear not to persevere in their reactions. The analyst may believe there is too little assurance in foreseeing how patients will respond to one provocation or another. But if he affords himself any clinical experience in a group, he encounters a real and characteristic continuity of reaction in each patient, even among the most heterogeneously stimulating membership.

The heterogeneity of a group makes room for the patients' more flexible choices. For the impulsive member, there are patients whose rigidity helps him to exercise greater control. For the superego-ridden member, there are patients in the group who support his right to allow himself more privilege. The mutual support of peers provides a less severe and more permissive influence than the illusory and actual authority of the analyst, whose interventions are experienced as more unequivocal.

The coexistent and synchronous presence of horizontal and vertical vectors is also a factor that promotes flexibility in response. If only one of these dimensions is available, as in dyadic analysis or in a leaderless group, there is less flexibility and greater rigidity.

FOCUS ON INTERACTION

In dyadic treatment, the analyst may promote the patient's responses to him, concentrating on the analysand's disturbed reactions to him with a view to resolving them. In the group, many of these responses are directed toward co-patients, and there is intense affective interaction, both realistic and transferential. Such profoundly emotional interactions rarely occur in dyadic treatment, in which the analyst circumscribes such an eventuality by his remoteness. He rather permits the patient's affect simply to unfold without himself becoming emotionally involved. He cannot become involved without jeopardizing the treatment relationship. He certainly cannot become inappropriately enmeshed. In the group, however, patients may be supported in response to one another and encouraged to interact without acting out. This interpersonal engagement has value. The therapist can preserve his reasonable, examining role. In the therapeutic dyad, such a posture tends to block the affective interpersonal exchange that occurs in a group setting.

WHERE ANALYSIS TAKES PLACE

Analysis takes place largely through the interventions of the analyst. For certain patients, generally in the early phases of therapy, the most striking progress may not come in the dyadic interviews or in the group meetings the analyst attends but in the alternate sessions. This advance occurs without analytic intervention. Such improvement becomes analytic when the character of the unconscious material is explored and made conscious, when the significance of the repressed material is grasped in terms of the total experience, and when the latent posture and design that produces the anxiety are analyzed.

A most significant function of the analyst is to promote that activity of the analysand in interpersonal relationships beyond the therapeutic dyad. Some analysts too nondiscriminately prefer to limit the analysand to his one-to-one involvement with the therapist. They make the analytic relationship too exclusive of connections with others. This treatment has questionable validity because it may insulate the analysand in symbiosis. It limits the patient's choices, freedom, and growth, it circumscribes his activity within the therapeutic frame, and it negates the value of transactions beyond the dyad. The same thing may take place in group analysis if the leader interferes with patient interactions beyond the group, rejects the alternate sessions, and supports responses primarily to himself.

The group therapist attends the unconscious processes and motivations of each patient. His confronting them with their resistance, his analysis of their dreams and fantasies, his uncovering their suppressed history with its associated affect, and his making them aware of its repetition in transference in the group all enable them to consider the sounder and more realistic alternatives inherent in conscious choice. If he simply allows the members to communicate without insight, he encourages resistance. His example promotes the patients to undertake some role in giving and getting mutual understanding by similar but less expert means.

One patient should not be given protracted attention. Mutually responsive members should be given multi-lateral insight. Exclusive preoccupation with one member should be explored as resistance or countertransference.

A patient under criticism by the whole group without a single ally among the members should receive the leader's support. The member's provocative role should be examined and the unconscious motives for the feeling against him investigated.

A group therapist encourages his patients to look inward, backward, and interactively in order to be able to move forward more freely in a wondrous expansion of understanding. The group therapist needs to be devoted to the members, versatile in his approach to their problems, and alert to their moments of accessibility or defensiveness. If the group therapist truly hears in their responses the conflictual cry for help, the plea for enlightenment, and the great fear of disappointment, he can lead them from confusion to clarity, from sickness to stability, from isolation to interrelation.

Most of all, the group leader needs to achieve mastery in the area of technical competence. To this end, he needs to listen more carefully to the unconscious communications coming from patients. But to hear them in depth he needs to exercise his own freely roving imagination. To hear them even more profoundly he needs also to listen to how his colleagues perceive, attend, and write about their work in the group therapies. Finally, his expertness can be realized only by having the courage and persistence to illuminate the way to reality, even if he stands alone.

TIMING

One criticism of group analysis is that a member may awkwardly or discordantly offer some insight that the recipient is by no means prepared to accept at the time. The judgment is made that a precipitate or untimely offer of understanding may be too hurtful to a patient who may not be able to cope with the anxiety provoked by the confrontation. The authors' experience is that group members are, in general, able to deal with insights offered by co-patients either by resisting them or by gradually accepting them. When the therapist errs in the timing of a confrontation, the analysand becomes more disturbed because the understanding comes from a figure of authority.

The analyst in groups soon learns that it is not he alone who has the delicate touch, the exquisite empathy to know just when and how to offer insight. Surely some members are at first indifferent and unconcerned with others, but a large number have from the start a sensitivity to the feelings of others. At times, the analyst may be overprotective with a patient in the group, doubtful about his capacity to tolerate some newly offered interpretation. He may, under such circumstances, inappropriately postpone the acquisition of insight.

A co-patient does not have the expertness in timing interpretations that the skilled analyst has. But it is a common experience to find untrained members making very valuable observations about one another with an intuition and an acuity that are surprising. It is not that psychoanalytic theory and practice just come naturally to them. It is their good sense, directness, spontaneity, naturalness, enthusiasm, and artlessness, free of analytic jargon, and their obvious wish to help, that give them the capacity to be reparative. The affective pitch of reaction is also a factor in their reaching one another.

In dyadic analysis, it is the therapist's exclusive jurisdiction and responsibility to determine when to offer a piece of insight. His mistakes in timing are burdened with his authority. Excitation, insight, and confrontation by group members are both more readily resisted and at times more welcomed because they come from peers. If dyadic analysts alarm patients less with confrontations, it may simply be that they make fewer interpretations and are more guarded than necessary. If individual analysts are careful about poorly timed offers of insight, they may be just as reserved in tendering properly timed comments, thereby delaying the progress of analysis. In the group, the therapist can more securely turn over the experience of interaction to his patients, who provoke less anxiety than he does. He need not then be fearful that their attention will be hurtful. He is also free to step in more discreetly and discriminatively at those times when his interposition can be most beneficial. A member may at times become disturbed by a poorly timed response of a co-patient, but interaction among peers usually animates, sustains, and augments the progress of group members.

SILENCE

Therapists are familiar with the resistive significance of silence and are usually impatient with it. However, it has other dimensions in the group. Silence is not necessarily resistive; on occasion, it represents a period of renewal, integration, meditation, or deep feeling without the need to express, act, or respond immediately to the other. While one member is quietly examining a problem, another may be unavailable in resistance. Still another may be too apprehensive of exploration for the moment, and two others may be involved in an intense interaction and invite analytic inquiry. The group analyst can turn productively from one patient to another while some are provisionally silent.

If an analysand is making himself known and requires a listening silence, it is necessary for the analyst to be quiet. His inactive attention is required by the patient as an act complementary to his own. The analyst's being quiet looks like passivity on a manifest level; it is, in fact, his chosen activity appropriate to the patient's needs.

ANXIETY

Anxiety emerges when defenses or resistances are attacked or dissolved. Some patients feel little apprehension in the bipersonal situation but are obviously threatened at the idea of entering a group. Often they are symbiotically tied to a mother surrogate and fearful of the environment and persons apart from her. Other patients who were historically in *dis-ease* in the nuclear family or with an original parental figure are more secure in circumstances outside the family and frequently find the group more reassuring than with the analyst alone. They appreciate the alternate meetings more than sessions when the analyst is there. The therapist may feel the same way. Depending on his original history, he may be more or less nervous in the dyadic or in the group situation. The analysand needs to be encouraged to examine the source of his anxiety and to resolve it in the setting in which he experiences it. If he does not do this, he is liable to avoid the circumstances in which he develops anxiety, evades confrontation, and escapes resolution.

Every patient experiences anxiety. The therapist needs to know whether his apprehension is determined by realistic perception or by transference. Psychoanalysis in groups provides three means for the elucidation of defensive operations used to suppress anxiety: the consultation with the analyst alone, the regular meeting, and the alternate session. In these three settings, the therapist can examine the differences in anxiety in various transferential relationships.

In dyadic analysis, there is anxiety in the transferential impression of threat from the analyst as parent, generally the mother. A sense of being threatened by forces outside the analytic situation, whether in fact or in illusion, is derived from the patient's associations. In the dyad, it is hoped that the analysand will become conscious of his anxiety in the society external to the analysis, and that he will be disinhibited enough with his therapist to tell him of his feelings. In the dyad, there is greater need to become aware of anxiety stirred beyond the couch; in the group, anxiety can be revealed more easily and quickly in the course of interaction.

Some patients are more anxious in the dyad and more relaxed in the group. Alone with the analyst, they are more apprehensive about closeness to the parental surrogate, about his intensive scrutiny of their strong and ambivalent feelings about him, and about the possibility of isolation with him and its attendant regressive possibilities. In the group, there is more flight from exploration and, as a result, less anxiety. For other patients, the co-patient peers are more anxiety provoking. It may be that for most patients, given a choice of milieu, they would choose the dyad over the group as less anxiety inducing. The belief that in the group there will be less skillful intervention, less benevolence, and more eruption impels most patients to seek individual treatment. In some measure, a patient's choice of milieu is dependent on his history with parents and siblings, as well as on currently popular styles of therapeutic intervention.

SHIFTING ATTENTION

The experience of attention shifting from one member to another in psychoanalysis in groups diminishes anxiety by providing respites from exclusive and sometimes oppressive examination. In dyadic analysis, the patient is continuously under scrutiny. This scrutiny may produce defensiveness and resistance—a reaction to analytic pressure that can at times be incapacitating. The group, on the other hand, permits the patient periods of time to repose—to reflect on what he has just previously experienced, to consider what interpretations have been made to him, to speculate on alternatives in the process of working through—and, after being helped, he can turn to others and offer help. The shifting of attention is itself an alternative way of conducting oneself. It confronts the patient with the reality that he need not compulsively engage in a limited kind of activity.

Alternating scrutiny gives the patient an opportunity to show himself at a speed that is not too overwhelmingly anxiety provoking for him. In the therapeutic dyad, he is under continuous scrutiny and is required to expose himself. In the group, shifting attention away from him without the ongoing expectations that he make himself known may provide opportunities for resistance.

DEPENDENCE ON THERAPY

The morbid clinging to the therapist that can develop in the course of treatment is more ominous in the dyad than in the group. It is more of a hazard, at least in its intensity and depth, in the one-to-one setting, not infrequently becoming a transference psychosis and removing the patient from reality. In a group, a member may become neurotically needful of the group, the leader, or one or another patient, but the analyst and co-patients push for interaction with others in and out of the group, which operates to resolve pathological dependency. This is valuable in exploring and working through the most serious transferential neurosis.

There is danger that some therapists may tend to develop in their groups an unhealthy association, in which patients may be encouraged merely to act out, rather than work through. Here regression is extended and appreciated, and the leader supports the patient's illness and entrenches his transference neurosis. The dyadic or group setting may be used by the analysand or the analyst to sponsor dependent ties or to resolve them. Treatment can become habituation, whether in the dyad or the group.

DREAMS AND FANTASIES

As in psychoanalysis per se, dreams and fantasies are of utmost importance in psychoanalysis in groups. In groups, dreams can have even more utility in one sense. They can elicit unconscious associations, not only from the dreamer but from other group members as well. In psychoanalysis in groups, patients are requested to recount recent dreams, recurrent dreams, and old nightmares. They are asked to free associate around the dream content and finally to speculate about and interpret the dream. In lieu of dreams, the therapist encourages the group to present fantasies, reveries, and daydreams. He asks group members to avoid censorship and encourages fanciful speculation about one another's productions. In this way, the dynamics of the dreamer are analyzed, as well as those who associate to another's dreams.

The essential difference between analysis of dreams in individual therapy and in psychoanalysis in groups is that, in groups, individuals can associate to others' unconscious productions as well as their own. Here it is the analyst's job to translate their associations in regard to the associator's dynamics and only secondarily to those of the person whose dream is being associated with, that is, he is taking another road to each individual member's unconscious, through associations to the unconscious productions of others.

For the dreamer himself, dreams are discussed because they reveal essential unconscious data reliably and with demonstrative and liberating effect. The analyst must ask for them in detail.

In one-to-one therapy, the analysand associates freely to his dreams, and the analyst seldom reveals his own associations. They are withheld—or are only partly revealed in a refined product—in his interpretations and other responses. In the group, the dreamer at first associates to the dream. Then everyone tries to interpret the dream and the significance of each person's subjective associations as applicable to himself. In this way, the therapist avoids individual analysis of each member's dream in turn and encourages multilateral analysis. He may enter the interpretive process from time to time to integrate what has been said, to underscore an essence, to make a point more intelligible, or to suggest an exploration of neglected elements in the dream when they seem to be meaningful.

Analysands who evade unconscious processes in the dyad may not present dream material. They justify their opposition by contending that they do not see any value in dream analysis. This resistance can be resolved more readily in the group than in the dyad, for, in the group, patients witness another member's presentation of a dream, its analysis, and the member's greater understanding and forward movement in treatment.

Some group therapists do not press for dreams in the group. In fact, they seem to reject the analysis of dreams in a group. But in most groups a number of members quite spontaneously tell their dreams, so it is more difficult for the therapist to discourage them in that setting. He is more obliged to pay them attention. Even in a group, however, if the analyst frustrates the emergence of dreams, they are likely to be recounted less and less often until they are entirely abandoned.

Dreams are also valuable therapeutic adjuncts in the clarification of transference. A member may, for example, project an associated woman patient in a dream in a dual role, both as a menacing figure and a lovable one. He may do this before free association or biographical acknowledgment has given us any indication of his mother's ambivalent attitude toward him. Interpretation of the dream enables him and the group to discover a destructive mother image with which he compulsively invests the woman. As he recognizes the transference features of his vision of her and sees her less threatening aspect, she becomes more lovable. As he progressively analyzes the compulsive character of his attachment to her, he dispels even this maternal hold, and she becomes simply an engaging friend, stripped of maternal qualities but with an attractiveness of her own. In these instances, reality proves much richer and more rewarding to the patient than his illusion.

FREE ASSOCIATION

Analytically trained therapists are often doubtful about whether patients can associate as freely in a group as in a dyad. True, there are more interruptions of free association in the group. But to look upon unrestrained, unbounded, and indefinite free association as fitting is to misunderstand the function of free association and the nature of analytic treatment. It is better to employ free association selectively, with recognition of when it is expedient. It is neither possible nor advisable to associate freely at all times. Discontinuity and bounds are essential to treatment, as they are in life.

The dyadic analyst may be doubtful of the effectiveness of group analysis because he does not believe that a patient can associate freely when he is interrupted by his co-patients. In reality, free association may be hindered by co-patients at certain times and helped at others. Where a patient is delving into as yet unexplored latent material, he usually stimulates and wins the attention of the other members and is therefore emboldened to go on. When he continues to reproduce the same psychopathology in free association, co-patients become bored with the recurrence and appropriately try to stay his repetition and ask for a more mutually invigorating alternative. When his free association is moving him to disclosure of appropriate, noncompulsive possibilities, his fellows are hopefully but quietly attentive, in the expectation that he will have the freedom to make a nonobsessive choice. When his stream of consciousness appears to be running down into estranging autism, co-patients resist his self-destructive and isolating free-association.

In dyadic analysis, the therapist interprets the free association of the analysand, whose associations are less free to the extent that he is aware of them. In group analysis, the patient not only freely associates but is required to operate with an awareness of the others. Although this obligation may appear to limit the freedom of his stream of consciousness, the demand for mutual awareness promotes good health. Unrestrained free association without the checking of feedbacks in reality leads to disequilibrium and derangement.

In analysis, whether individual or group, the patient is expected to reveal the truth about himself. In the dyad, the analyst is not required to expose himself. In the group, all the members are encouraged to show themselves and interact in an open way. The result is that every patient becomes aware of the effect he has on others in a way that is not available to him in dyadic treatment.

Each member finds out what his own provocative role or behavior patterns are.

The group analyst's preoccupation with interruptions of free association may represent his wish to conduct individual analysis in the group setting. But such a commitment prevents the leader from using the resources of his assembled patients and interferes with proper treatment of them. The interruptive contributions of fellow patients not only clarify the presentation of a given patient but may be used as free associations in themselves. In discussion of a dream, for example, the free associations of various members stir the further exposure of the dreamer's unconscious material. They also give the analyst more hints for understanding the dream, and clues to the psychodynamics and psychopathology of the others, which can be multilaterally interpreted.

The analyst's conception of fellow patients' communications as interruptive denies to the group the value of multilateral analysis. Instead, it imposes individual treatment in a group setting and encourages a rivalry to interrupt one another, becoming a competition to be heard by the analyst.

Encouraging patients to enter in with their own free associations, which are also acknowledged and examined, promotes the feeling that all are in analysis, rather than just a single member at a time in rotation. It is, therefore, necessary for the analyst to deal with any presented material as interactional, so that the number of patient interrelationships is enhanced. In so doing, he augments, rather than circumscribes, all the streams of consciousness in the group. The analyst's aim to give space to each patient in which to associate freely is commendable. But by limiting the free play of the others, he really hinders the achievement of his goal. In group analysis, all the analysands should be encouraged to be collaborative and active participants.

RESISTANCES AND DEFENSES

Resistance yields more readily to the psychoanalysis in a group. Patients directly challenge one another's resistive maneuvers. They do not permit a member to escape in sleep. They do not long permit a nonparticipant to remain silent. They vigorously demand an end to resistive operations. They push for change and new activity, demand interaction, and object to anyone's retirement or dominance and to obsessive intrapsychic preoccupation or grossly fantastic ways of nonrelating. They press for coexistence, verbal intercourse, and plain speaking.

By sustaining and criticizing one another, patients penetrate defenses more readily. Some therapists believe that defenses are weakened under attack in the group but that the anxiety underlying these defenses needs to be analyzed only in the dyad. The analyst in the group may on occasion be obliged to support a defense at a particular moment. But the idea that defenses may be resolved in the group, but the subjacent anxiety may not, seems to be a fallacious view of the nature of the group experience. In the dyad, the technical skill and timing required for dealing with defenses are the analyst's. In the group, the breaching of defenses of certain patients often promotes corresponding breaches among the more defended, who experience vicariously the understanding, progress, and working through of the need to maintain certain inappropriate defenses.

Analysis of Resistance

Resistance in groups manifests itself in the forms encountered in individual analysis, but the group setting provides a special environment that lends itself to the elaboration of resistive forms peculiar to it.

For the patient "in love with" the analyst, being in the group is enlightening. She may become as emotionally attached to another group member as she was to the analyst. Her "unfaithfulness," the rapidity and completeness with which she moves from one man to another, confronts her with the irrational and compulsive character of her behavior, and the nature of her activity becomes obvious to her as transference.

Another manifestation of resistance is the compulsive missionary spirit. Here the provider persists in looking after group members in a supportive, parental way, using this device subtly to dominate and attack the other members and to repress more basic pathology. The group resents this false charity and demands and evokes more spontaneous participation by rewarding the messianic for unguarded slips of feeling, and by rejecting dogmatic helpfulness. This does not imply that warm and spontaneous offers of assistance are rejected; rather, as long as supportiveness is not compulsive but thoughtfully sympathetic, it is welcome as a sign of good health.

Voyeurism is resistance that is more general in psychoanalysis in groups. Some patients try to escape personal examination and engagement by retreating. They seem willing and even eager to allow others full interaction, while they assign to themselves a tremulous watchfulness. The group, however, has little tolerance for nonparticipants. It engages the voyeur by its welcoming self exposure. It moves him by inviting and provoking him to become involved in the warm emotional life of the new family. His resistance begins to melt when the sideshow to which he was drawn by dubious motives becomes a wholesome drama in which he is impelled to take a legitimate part.

Hiding oneself behind the analysis of others is also a common form of resistance in psychoanalysis in groups. This resistance is characterized by a concentration on the neurotic behavior of other patients and is accompanied by an evasion of analysis directed toward oneself. Such a patient cleverly shifts attention from himself to the associator in order to defend himself against disturbing examination. He manages to redirect the group's attention to any individual who dares to analyze him. He handles what is said of him, for example, by remarking that his critic has an interesting overtone in speech that he ought to examine. Using endless devices, he deflects what could add to deeper insight, tackling the examiner. The other patients, however, gradually dissolve his resistance by expressing their appreciation for his incisiveness and by simultaneously demonstrating to him that, behind his emphatic lecturing, he makes himself inaccessible to the helping hands of the group for fear of humiliation. It is pointed out that fear of his vulnerability to parental substitutes in the group is forcing him into this compulsive role. To the extent that the members understand the frantic insecurity that underlies his bravado, they extend a reassuring friendliness that enables him to relinquish his insistent critical study of others for self-examination.

INTERPRETATION

The analyst guides the group members from multiple interaction to the search for unconscious motivation, from the manifest to the latent. By this means, the historical bases for the activity are brought into consciousness. Patients who object to the movement from manifest behavior to the investigation of unconscious motivation and persist merely in catharsis or verbal acting out of affective interaction are in resistance. When they accept the idea of the relevance of the latent material, they begin to offer interpretations of their own. Some of these interpretations are most valuable. In the main, however, they are not systematically timed. An analyst may carefully consider when to introduce an interpretation, but a patient reacting spontaneously is liable to be wild, and a poorly timed interpretation is only partially heard or not heard at all.

WORKING THROUGH

The necessity for working through is often neglected in treatment, particularly by group therapists, probably because so many of them repudiate psychoanalysis or are inadequately analyzed themselves. As a result, they are confused about the analytic process and are unable to formulate a unified theory of analysis for members of a group. The perplexity is evinced in the multiplicity of group therapies reported in the literature. The enormous volume of material made available in interpersonal reaction in group therapy may be disequilibrating to some group leaders and may make them feel that working through is not achievable.

Clinical experience indicates that working through can be effected in a group. The profusion of material can make it easier to discover the repetitive core of psychopathology, even the transference neurosis, and can facilitate working through. Recurrence is characteristic not only of psychopathology but also of treatment. After ventilation and insight into the psychodynamics and the psychopathology, the therapist again and again suggests more reasonable alternative choices. Only in the group is it possible to work through the bilateral and multilateral entwined neurotic manipulations involving two or more patients. The resolution of various facets of the disorder of members at different phases in their treatment is useful in making clear the analyst's recurrent preference for reality over illusion. It is their reiteration that promotes the working through of compulsive and archaic yearnings toward the final choice of more reasonable alternatives.

A good many patients come to psychoanalysis in groups after a failure to respond to individual treatment. Frequently, they have developed an increasing dependency on the therapist, with a deeply entrenched neurosis or psychosis. Such patients often demand concurrent individual sessions immediately after their transfer to an analyst in groups. They do so out of anxiety about breaking the symbiotic tie to the mother surrogate. The group analyst must resist these maneuvers. Instead, he must help such patients develop some independence, stronger egos, and responsibility for themselves. If group members insist that such patients function with them and the therapist resists the wish for exclusive individual support, these patients become more securely involved with their peers, more removed from the mother tie, and more self-reliant. They become less needful of the therapist, and more self-reliant. They become less needful of the therapist in an infantile way, and more relaxed with group members and in social situations apart from the therapeutic group. A significant derivative of the group analytic experience is that each patient becomes more ego-oriented. Other patients are able to work through their symbiotic tie to the projected tie to the therapist— often with the group members' support and understanding.

TERMINATION

It is probable that successful conclusion of treatment is more easily attained in the group because it fills the therapeutic need for interaction and engagement apart from the analyst. It is the judgment of the therapist that generally determines when a patient is ready to end treatment. But, on occasion, the leader may not be fully aware of the extent to which a member has improved. Then other patients may call his attention to the fact that a progressing member has made substantial gains. A patient may feel freer to show his good resources at alternate sessions than at regular meetings, and so the leader may not be as aware as the members of the patient's considerable improvement. What requires resolution in such a case is the patient's hesitation to show his effectiveness in the presence of the group leader.

Resistance to ending treatment may be a problem not only for the patient but for the therapist as well. The observing group members help to reduce the patient's or the analyst's resistance to termination. This validation by the group does not depreciate the competence of the analyst. It simply offers him another impression on which to base his estimate and assessment. In dyadic treatment, the material is always derived from the analysand, except in the relationship to the analyst. The patient is a partial and one-sided source of enlightenment. Group members offer more evidence and reasoning for reaching a conclusion as to the propriety of ending at any given time. The patient considering termination usually seeks the opinion of the analyst. If his wish to leave is resistive, he commonly looks to his peers for allies who will support his inappropriate flight from treatment.

The recovery of one patient heartens another member with the hope that one day he, too, will be well. The release of one member is a stimulus and a promise to the other. Such an experience is not available to the patient in individual treatment. Only the member of the therapeutic group can observe another patient's getting well. The improvement of one induces the rest to try harder to attain a similar well-being. The departure of a recovered patient may re-motivate another at a time when he is feeling despondent. The more disconsolate are stimulated by being witness to another's restoration. They become more inquiring and searching about how this particular co-patient managed to get well in order to achieve the same for themselves. They may become more rivalrous with the departing or remaining members in the competition for return to health. This competition may have its resistive aspects. If one member is discharged as well, another may insist that he, too, has been cured when he is still quite ill. It takes little examination by the group and the analyst to expose his resistive maneuver.

RESOLUTION OF PSYCHOPATHOLOGY

It becomes manifest in the group therapies that the therapist's counsel to speak freely results in various spirited, interpersonal exchanges. These communications are both reasonable and unreasonable. Patients become more and more conscious of the characteristic misperceptions that typify each of the members. In the nonanalytic group therapies, these distortions are not pursued to their origins, in particular nuclear kinfolk. In analytic group therapy, these transferences are traced to specific familial antecedents in the hope of uncovering and releasing the suppressed associated affect and working through the persistence of conflict. Working through in either setting requires a conscious exertion to adopt more appropriate and rational expedients to repetitive pathological patterns.

Individual therapy is less reality bound than the group therapies. There, even as the patient exposes his feelings and thoughts, he is expected to consider those of his co-members. This regard for them precludes abnormal withdrawal into autism and psychosis. It helps each patient to become conscious of his causal role in eliciting the responses he gets from others. Not only is insight into oneself significant, but awareness of one's impact on other persons is just as meaningful and rewarding.

The leader and group members proffer distinctive types of usefulness. Benefit from patients is volunteered more extemporaneously, more unpremeditatively, but also more obsessively. The leader's aid is more carefully selected, is more serviceable, and is imparted with more thoughtfulness and better timing.

8

Analysis of Transference

Since transference and countertransference terminology is used differently by different theorists, the following glossary of transference and countertransference terminology is provided to facilitate the discussion to follow. Some new terms will be introduced as well.

To begin with, the authors utilize the terms *projective transference* and *introjective transference,* the former being the projection of early parental figures onto present-day others and the latter being the introjection of the early parental figures into the self. The concept of introjective transference, coined by Kutash (Wolf and Kutash 1985) and described in detail in *The Submerged Personality* (Wolf and Kutash 1991) we believe is as important as projective transference. Other transference definitions include the following.

Transference—unconscious investment of any present figure inside or outside the therapeutic situation with qualities linked with an early familial figure.

Direct transference—when a patient invests the therapist with qualities linked with an early familial figure, or vice versa.

Lateral transference—when a patient invests another patient with qualities linked with an earlier familial figure. This can occur singularly, bilaterally, trilaterally, and so on.

Split transference — when a patient or therapist invests several group members with diverse aspects of the same early familial figure.

Penumbral transference — when a patient or therapist invests one other group member with both a primary transference to one early familial figure and a shadowy or secondary transference to another early familial figure, the latter is a penumbral transference.

Homogenized transference — when a patient or therapist invests several group members as if they were one person with qualities linked with an early familial figure.

Group-as-a-whole transference — when a patient or therapist invests the group-as-a-whole with qualities linked with an early familial figure.

Kutash (see Kutash and Wolf 1982), believing that the individual's self as a child can be considered an early familial figure, identifies the following as a form of transference.

Projected identification transference — when a patient or therapist identifies with another group member and projects his early feelings from his own original family onto the other, thereby getting vicarious transference satisfaction through seeing the person gratified.

Kutash (see Kutash and Wolf 1982), believing the introjection of an early familial figure into the present self as opposed to projecting it into another can be considered a transference of an early familial figure's characteristic into a present day figure, identifies the following as a form of transference.

Therapist's introjected transference — when a therapist takes on the role of his own parents in the manner in which he ministers to the patient or patients, whom he has come to see as early familial figures. He or she acts as his own parents might as leader of a recreated original family.

Cross transference — when group members or leader are simultaneously having transference reactions to each other or the leader. In a group of eight, this may involve sixty-four permutations.

Counter gratification — when a patient gives transference satisfaction to a co-patient or the therapist.

Countertransference—when a therapist is responsive to a patient's transference in a way that provides the member with transference gratification.

Transference neurosis—when a patient develops a strong emotional attachment to the therapist based on investing him or her with qualities linked with a familial figure and this misperception is repetitive, profound, regressed, and prolonged.

Countertransference neurosis—when a therapist experiences intense countertransference of long duration.

Transference psychosis—when the patient's observing ego is no longer able to distinguish the analyst (direct) or a patient (lateral) as himself but sees him as an actual familial figure.

Countertransference psychosis—when the therapist in response to the patient's transference gratifies the transference by believing that he is in fact the particular familial figure projected by the patient.

PATIENTS' TRANSFERENCES

One of the most important aspects of psychoanalysis in groups is the identification and resolution of transferences. Under the therapist's leadership, patients discover the extent to which they invest one another with early familial qualities. In the group setting, when a member may not only project a significant historical figure onto the analyst but may also single out members of the group for the same purpose, the field for transference is appreciably extended.

Certain truisms about transferences are stressed. The analyst explains that all human beings carry out a childhood heritage of responses that impel them to endow the present with the old forms; that investing others with attributes they do not possess is revelatory of distorted character structure in the investor; and that therapeutic progress is measured by the success with which a patient can revise these erroneous imputations and by the tolerance with which he can accept similar unwarranted and invalid appraisals directed against himself. Patients are alerted to their analytic role to recognize and point to transference reactions whenever they appear. The qualities of transferences are described to them so that they can more readily become conscious of its nature. It is demonstrated how every transference reaction has the qualities of irrelevance, compulsion, repetition, irrationality, and that these are accompanied by emotional disturbance and a sense of helplessness or grandiosity.

The discovery and analysis of transference is the most important work of analysis in a group, since it repeatedly interferes with the patient's true estimate of reality. Transference prevents each member from being able to accept another by conferring traits on him that originally stood in the way of a more wholesome relationship to a member of his original family. Accordingly, patients need to be made aware of its derivation, qualities, and purpose. It is indicated that the transference response is unconscious and that as a result the patient making the investment will usually resist recognition of his projection; that transference is inappropriate to the situation at hand, since the patient is responding to a mask that exists in his mind, rather than to the objective actuality. It is noted that transference has the elements about it of the illogical, unreasonable, and absurd, that these qualities aside, the patient inevitably persists in his untenable position with compulsive insistence and that he reproduces his irrelevant projection over and over. It is specified that the transferring patient experiences and usually exhibits some affective disturbance, such as mild anxiety, irritability, depression, and fearfulness, which may mount to the most unrestrained panic and terror. It may be associated with eroticism, infatuation, or romantic sentiment. It is accompanied by enormous feelings of helplessness or grandiosity that overwhelm rational considerations. Even though all its disarming and disadvantageous features are repeatedly demonstrated, the patient seems unable to control its imperative recurrence. It is revealed that the transference response is always excessive, well beyond what is called for by the provoking circumstance and, hence, overcomes and renders the member ineffectual. It tends simultaneously to startle, upset, and inhibit or provoke persons in the immediate environment by the enormity and suddenness of its appearance. Its unyielding quality makes it difficult to modify, and it takes a fixed course of its own, which the patient and analyst seem for a long time unable to disturb or deflect. All of these characteristics have an immediately gratifying but ultimately immobilizing effect on the patient. Bound by these limiting restraints, he cannot react with the freedom and plasticity demanded by diverse environmental stimuli. It is suggested that any transference reaction, at that moment, should be traced, if possible, by historical flashback to those earlier experiences that determined the nature of the present response.

By example and illustrative demonstrations from material at hand, the analyst repeatedly verifies the singular features of transference outlines. To this end, he does not avoid any opportunity to clarify any one patient's investment of another or the analyst. In the beginning, whenever a reaction appears that has the characteristics of projection, he points out to the reactor the transference character of his response. With increasing experience, patients become more adept in identifying one another's transference reactions. The extreme disparity of various investments confronts each member with the patently illusory nature of these responses, and he learns to see his own particular masking of others with parental or sibling surrogate cloaks as equally inappropriate. It is emphasized that transference must ultimately be dealt with, the timing depending on the readiness of the patient. Anything short of this is resistance.

In some respects, transference is so rigidly fixed in the character structure that the patient projects the same distortions regardless of the personalities around him. But there are penumbral variations in his reactions to every patient and to the analyst that are part of the transference. That aspect of investment, which is so fixed as to be the same regardless of the personality on which it is projected, is discernible fairly readily. Those nuances in the transference that vary, depending on the nature of the provocative personality, are less obvious: they require vigilant attention. But the close pursuit of these shadowy variants in transference relationships is most rewarding. It is the analysis of these trends, peripheral to the central transference, that makes psychoanalysis in groups an intensive process. While in individual analysis a patient may project onto the therapist at different times father, mother, or sibling images, the analyst is less likely spontaneously to arouse these multiple investments than a group of people with variously stimulating personality peculiarities. The central or thematic transference reaction, most generally elicited, appears as a reproduction of a relationship to a more significant parent with whom the patient was more ambivalently and affectively bound. Less peripheral or penumbral transferences that appear with more subtlety and that are often altogether neglected in individual analysis reproduce more conflicting but less painfully traumatic relationships to the less significant parent and siblings. The multiplicity of ways in which a patient dresses up the other members accurately reanimates the old family, disclosing in the action both his history and the richly divergent facets of his personality.

In individual analysis, it is often difficult for patient and therapist to follow the projection onto the therapist of the roles played by a number of significant members of the family. The group provides all the familial actors and lateral transference possibilities. Not only the number of patients, but also the presence of men and women expose and more rapidly precipitate aspects of transference relationships in both male and female parental and sibling surrogates. The presence of patients of both sexes facilitates the appearance and resolution of early conflicting unconscious trends formerly elicited by father, mother, sister, and brother. The group re-creates the family unit in which the patient can more freely reanimate the impelling and denying emotional demands whose contradictions he was once unable to solve. As he gradually becomes able to dispose of compulsive investments and discern group members in fact, they become the social bridge to the establishment of normal interpersonal relations.

A patient will not infrequently select several other participants who represent for him diverse aspects of the same parent on whom he projects the psychological heritage of the past. The choice of a particular patient or of the analyst as a target for a specific aspect of transference depends on the extent to which certain trends in the provocative personality most nearly resemble special characteristics of an earlier familial associate. The likeness may be near or remote. The approximation is usually in terms of sex and age but primarily in phases of character structure. The evocation of particular facets of transference by specific patients itself becomes a matter for study from the point of view of the provocateur's unique neurotic and healthy qualities that inspire revivals of outmoded forms in other members. For some patients, it does not matter in the slightest what the age or sex of a given member is, with regard to eliciting a transference; they will project the mother image onto a man and the father image onto a woman. For them, as for most, the important element evoking a particular familial mantle is the behavior at the moment or fragment of character structure in the provocateur rather than his gender.

Wolf had the opportunity some time ago to alternate sessions with a female analyst, both conducting a meeting together once a week. The purpose in organizing a group with multiple therapists was partly to teach and learn and partly to see the effect of introducing what might turn out to be maternal and paternal images in the persons of the two analysts. There was no uniform response to them. For some, both evoked parental projection. Occasionally, negative transference was directed by a patient toward the male therapist if there was historically greater hostility toward the father, and toward the female therapist, if there was early resentment of the mother. But just as often, it appeared that parental roles were reversed by members. And perhaps just as frequently, patients did not use the analyst as father and mother surrogates at all, but utilized one another instead. This experience seemed to show that there is no special advantage in introducing two analysts of opposite sexes. When a single therapist conducts group meetings for the duration of treatment, patients may choose some member of the group of a sex opposite to that of the analyst as a representative of the missing parent. Sometimes if the analyst is seen as a mother image, the patient may choose another male or female member as a father image. Occasionally, a patient discovers two or three father and mother surrogates in the group and variously any number of sibling substitutes. Sometimes the analyst is not regarded as a parental equivalent but as a sibling or child, and parental proxies are chosen entirely from patient membership. However, there are some few members who never seem to desex others in a projection. For them, the presence of both sexes among the membership provides a target for the investment of heterosexual transference reactions that are elicited with more difficulty when patients are obliged to project them onto a parent or sibling deputy of the same sex. Thus, a mixed group enables each patient to excite, evolve, study, and analyze projected relationships to meaningful figures of both sexes in the past.

An aspect of transference that receives repeated emphasis in the group is the analysis of such an action in the moment of its occurrence. It will not do to let a patient evade a consideration of his present irrational behavior by looking backward into history to seek the origin of peculiar conduct. It is a valuable exercise to search out critical causes. But the persistent probing into historical beginnings can become obsessional. It can enable a patient to neglect grappling with the forces that compel even now to reconstruct the past against his better judgment. In individual analysis, in which the tendency may exist to explore biography in excess, transference attitudes are not always revived with the startling vividness encountered in analysis in a group. This is true, in measure, because in individual analysis the therapist probes, while in group analysis the patients react and interact. Inquiry leads to insight, but interaction has a boomeranging, repercussive effect that stirs echoes of former times with resurgent clarity. In individual analysis, a patient can unconsciously falsify his record by reanimating perjured likenesses of parental figures. No such distortion is possible in the group, if the therapist holds the patient to his projection in the moment of its occurrence. And while it is true, in individual analysis, that the analyst can likewise insist on interpreting transference responses to him as they appear, he is frequently so unprovocative and so commonly bent on searching that the reactions to him are often minimal or else such subtle transferences that they are too obscure to be interpreted.

Once again, this does not mean that the therapist and the patients neglect history altogether; they look upon biographical records as being of central importance, but only insofar as they clarify transference, and only to the extent that they appear in significant bursts of recollection in association with the analysis of transference. By utilizing history in this way, long, irrelevant excursions into biography that are largely resistive are eliminated.

There is a curious correlation between biography and transference. To the extent that history is studied outside the context of immediate transference, it is relatively unrevealing and useless as therapy. To the extent that history is studied within the context of immediate transference, it provides understanding and is useful as therapy. Furthermore, the recollection of valuable fragments of the past is enormously facilitated by free association around and examination of an acutely neurotic reaction in the moment of transference. And there is rewarding interplay between history and transference, one elaborating the other until their close relation is established in detail. In spite of the therapist's emphasis on this procedure, patients manage in early alternate meetings to ventilate many aspects of previous experience. As they come to see the misleading character of extensive biographical rambling, they abandon this form of resistance. To the degree that the analyst is able early in treatment to effect such concentration on the analysis of transference, he shortens the duration of therapy. The handling of immediate projection stirs and highlights the salient repressed past—and it is this history suddenly welling into the present under the stimulus of transference that has illuminating value.

There is an element in the group setting that facilitates the analysis of transference, namely, the confrontation of each member with his disparate projection on the same person. It is often baffling in individual treatment to try to convince a patient that his estimate of the analyst is far from realistic, but is rather a reproduction of an unresolved conflictful attitude toward a parent. The neurotic person stubbornly insists that his feeling for and impression of the therapist are accurate. And while the analyst may grant their tenability, he has great difficulty in persuading the patient that they are also an attempt to maintain archaic familial constellations. His obstinacy melts more easily in a milieu in which he is faced with divergent impressions of the same person projected by many present. He is forced to reexamine his perceptive faculties. He cannot maintain so readily his critical obstinacy that the analyst is brilliant, strong, and all-providing when another patient insists just as mulishly that the doctor is stupid, weak, and unreliable. He is obliged to reconsider his original investment in the therapist for possible misrepresentation. And in his reactions to other patients he is also forced to reinvestigate his projective devices.

There is another element in the group setting that is conducive to the fuller evocation of transference possibilities. And that is the variously provocative characteristics of the multiple personalities in the group. No matter how versatile a therapist is, he is still bound by the limitations of his character structure. This has an unstimulating effect on the patient as far as calling forth the multiple projective potentials in him. The disparate personalities in the group furnish a larger number of eliciting agents whose particular differences elicit wider and more subtle facets of transference than is attainable by the analyst alone. If he is skillful, he may, by uncovering successively deeper levels of the patient's personality or by playing different roles, evoke less obvious and more many-sided penumbral transferences, but, in general, these shadings are lost. With little effort on his part, but with mere attention he can discern how naturally one patient animates another into revealing peripheral sides of neurotic investment or wholesome responses that would otherwise be missed or extracted with great difficulty. This fact is underscored by the discharge of a recovered patient or the introduction of a new one. Under these circumstances, the absence of an old or the insertion of a new infectious element stirs each member unconsciously to present a fresh side of his nature, projected or normal. This has the effect not only of enlarging the view of transference but of giving the patient an opportunity to test his developing healthy resources in ever-widening circles of society. Further striking evidence of the provocative effect of the group members, as compared with the therapist alone, becomes manifest following the movement of a patient from individual analysis to psychoanalysis in groups. From a comparatively static, single-sided individual, he turns into an active, complex person with multiple facets that challenge investigation.

Each patient's provocative role must be explored in terms of the healthy and neurotic responses he elicits. Members are asked to assist in discovering one another's inflammatory tactics. This becomes apparent gradually as eight to ten patients continually tell each other what he does to them in emotional terms. But how then can he distinguish what is truly provocative, originating in the provocateur, and what is neurotically derived from the reactor? In the interplay back and forth of mutual interreaction, there are healthy and unhealthy forces at work between any two people. The therapist may take the lead, in the beginning, in demonstrating this. He shows that in every interpersonal encounter there is the possibility of developing vigorous and bilaterally rewarding interchange, but he also points out how, by pursuing neurotic investments in bilateral transferences, any two individuals may end up in attempts to dominate, control, exploit, or separate from one another. To intercept mutually destructive or detaching interplay, he is continually alert to bilateral transference possibilities. It is sometimes very difficult to discover the actual initiator of a neurotic circular movement. It is, however, most important to analyze the movement once it is under way, and to pursue and finally establish the healthy and neurotic deportment of the players in mid-scene.

Perhaps the citation of an example of the transference process as it occurs in the group will be illuminating.

In prior individual treatment, Helen evidenced erotic interest in her analyst that was associated with some fear and anxiety. Feelings toward her father during childhood were never conscious nor expressed. During an early group meeting, the analyst complimented George on his brilliant intuitive appraisal of her. She felt, at once, that he was being favored and reacted with jealousy, feeling that he was more highly regarded for his intellectual talent. Immediately anxious, she challenged his statement and reacted with marked hostility toward both throughout the duration of the meeting. Despite her competition with him for the analyst's esteem, she felt that he would inevitably do better than she and that the therapist would just as certainly always promote him because he was a man. The compulsive nature of her conduct together with its interesting sequel came out at the next session. Helen told that upon leaving the previous meeting, she had gone automatically to a florist to order an elaborate bouquet for her mother. Suddenly confounded in the flower store, she stopped and tried to realize what she was doing. There was really no occasion for sending her mother a bouquet, for the latter was not ill, nor was it a holiday or an anniversary. Understanding followed directly. She knew then that in the group the analyst had changed from a father to a mother image; George, the man the therapist had complimented, had become a brother substitute with whom she had been in perpetual rivalry for her mother's attention. Praise of him elicited the projection of the mother image onto the analyst. It also aroused a keen hostility toward George and especially toward the analyst. The gift of flowers was to propitiate a mother who was annoyed by her conduct, to conceal her welling resentment and to appease her conscience for coming so close to fully expressing her anger against her mother. Of striking interest was her abandonment of the father image in the therapist, as soon as the group provided a situation in which the analyst could reward a man who was at once invested with brother quality. Apparently, she was able to re-create the father image as long as the analyst was alone with her. As soon as the original family was reanimated by the group setting and more particularly by the authority figure's approval of a man, a particular familial constellation was revived that necessitated a revision in her earlier investment on the analyst. The therapist's complimenting a man unconsciously recalled greater admiration of her brother and disapprobation of herself. Her mother was the prime agent in the construction of this historical configuration.

Later meetings brought out her mother's actual preference for Helen's brother because he was a boy. Helen's compulsive penis envy, her disregard for her feelings, and excessive regard for excelling intellectually, an area in which she always felt doomed to come off second best reproduced her relationship to mother and brother. By attention to the aspects of her shifting transferences to the analyst and to George, we were at last able to help Helen relinquish familial claims on her and to react in her own and the other's right.

There are at least three salient points in Helen's story. The first illustrates the sudden appearance of occasionally unforeseen bursts of transference toward the therapist or another member after a patient has been introduced to a group. The second throws light on the inevitable appearance of previously latent facets of personality, new and multiple transferences in the re-creation of the old family, so that movement into a group changes behavior. The third illustrates how significant incidents in early life are recalled by the flashback method in relation to the analysis of immediate transference.

9

Countertransference

Countertransference has become an ideological and semantic battleground. At this moment in the development of psychoanalysis, greatest emphasis is being put on the analyst, his real and illusory problems, his personality, his training, and his technique. The literature indicates that confusion of opinion exists, especially in group psychotherapy, as to what transference, transference neurosis, and countertransference really are. Just as transference has been misconceived as equalling the total relationship of the patient to the therapist, so has countertransference been misapplied as equalling the total relationship of the analyst to the patient. Berman (1950), for example, says countertransference is the sum of the analyst's emotional reactions to the patient; it is the same as transference except that it now stems from the analyst.

It is not always clear what is being described under the rubric "countertransference." Are such reactions all good or bad, or sometimes good and sometimes bad? Some therapists feel countertransference is any rejection of the patient, for example, sending him to another therapist. Some feel any anxiety of the therapist is countertransference, for example, castration anxiety as the therapist's defense against his success, or anxiety before his dependency or when his omnipotence is threatened. Others feel any exploitation of the patient is countertransference. On the other hand, still other therapists feel countertransference is the essence of the curative experience. In the main, however, countertransference is viewed as something "bad," something to be avoided, and the assumption is made that the better trained the therapist is, the more appropriate will reactions on his part prevail, and the less countertransference there will be.

Countertransference is thought to be the analyst's transferences. Here, a distortion in perceiving the patient as if he were a member of the analyst's original family is meant.

Empathic countertransference, according to both Reich and Nunberg (Symposium 1953), is based on the analyst's identification with patients and projection of his own feelings. This can be partial motivation for becoming a child analyst, for example, through identification with "the child in the patient" or with "the underdog." It reflects a subject–object conflict.

Defensive countertransference is conceived by Gitelson (Symposium 1953) as a consequence of the intensity of conflict in the analyst.

Reactive and nonreactive countertransference arise in response to pathology in the patient, such as projection, or an acting or acting out. These are similar to induced or suggested countertransference, which appears when the therapist accepts or rejects exclusively a certain kind of communication.

Utilizing what Menninger reports as a current error with regard to transference, Slavson believes there are positive, negative, and ambivalent countertransferences, and semi-attached and telecountertransference. In transference or countertransference, all kinds of thoughts, feelings, and attitudes exist. The expressed affect does not define the nature of the transference or countertransference.

Flescher (Symposium 1953) insists countertransference can be conscious and rational. Lewin (Symposium 1953), however, declares that it is rational or irrational, scientific or emotional, conscious or unconscious, appropriate or anachronistic. This definition is so nonspecific that any response of the analyst becomes countertransference.

To understand its real nature is complicated because of difficulties about countertransference, since it is of unconscious origin. Moreover, reports of its effect are contradictory. In simple terms, countertransference is, for us, what it says: namely, activity of the analyst in response to the transference of the patient. Schilder believes that transference requires by psychological law a complementary response. Ferenczi maintains the analyst must not even yield inwardly to his own emotions; or, as Schilder puts it: "He must never answer his patient in a human way."

Freud (1907) writes that the analyst must not offer his patients any transference satisfaction. Later in the same volume, he says:

> A certain amount (of transference gratification) must of course be permitted to him, more or less according to the nature of the case and the patient's individuality. But it is not good to let it become too much . . . I do not think that I have exhausted the range of useful activity on the part of the physician with the statement that a condition of privation is to be kept up during the treatment. [p. 398]

Berman (1950), too, asserts that countertransference within limits is good. What is "within limits" is nowhere defined. What is meant is not too much and not too little, but how much giving and how much depriving are not explained.

These opinions should not be interpreted as a call for unduly strong control of affect on the part of the patient or therapist, or the absence of such control. We are dealing here with the question of overreaction. Hopefully, overreaction and underreaction will be less frequent or binding and of shorter duration in the analyst than in the patient, due, among other reasons, to self analysis. As long-lasting transference develops into transference neurosis, so, we postulate, intense countertransference of long duration develops into countertransference neurosis.

COUNTERTRANSFERENCE IN INDIVIDUAL THERAPY

In our opinion, transference reactions of the patient may facilitate therapy, but countertransference reactions interfere because they fulfill illusion and deny reality. Transference may on occasion, and by chance, be a new way of relating for the patient. It is the therapist's responsibility, however, to frustrate illusion rather than to reenforce it.

The therapist has a discriminatingly flexible role adaptive to each patient. This is especially true in group therapy, in which greater possibility for bilateral gratification exists. For us, countertransference is descriptive of behavior induced in the therapist that is responsive to transference and provides the patient transference satisfaction. In every transference of the patient, there is an implicit demand on the analyst that he fulfill or satisfy some aspect of it. This is the transference expectation. It is our position that, by definition, countertransference is that kind of activity that fulfills the transference demand of the patient.

Greenacre's (Symposium 1953) conceptualization is related to our understanding. According to her, there is a primary transference: namely, to misperceive the analyst as if he were the patient's mother, and the transference demand of the patient is to be the analyst's child. Primary countertransference exists when the analyst acts as if he were the patient's mother. Secondary countertransference occurs when the analyst responds to the patient's transference demand that the analyst be a certain kind of father or sibling, for example.

Countertransference provides object relations in the analytic situation. It is the therapist's unconscious, involuntary, and inappropriate response to the patient's transference demands in the therapeutic situation. It is irrational and ultimately disagreeable to both analyst and patient.

Distinction should be made between the therapist's transference and his countertransference. Kubie (Symposium 1953) asks, "Who is the analyst to the patient: father, mother, sister, brother?" We may also ask, "Who is the patient to the analyst: father, mother, sister, brother?" These are transferences. It is not sufficient merely to know who the analyst is to the patient and who the patient is to the analyst: we must see the connection between these two. If the analyst is a mother to the patient, and if the patient is a child to the analyst, we have fulfillment of the transference demand of the patient, and countertransference on the part of the analyst. If, on the other hand, the analyst is a mother to the patient, and if the patient is also a mother to the analyst, we have bilateral transference and not countertransference. In both, there is interference in treatment due to distortion and conflicts of interests. Since our goal in treatment is objective cure, being aware of these fine distinctions is not enough. It is an important first step, but we need to know what to do with interferences in the patient and in ourselves.

It is theoretically probable that for every countertransference reaction there is an antecedent transference of the analyst. The analyst's function is to disappoint the patient's transference expectations, and then to analyze the disappointment. It is likely that the therapist's transference impedes such analysis. Countertransference tends to fulfill bilateral irrational needs. This circular effect converts the process into a continuing spiral and leads to the frustration of successful termination. Countertransference then represents a general phenomenon in which not the real needs of the patient are central, but the illusory needs of the analyst. Other aspects of the personality of the analyst may also have to be differentiated from his transferences and countertransferences.

Countertransference results in a kind of oscillation between gratifying and frustrating the patient. It is a persistent temptation and probably present in all therapy, but some patients elicit more, and some less, countertransference. It is unconsciously provoked by and unconsciously responsive to the patient's unconscious demands. Freud points out that it is equally bad to respond to or ignore the patient's love. He suggests that it is to be analyzed. The two pitfalls for countertransference are identification and projection.

Some general considerations regarding countertransference are (1) the repetitive character of the therapist's reaction, (2) difficulty in relating to the patient as a patient, (3) if the therapist's needs must be gratified, this is countertransference except in the matter of fee; (4) if the patient's real needs are kept central, there is less likelihood of countertransference; and (5) even if the fee is symbolic to the therapist, he is entitled to it.

COUNTERTRANSFERENCE IN GROUP THERAPY

In the group, every therapeutic problem is exaggerated. The issues around transference and countertransference are no exception. Quantitatively and qualitatively, countertransference becomes an even more complicated matter in the group. Simply the presence of a variety of persons multiplies the transference manifestations and provocations in both patients and therapist. Locke (Symposium 1953) calls bilateral transference responses among patients *cross transference*. Some of the multiple transference reactions among patients in the group will fulfill transference demands. When a co-patient gives transference satisfaction, we recommend it be called *countergratification*, and the term countertransference be reserved exclusively for the analyst. Although countergratification and countertransference meet the archaic needs of the patient, the source of such satisfaction must be differentiated. Gratification of the real and maturating needs of a co-patient is similarly different from countergratification.

We wish now to offer some suggestive samples of the unconscious participation of the group therapist that should be examined with openness. In part, we are dealing with the trend toward humanizing the analytic experience, whether in therapy face-to-face or in a group. Unconscious factors may be as much at work in the treatment-group setting as when insisting that the patient be seen alone on the couch. In some instances, treating patients in a group may be motivated by unresolved conflict in the therapist and his identification with peers rather than authority figures. In others cases, the therapist may reverse roles or symbolize the group or particular members. Such a group therapist expects patients to become adjunct analysts. Because of his sense of limitation, such a therapist turns to the group to supplement his capacity to be helpful to patients and fosters the illusion that it is the group that supplies the therapy.

Following is a list of possibilities that, in our experience, need to be explored for the presence of the group therapist's transferences and countertransferences.

1. The therapist may relate to the group as if it were his own projected family (therapist transference).

2. The therapist may enjoy watching the women and men fight with each other.

3. The therapist may want to induce the group to be quiet, friendly, cooperative, and reasonable.

4. The therapist may find a member being seductive or seduced by another patient vicariously enjoyable.

5. The therapist may act so as to be admired or, conversely, to be perceived as overly humble.

6. The therapist may maneuver patients into roles and integrate his defenses with complementary ones in them.

7. The therapist may arbitrate like God or judge instead of analyzing.

8. The therapist, out of a sense of omnipotence, may deny patients freedom.

9. The therapist may demand activity out of his own depression.

10. The therapist in attending to group process or group-as-a-whole dynamics may homogenize the members, see them as if they were one patient, without listening to individual voices and knowing them as separate persons.

11. The therapist may not listen to projected peers or authorities.

12. The therapist may wish to be the only child in the group, or he may treat patients as only children.

13. The therapist may take an attitude of nonresponsibility to a member and allow scapegoating, or he may join the mass against the individual or the individual against the mass.

14. The therapist may stimulate acting out.

15. The therapist may need to control the group for fear of patients running wild.

16. The therapist may introduce into the group any and all patients whether they fit the group or not or, conversely, form groups of sharply defined characteristics or homogeneous groupings.

17. The therapist may fail to analyze latent lateral transferences when they are masked in suggestions by one patient as constructive alternatives to a co-patient. This can also be true of the analyst whose manifest proposals of constructive alternatives may conceal countertransference.

18. The therapist may demand that patients shape their way of life and their values to his. The expectation that the patient fulfill the therapist's superego or id demands retraumatizes the patient.

19. The therapist may identify with the patient or patients and project his own feelings from his own family onto the patient (projected identification).

20. The therapist may take on the role of his own parents in the manner in which he ministers to the patient or group (therapist introjection).

An example of transference in a patient in a group, met by transference as well as countertransference in the therapist, will now be offered.

> Upon the death of his sister, Bob spent the following group session projecting the group as a family, which, unlike his own, would comfort and be with him to the point where he invited them all to his house while he sat *shiva*, a seven-day mourning period observed by Jews, during which friends and relatives visit. He called upon the group leader to take the role of his long dead father, who had shown him some affection, calling him to ask him to call group members to let them know he was sitting *shiva* at his home. The group leader, under supervision with Kutash, described how he identified with this neglected patient now without the father from whom he had gotten some sustenance. He found himself encouraging group members to attend. When one gentleman said, "I'm confused, are we supposed to be a group or a family?" the therapist caught his transference and countertransference and answered "a group. But you may of course have your alternate session at Bob's."

We wish to give an example of the transference–countertransference cycle in a group setting. It is possible to illustrate this effect because we know the patients' transferences and their implicit expectations, as well as the analyst's psychodynamics.

> Mary lent Fred, a co-patient, some recordings. These patients were both music lovers. Their transferences were similar in that both patients projected bad mother images on the other and turned to the analyst as the good mother who would side with each of them against the bad mother projected on the other patient. The transference of the analyst was having to settle arguments between the symbolic mother and father, which always gave him some anxiety, but his counter-transference was immediately to fulfill the passionate, irrational

demand of Fred and Mary by attempting to settle their argument. The chances are that the analyst could avoid countertransference if he were not also in transference. Most parents want the child to side with either father or mother. There is much opportunity and pressure in the group for the analyst to become an omnipotent judge as a way of handling his anxiety and helplessness.

Our transferences and countertransferences may account for many failures, because they elicit co-patient transference and countergratification, and encourage patients to try to meet our transference and countertransference operations. Countertransference may be concealed in what the therapist chooses to emphasize or analyze in the contestants when he is, in fact, favoring one or rejecting the other. Often, by some technical or theoretical device, he rationalizes the taking of sides, or an irrational, inappropriate action in a contretemps among patients. Sometimes the analyst has a pressing need immediately to solve a conflict, and thereby to cut off any interaction among or between patients. This is true of patients' expressions not only of anger but also of positive feelings, which may give rise to anxiety in the analyst and his need quickly to interpret.

A therapist may introduce patients into a group in order to avoid direct interaction that threatens him. By identification, every patient misperceives himself in fantasy as an extension of the analyst. The latent communication to the analyst in one patient's interaction with another should not be missed: that is, "going around" involves the therapist as well. If the therapist is not manifestly included, he may assume that in fact he is. When the therapist acts as if one patient is right and another is wrong, he is probably in countertransference, executing cultural attitudes incorporated in his own superego. His role is to try to understand and to analyze.

Countertransference reactions are probably to be recognized also in technical defects and failures. They may show themselves in strain in the analyst. The group is indeed more demanding of the therapist, but the strain he feels may be founded on real or unreal causes. An examination of the level of treatment may also indicate the presence of countertransference; the level may be superficial, repressive, controlling, or noninteractive. By passivity and overpermissiveness, the therapist may cloak his hostility and aggression. "When I don't know what to do, I do nothing and remain silent."

Sometimes countertransference problems arise out of omnipotence in the assertion of power, in teaching, in sexual involvement with a patient, and in other forms of pathologic acting. Moreover, the patients may act out with sex and violence, the therapist's unconscious wishes. He may forbid activity by an exclusive emphasis on conscious or unconscious processes, on nonverbal communication, on the present, past, or future, or even on transference.

It seems clear that in the complexity of the group, there is greater opportunity for selective attention, listening, recognition, and interpretation on the part of the therapist. Therapy then takes on a monolithic quality, a monodimensionality. Heterogeneity and openness to new ideas represent forces against the pathologic problems of the therapist. Group members are exceedingly responsive to transference or countertransference in the analyst, and they recognize quickly its excessive quality in him.

Countertransference represents fulfillment of the fantasy of the patient with regard to the therapist, in the expectation that the therapist play a certain role. Such fulfillment is more difficult in a group in which the membership is heterogeneous, and the fantasies and demands projected onto the analyst are more varied. Scrutiny will reveal whether the therapy has been unplanned and the goals defeated. In such instances, we may assume that countertransference has been at play. But always we would need to understand the intensity or degree of interference. Flescher (Symposium 1953) states that we must not react to patients, that we must control our reaction. For Slavson (Symposium 1953), the analyst is, ideally, completely neutral and devoid of feelings about the patient and the outcome. In our opinion, this is an improbable and undesirable role ideal that can result only in contactlessness.

Slavson sees in the intensification of feelings of anxiety, inadequacy, and uncertainty in the group more transference and more countertransference than in the non-face-to-face situation. Yet, he insists that no transference neurosis appears in the group. Such a position, we feel, is contradictory. For many patients, non-face-to-face therapy probably provokes more projection, very much as in the child with an absent parent. Reality is a corrective to transference manifestations and impedes or inhibits their appearance.

Countertransference can be seen in the excessive forms of behavior of the analyst that are repetitive and over prolonged time. Patients have needs and the analyst has needs. Transference and countertransference do occur. The question is whose real needs are central to the particular activity in duration? In group therapy, multiple transferences and, probably, countertransferences occur. The therapist is committed to being realistic and not giving in to the network of multiple transferences and transference demands with multiple countertransferences. We believe countertransference neurosis can also occur in the group, and is facilitated when, for example, the group is misperceived as one patient, or when treating the group as if it were one person. In such a distortion, it is easier to fulfill the transference demands of both patients and therapist.

There is an idea current among some therapists that the criterion for termination is when the therapist resolves his countertransference. This is used as the indication that the patient has improved. Here, too, we raise the question as to whose needs are being served. There is also a prevailing assumption that the analyst has conscious control over countertransference. Schindler (Symposium 1953) says that the group analyst should refrain from unconscious, uncontrolled attitudes toward patients. It has also been recommended that the therapist refrain from aggression and favoritism, since both of these are based on narcissism, from giving or depriving, from activity or passivity, from authority or autonomy, from destructiveness. Such suggestions for refraining only complicate the problem and add little to our understanding of the unconscious forces at work.

Waelder (Menninger 1958) says, "Since we are all partially blind, the best we can do is to support each other so that the vision of one may make up for the myopia of the other, and vice versa" (p. 90). What can we do about countertransference problems? We do not want always to be in analysis and/or under supervision. Menninger (Symposium 1953) suggests the possibility that we work with a trusted colleague to talk over problems for mutual benefit.

COPING WITH COUNTERTRANSFERENCE

We should like to consider the following, separately or in combination, as possible methods for coping with and working through countertransference trends: (1) personal analysis, (2) personal analysis in groups, (3) self analysis (to be sure, additional analysis is not the only way to deal with countertransference, but surely self analysis can be used, especially when listening to the patients' free association, dreams, and interactions); (4) talks between trusted colleagues, (5) consultation, supervision, and control; (6) supervision in a group, (7) multiple supervisors together or separately, sequentially or simultaneously; and (7) use of films and tape recordings.

We should like to suggest that the current preoccupation with countertransference may itself become countertransference. All the problems in treatment become the analyst's. This can immobilize and castrate the analyst and often results in status denial. An omnipotence problem that needs further analysis may be hidden here. For, in such an attitude, the therapist becomes the alpha and omega, the "be-all-and-end-all" of treatment.

As we have already pointed out, countertransference is recurrent, persistent, compulsive, repetitious, and of a continuing nature. It is obsessive, involuntary, unconscious, entrenched, manipulative, and exploitive. As we see it, the more serious problem is not countertransference, but the countertransference neurosis, as we have described it earlier.

One of the antidotes against countertransference, in our opinion, is the presence of the group. The analyst alone with the patient can more easily develop a countertransference neurosis. The whole group will not be uniformly worshipful of the analyst and, therefore, attenuate countertransference grandiosity. Waelder (in Menninger 1958) writes:

> There is always a danger of deterioration in the work of people who do not have the benefit of comparison with the work of others and who are in no way supervised. I do not think of deterioration in the crude meaning of a blurring of responsibility—such instances happily are very rare—but in a more subtle sense. An analyst knows what he has seen in a patient but he cannot know

what he has not seen but might have seen, and he may get an exaggerated idea of the completeness of his observations and the adequacy of his interpretations. [p. 92]

In the group, if the analyst has need to defend the position of omnipotence or omniscience, the members can nevertheless be insightful about one another and about the analyst. To quote Grotjahn (1950), "It is easier to develop a folie à deux than a mass psychosis" (p. 62).

10

The Role of the Leader

What, it is pertinent to ask, are the particular qualifications and functions of a successful group analyst?

Psychoanalysts are not ipso facto good group analysts. Special attributes are required of the group analyst, who must be first of all a psychoanalyst. He must have adequate training, intuitive insight, a capacity for empathy, and an ability to dispose of countertransference attitudes. He must expect concerted efforts to deflate him. He must have the capacity to withstand neurotic attacks on him with composure. He must not be discouraged or thrown off balance by the intensity of interpersonal enmity that occasionally develops in early meetings. Such outbursts are largely projective in character, and his function is jeopardized if he fails to react to them with appropriate analysis. Even the most timid will assail him from the vantage point among the group, and destructive patients will test his tolerance of neurotic frustration and aggression to the utmost. In spite of the therapist's attempt to create a new, more benevolent, and permissive family, the old one with all its rivalry, aggression, and dictatorship, may assert itself and tax the new parent in the extreme.

He ought to be able to welcome patiently the manifold variety of transferences with which he is invested and not be misled to accept them as real by inappropriate reaction. To be sure, the analyst is afforded the same protection from some in the group as his patients. If he is unreasonably attacked, some of them will come to his rescue and support him when the occasion seems to demand it. For, acting upon his injunction, they are continually engaged in reacting spontaneously to everyone present including the analyst. He, too, must expect both blame and praise according to their changing concepts of his desserts.

The function of the group analyst is to guide his patients to fuller awareness and social integration. He can best accomplish this by avoiding conceited and compulsive leadership. He can more surely achieve such a goal by attentive regard to what group members can teach him. The therapist alone need not know all to provide adequate leadership. His nuclear, professional, and leading position is not by itself enough to provide his patients with the full insight they need.

Experience with him is not comprehensive enough to ensure healthy, social restoration. Therefore, it is necessary that he supplement his clinical knowledge with an understanding of the interaction of the various group members. This means that he must constantly maintain an alert and intimate connection with the rich reservoirs of understanding that are potential in the group, catalytically interplaying their intuitive insight with his own. He must attend the least small voice as well as the loudest. It will not do for him to detach himself at his desk and hand down well-prepared instructions. While he seeks solutions to neurotic problems, the proper answers cannot be found without vigilant regard to group experience that is continually testing his leadership. While the plan operates for the resolution of conflict, he cannot achieve his objectives without the help of the patients. The patient members are an essential and final check on the extent to which therapeutic aims are being fulfilled. The patients' interactivity with each other and with the therapist guarantees status to each individual and finally enables him to utilize his own resources and those of the other members.

The group analyst's view of things tends to be one-sided. He sees patients and their behavior from above. Accordingly, his impression of what is happening is limited by his paternalistic, relatively nonparticipant position. While he engages in group activity, the quality of his participation is different and modifies his perception of events. The group, on the other hand, appreciates interpersonal forces at work from another side. Its awareness is likewise limited by its position and function in the group. To accomplish the harmony that will lead to integrated group activity, the analyst and patients must interweave their complementary roles. Leadership that achieves this is therapeutic.

The successful analyst learns never to underestimate the significance of the contribution that can be made by the members to mutual insight and social integration. Patients sometimes show themselves to be close to unconscious truth. If the therapist is wise, he consults them and often supplements his experience with theirs. It may be said that neurotic conflict in part develops in the child because of contradictory influences imposed on him by his parents, who are exploitative, dictatorial, and selfish and at the same time cooperative, democratic, and supportive of the child's developing resources. In the new, permissive family of the group, to the extent that the therapist is authoritarian and detached from the group, he duplicates the destructive role played by the original parents. In this way, he may reinforce the patients' difficulties and undermine their actual effectiveness. To the degree that he is continually attentive to the emerging intuitive potentials in the various members, he helps to create a new family unit of the group, in which each participant can realize increasingly gratifying levels of adjustment.

The analyst who regards himself as the most active, critical thinker in the group and the patients as a relatively inert mass is likely to be led far astray. With such a misconception, he tends to overestimate himself and look down on the group; he has the illusion that success or failure depends pretty much on him and that the group is lacking in creative, contributory power. He believes that his acuteness alone determines the successful outcome of treatment. Such a view condemns group members to passivity and excludes them from the active participation essential to their recovery. It also reduces the group activity to a series of dictated or accidental psychodynamics whose ebb and flow are determined by the prescriptions, needs, and fantasies of the authoritarian therapist. While the development of patients in a group moves on according to certain principles, the therapist and each patient are constantly modifying their progress. The therapist can play a most significant catalytic part in facilitating patient movement by seeing further ahead than his patients. He can do this also by desiring and struggling to accomplish healthy integration more vigorously than they. His effectiveness lies in his deep contact with each member, in his ability to understand them, in his skill in foreseeing the historical course the individual takes, and in his confidence in the potential resources of the various members.

The course a group takes is primarily determined by the various character structures of the participant members, itself a product of their previous histories. The personal qualities of the analyst modify this course. This does not mean that the contributions the analyst can make should be ignored. Nor does it mean that progress is exactly predetermined by the constitution of the patients in it. If this were so, it would make no difference whatsoever on the movement in the group if one therapist were substituted for another. The role of the group analyst would be a passive one in the face of the group's fatalistic course. The influence of the therapist, however, cannot be reduced to this kind of insignificance. He must possess skills that make him most capable of resolving intragroup conflict, of interpreting the problems presented by the patients' previous histories, of pointing up the new needs created by the preceding development of the group's interactivity, and of taking the initiative of satisfying these needs.

In this relatively new field of analysis-in-a-group, the therapist must be a person who is venturesome, for there are many new, experimental areas to explore. He should, therefore, avoid assuming dogmatic attitudes in the group's interest as well as his own. If he is authoritarian, he prevents the members' full emergence and contribution, which may enlighten him also. He seeks to be capable of admitting his own mistakes openly, of examining the reasons for them, and of analyzing the conditions that gave rise to them in order to correct them. He needs to be able to show his own shortcomings, if necessary, and so be an example to the others.

The psychoanalyst cannot encourage an inspirational atmosphere that represses unconscious factors and creates unstable illusions of success that are bound to be short-lived. He promotes a spirit of deep, mutual examination and review of personal strengths and weaknesses. Such a procedure does not destroy the patient but explores his neurotic character structure.

At times when the group falters, the analyst must remain firmly and consistently optimistic. He takes a stand against any one patient's exploitation of another. He must avoid in himself and discourage in the members the intellectual cliche that obscures the simple, richer, and more elemental meaning for which the patient is groping. A calculated, scholastic approach leads to an evasion of affective contact indispensable for rehabilitation. Here, as elsewhere, he can turn to the group for the naive phrase that is poetic, refreshing, and apropos in order to escape the compulsive use of the more restricted language of professional associates. He should set an example in simplicity, honesty, and straightforwardness to encourage those patients who underestimate their great ability to make meaningful contributions. He does not always emphasize what is said, but rather how it is said. He tries to treat complicated questions without complexity. He should not strive for the eloquent phrase. His thoughts need to be clear and distinct—their intent plain. While he plays a leading role, he strives to help the members feel he is one of them—not apart. He ought not to teach too much, for if he does, he will find himself governing rather than liberating. In this regard, it would pay him to lend an attentive ear to what is said of him in the group. There he will find his severest critics as well as his staunchest defenders. Regard for what they say will help him to enlarge his understanding of himself. Again, he should not hesitate to show his appropriate feelings in the group. In doing this, he sets an example of freedom and emotional contact that is infectious. If he hides affect, the group will respond in kind. His sadness or gaiety will strike healthy reactive chords in others. But, if he is well, he will be realistically optimistic.

The analyst is on guard against alliances in the group that conceal deeper, unrealized, and unspoken attitudes, which should be ventilated. Two patients, both fearful of criticism, may evolve a superficial and precarious neurotic amity, which undermines the therapeutic process. Their fraudulent harmony is resistance and works to prevent the exposure of facets of character structure. Patient progress cannot take place in an atmosphere of insecure and evasive peace and goodwill. It can move on if the analyst presses for mutual exertion and cross exposure, which develops contradictory positions. Thus, when intra- and interpersonal conflict is exposed, the group can proceed to overcome these seemingly irreconcilable attitudes. The neurotic character structure must sooner or later be exposed, not coddled. Otherwise, it fights for its existence and defends an outlived cause. At the same time, the new and healthier personality is also struggling to emerge. The analyst must ally himself with the healthy and make himself the implacable opponent of the outmoded pathology. He can do this by openly and honestly exploring unconscious conflict and screened attitudes and encouraging the group to do likewise. In examining the neurotic framework of the personality, he must concentrate his analysis on oppressive or prohibitive trends, on overprotective and exploitative tendencies, and on ever-present compulsive struggle for power, whether it shows itself in men or women.

Conscious and unconscious overestimation of what is generally regarded as masculine plays a part in the evolution and resolution of every neurosis. The analyst resists the obvious and insidious ways in which the masculine is overvalued. To this end, he takes every opportunity to establish the complementary equality of the sexes in difference. He exposes the devious and subtle ways in which the equivalents of masculinity are taken for granted as superior. He shows each member how, unconsciously, he has hardly progressed from the phallus worship of his ancestors. Among male patients, the analyst indicates how this may manifest itself in compulsive pursuit of women to prove sexual prowess and to relieve castration anxiety. Among female patients, he points out how male supremacy notions are reflected in what amounts to the same thing: the manifold varieties of the need to dominate and control. The analyst exposes the social counterparts of this overevaluation of the male sex organ as an incessant power drive that shows itself in diverse, antisocial efforts to establish individual dominance. He traces these sexual and social correspondents to their common cultural and personal origin. He challenges psychopathic values. In this way, the therapist persists in analyzing aggressive interactions. Members must be schooled not to value each other only as men or women to be exploited as competitive sexual objects.

The analyst can foster harmonious accord if he takes pains to oppose every psychopathic alliance against healthy mutuality. He strengthens individual growth by trying to expose the destructive quality of such unwholesome compacts. He is alert to the fact that not all affinity in the group is necessarily salutary. The devils too may be in league. Under the pretext that "it is necessary to express hostility"—at times a true enough observation—patients deviously, compulsively, and sadistically attack and provoke discord and regression among others who are progressing. The analyst supports forces in the group whose interests are not partisan, but generally and reciprocally emancipating. He stands firm against and thwarts clannishness and narrow self-interest. He analyzes attempts on the part of one patient to misuse another by exposing the act and its motivation. He resists appeasement of pathologic tendencies that would dominate or manipulate members. Such concessions will inevitably bridle and delay patients' progress.

The analyst constantly seeks a theoretical base to keep pace with his practical work. A flexible theoretical background, continually modified by concrete experience in the group, gives patients and therapist alike the power of orientation, clarity of perspective, faith in the work, and confidence in ultimate recovery. But he must be equally strong in practical work. Study of theory and practice will enable him to see a long way ahead and thus anticipate successes and impasses in the patients' best interest. Attention to the interplay of hypothesis and fact leads to the continuous elaboration and modification of each, establishing ever clearer insights into reality and corresponding changes in technique.

Every form of therapy is limited in what it can accomplish. While the analyst hopes to help the patient develop and realize his full possibilities, both he and the patient are partially blocked by a frustrating reality. Yet even within the present social context, certain things can be achieved. The movement of a patient from individual to group analysis is a considerable step toward socialization. It is a vital step away from misleading glorification of individualistic acts that merely subject each of us to a compulsive

competition and isolation. To this unsound emphasis on detachment and individuality, the therapist offers genuine regard and
relatedness to each patient in the group, with a chance to liberate
and coordinate unrealized reserves. The therapist opposes purely
narcissistic interests at the expense of others. He sees that no
individual really gains anything at the cost of others.

An important function of the group analyst is to make clear in
the terminal phase of treatment the relation between the individual patient's freedom to act as he pleases and the needs of
others in any group of which he is a part. He needs to become
aware that his compulsivity demands a lack of freedom to behave
in any other way. He learns that his real needs and those of others
are not necessarily always in opposition. He does not feel
restrained or controlled by interpersonal demands. He finds this
lack of freedom to be only apparent and unreal. His seeming
restraint is really an increased consciousness that roles and
fulfillments are complementary. He becomes able to relinquish
his detached, masturbatory egocentricity. The neurotic's compulsive insistence on personal liberty frequently masks a wish to
exploit and dominate, which needs to be analyzed. When he can
recognize the congruence of self-realization and interpersonal
fulfillment and can act accordingly, he is on the way to getting
well.

An example may clarify this notion. A patient insists on his
right to masturbate. It is only when he is alone that he feels free
enough to enjoy an ecstatic orgasm. He is inhibited during coitus,
when his penile skin feels anesthetized. As he is liberated from
unconscious prohibitions, he learns how to reach new heights of
personal pleasure in mutually gratifying sexual intercourse, more
pleasurable to him because it also delights his partner. Rid of the
illusion that contact involves demands, he realizes himself interpersonally.

11

A Reappraisal of the Field

"Tell us how you work in and with a group," an editor said to us when inviting us to contribute to his volume. "A 'how-to' piece would be a welcome contribution."

The request stopped us for a moment. We had been vaguely dissatisfied with the current literature on group psychotherapy, including our own writings. The zest and searching seemed to be gone. Instead of the adventure and excitement of the early years, we were now being inundated with evermore parochial and partisan clinical points of view presented as the preferred way to function, or conversely, bitter denunciation because we were not practicing according to one another's prescriptions. It seemed to us a new, overall look at our own lives in the work might prove interesting, at least to us. This essay is a reappraisal of a field that still commands our zeal and devotion.

A frequent question asked by analysts of their patients is, "How did you happen to choose your life work?" Answering that question for ourselves, it seems to us, in retrospect, that we had found manifest reasons for becoming interested in group therapy and for continuing our work in it. Also in retrospect, we realize today that those reasons were not personal alone, but were dictated by the larger forces in the world of which our craft, or science, or art, or whatever one wishes to call it, is a part.

In 1938, Wolf came across some articles by Burrow, Wender, and Schilder. These three therapists, from different points of view and for different reasons, had begun experimenting with the analytic treatment of patients in groups. Burrow stressed the need to challenge the authoritarian position of the individual psychoanalyst. Schilder was concerned with the culture's influence on the individual, with his values and mores, while Wender occupied himself primarily with the disturbed person's need for a community and the responsibility of the community at large to understand and, possibly, fill that need.

We cannot document specifically why these papers caught our attention or commanded our own interest at the time. In all likelihood, some dissatisfaction with the existing psychoanalytic experience had something to do with it. Whatever the reason, we communicated this new interest immediately and enthusiastically to some colleagues who were in analysis with our own training psychoanalyst and proposed that we form our own group in order to experience for ourselves the advantages and disadvantages of group psychotherapy. Our suggestion was met with a thunderous silence. Only our analysts found words to discuss the matter with us. They felt, and not without reason, that our plan was evidence of our own resistance to our analytic relationship, which is what we worked on, while our experimental idea died aborning.

While we were in analytic training, the United States was in the depths of a great economic depression. Fortunately, we had been able to build a private practice in psychotherapy, but after a few years, the numbers of patients who had to be turned way because they could not afford private therapy began to haunt us. Was psychoanalysis going to turn out to be a therapy only for those who could afford it? Undoubtedly so, if no compromises could be found. At the same time, we had begun to feel that even if the process of psychoanalysis could not be shortened, it must somehow become a more immediate, dramatic, and meaningful experience for patient and analyst alike. It was then that the idea of trying to work with groups re-occurred to us. This time we were in the fortunate position of being our own "authority" and could put our ideas into operation. Without being too insistent, we began to present the possibility of group therapy to the patients already in analysis with us. To our surprise, we found that most of the patients shared our enthusiasm at embarking on a new adventure that had a serious base and held the promise of increased personal fruition.

The original group consisted of ten patients, five men and five women. They met with us three times a week in sessions lasting one and a half hours. Shortly after the group became cohesive, they reported back to us that they were continuing their meetings in a nearby coffee shop and that many different things were being observed during these extracurricular gatherings. We saw no reason to forbid these meetings without us. And so, almost immediately, the "alternate session," which we will discuss in more detail later, was established as an integral part of our plan for the practice of psychoanalysis in groups. This psychoanalytic orientation did not change, and now after 50 years, we still find the precepts of psychoanalysis the broadest, most reasonable base for effective group therapy.

Although this personal beginning was still in the pioneering days of psychoanalytic group psychotherapy, the first actual record of group psychotherapy in the United States was presented by Dr. J. H. Pratt, a Boston physician, in 1906. Dr. Pratt, working with tuberculars who could not afford institutional care, quickly found that his classroom instruction on tubercular home care had beneficial emotional side effects. By 1956, he was referring to his work not as "Home Sanatorium Treatment for Consumptives" (1906) but as "group psychotherapy" (1956). Between these two dates, group psychotherapy came of age. Moreno has written how he worked with groups in Vienna in 1910. Lazell reported on group treatment of psychotics in 1921. Burrow introduced the term group analysis in 1925. Wender reported on his work with psychoanalytically oriented groups in 1929, and in 1930 Slavson introduced, among other noteworthy innovations, activity group therapy. And in 1934, Schilder introduced group psychotherapy at Bellevue Hospital in New York, combining social and psychoanalytic points of view with his technique.

By this time, the economic depression in the United States had hit bottom. Tensions were further increased by the threat of imminent war, and the combination of these social forces undoubtedly did much to spur the acceptance of group psychotherapy as a recognized method of treatment. It was World War II, however, that gave group psychotherapy its greatest impetus. One of us embarked on our tour of military service with 4 years of clinical experience in group psychotherapy behind us. During our term of service, we had the rare and invaluable opportunity of working with hundreds of groups of men on a short-term basis and of training younger therapists in a method that had now become one of military necessity. Many devoted practitioners of group psychotherapy were developed during this trying period, and all of us were pleased by official recognition when, in 1944, a War Training Bulletin, issued by the United States Army, stated that the favorable response of patients to relatively brief treatment in groups warranted widespread adoption of this method of therapy.

MAJOR TRENDS

In the postwar period, despite the misgivings of many individual therapists, the number of group psychotherapists continued to grow. Probably the last holdouts among psychotherapists were the psychoanalysts. Nevertheless, today hardly a psychoanalytic school exists that does not admit the technique of psychoanalytic group psychotherapy to its course of training. In addition, many new schools of psychotherapy have grown around the practice of group psychotherapy. For our purposes here, a brief discussion of certain major trends may serve to clarify our own position. For example, there is the *experiential school*, which considers the immediate emotional experience of group interaction to be of paramount importance almost to the exclusion of history and working through. Some of these therapists also believe their own feelings, reactions, and so forth should be exposed as freely as those of the patients. To many of this school, thinking is the enemy of therapy and rationality only a repressive and destructive influence.

The group-as-a-whole therapists, currently very much in vogue, are also dedicated to the *here and now* and to the supremacy of the group over the individual's problems. They, however, are not as inclined to include the therapist as a superpatient, as it were, nor even as an authority figure above the authority of the group. Group dynamics, pioneered by Lewin, has proven itself very helpful to community organizers, educators, and business organizations. However, because of its nonanalytic stance and its lack of theory of the cause and cure of mental disorder, we have serious reservations as to its value as a method of treating the mentally and emotionally disturbed. We also find ourselves out of sympathy with the tendency to look on any sort of group activity as a form of group therapy. Many such activities may have constructive outcomes with no justifiable claim to being regarded as therapeutic techniques. We must confess that the heat generated at discussion of these various points of view (to which heat we have made our own considerable contribution), on sober reflection, leaves us slightly bewildered. Anyone who has participated in group psychotherapy knows that nonverbal communication, for example, is important, provocative, disturbing, supportive, and so on. Why then is it necessary or even desirable to build an academy of nonverbal communication therapy around the concept, or even to denigrate verbal communication? And why should there be any contention against the appropriate use of both? By the same token, any experienced group therapist will learn very soon that every group has a life and character of its own and that group cohesion is necessary in some measure for productive therapeutic work. But is it necessary or wise to put the group above the individual at every instance? Or at any instance? We happen to think that a group worthy of its name can often handle recalcitrance, destructiveness, or acting out on the part of members better than a single authority can. In other words, a group can usually set its own limits, can interrupt its own members' acting out. What is less hardy is the status of the individual self. And if there is a choice of emphasis, we prefer to put that emphasis on the side of the preservation of each individual's integrity, without removing him from the group but encouraging him there to achieve effective and successful peer interaction.

GENERAL PRECEPTS

To this end, we have found these general precepts to be of immeasurable help. First, to provide a reasonable serious, relaxed, purposeful atmosphere so that concentration and freedom to work and play are encouraged. This requires the setting of some ground rules that each therapist will choose according to his own personality. We prefer to make our ground rules very general for the most part and quite specific in some parts. For the general rules, we ask that each patient try to discuss his associations, reactions, fantasies, and feelings as frankly as possible, about himself, and his fellow group members, his family, friends, work associates, and his therapist. We ask further that the alternate meeting be considered an integral part of the therapy plan, to be attended as faithfully as the regular meetings, and that any interchange that takes place outside the group setting among individual members or subgroup of members be discussed within the group. These rules are not given as either/or propositions: either obey or get out. Nor is there any intimation of laissez-faire. The instructions are given with the full knowledge that each member of the group will absorb them according to his own level of understanding, organization, degree of resistance, and attitude toward authority and peers. Chances are excellent that collectively the group will regulate its own behavior toward constructive work.

Another rule we follow for ourselves and indirectly impart almost immediately to the patient is that any material that is compulsively emphasized or repeatedly left out of discussion is something to be investigated and analyzed as evidence of resistance. Therefore, if a patient discusses only his family or never his family, always the therapist or never the therapist, always others or never others, always his dreams or never his dreams, only history or never history, it can be assumed that he is hiding something it would be better for him to explore. This eliminates a good deal of endless discussion about which technique is more therapeutic or more effective: here-and-now activity or probing into history, interaction or introspection, verbalization or nonverbalization. They are all important, all at some time used in the interest of self revelation or resistance, depending on the particular situation of the particular patient at the particular moment of study.

In other words, we do not believe that emphasis on any one level or modality of the human being—conscious or unconscious, interpersonal or intrapersonal, interpsychic or intrapsychic, intellectual or emotional—is of any help to therapy if it willfully excludes the other levels. All are important, all must be studied as they emerge in the individual patient, to the end that more and more doors are opened for further insight into his psychodynamics and psychopathology, their effect on the group members and they on him.

It is our further conviction that to practice this way requires intensive training in theory and in actual experience of both individual and group analysis. When we first started training group psychotherapists, the students were members of my heterogeneous groups. Today it is not unusual for the therapist to have his group experience with members of his own profession. We deplore this tendency as violating the true principle of heterogeneity and would very much like to see the student forgo the protection of his professional peers and grapple with the problems in a cluster of garden variety mortals present. In this way, he will learn more about his own unconscious operations, his ability to expose himself appropriately, his attitude toward authority, peers, and so-called inferiors. Certainly, the more heterogeneous and vivid the group analytic experience, the less rigidity and the more reasonable spontaneity should result. And these qualities are the sine qua non of the group analyst who is prepared to deal with the multileveled analytic design with which this chapter deals.

Now to some specific details of how this basic design for psychoanalysis in groups might work in actual practice. In our original writings on this subject, we found that our own need for structure forced us into a "stages" design, which we feel has not proved itself clinically. Stages of therapy occur at different times with different patients. Some come concurrently, some earlier, some later. If one is conversant with the basic precepts of psychoanalysis, if one can handle one's own transferences and countertransferences, it should not be too difficult to pursue a reasonably disciplined plan of therapy for each individual, always seen against the background of his interaction within the group.

Many images have been used to describe the therapeutic group and group therapist. Some have likened the group to an orchestra with the therapist in the role of conductor. Others think of it more as a theatrical improvisation with the therapist as director. An image that often presents itself to us is that of a beach. The sand is always there, but every breath of wind, change of sea, or faintest footfall rearranges the sand particles. To try to prearrange the configurations of sand particles according to any rigid pattern, set of patterns, or stages would be futile. To maintain that these patterns, stages, or even results are constant or absolutely predictable would be untrue. And what holds for the sand holds for the therapeutic group. Is there nothing for them to hold onto but shifting sands? No. Each patient has his characteristic pathology, his characteristic resistances, and a set of transferences, which he repeats over and over again. We come to know and expect these particular responses of his, behavior that typifies him, that gives him a stamp, so that we learn: if we behave so, we can predict that he will react thus and so.

We shall try our best to describe the process of psychoanalysis in groups as we have experienced it and as we have practiced it.

Question: How does one establish a comfortable, relaxed atmosphere? The first necessity is to realize that the setting is important as a background for group members' interaction. To use a modern colloquialism, it is the *scene*. We ourselves prefer to hold group sessions in a squarish room, large enough to hold a circle of ten comfortable chairs, clustered around a rather large round coffee table, a setting not large enough to substitute for a living room or small enough to be a den. In one corner is our own leather chair, quite different from the other chairs, but not ostentatiously so. There are two clocks, one in our line of vision so that we do not have to refer to our wristwatches during the session, the other placed so that every group member can be aware of the passage of time if he so wishes. The walls are lined with bookshelves, and there is an air conditioner in the single window.

These may sound like petty details, but one soon learns that no details in group can be too petty. Our chair, for instance, has sparked more transferential hostility, speculation, and acting out than any other single item (except perhaps our passivity). One of the patients is angry at us. Why? Because we reserve the most comfortable chair for ourselves (like his father or brother or mother or whatever his transferential button is). We have our own clock. What's the matter? Are we afraid we'll be giving them an extra five minutes and so lose some money, or that we'll catch ourselves giving somebody something for nothing? Our walls are rather dark. Is that so they won't show the dirt? What are all the books doing on our shelves? We don't sound as if we ever read any. Are they just there for window dressing? These slightly humorous, critical, and half-truthful observations may relieve a great deal of the tension accompanying the expression of hostility and may hopefully open the door to deeper levels. In the same way, we have found that a straight sofa may be separating in the sense that one of three people on either side may be separated from the sofa subgroup. The circle of independent chairs is part of the atmosphere we want—separate but together as a group—in a room that is neither overwhelmingly luxurious nor antiseptically bare.

FORMING A GROUP

Now, with the group room ready, we are able to begin the formation of a group. The first step is to prepare the individual patient for joining the group. Sometimes this is not necessary, since some patients with prior individual therapy come specifically for group therapy. Even these patients, though, may need some time with the therapist alone before entering a group. In the majority of cases, some individual preparation is necessary in order to overcome fairly common resistances to joining a group. Usually, these resistances fall into the following categories: The patients who (1) think group will be a mortifying invasion of their privacy, (2) fear their difficulties will be publicized; (3) want exclusive possession of the therapist; (4) fear the group will reproduce a nightmarish family situation; (5) cannot take even a breath of hostility; (6) cannot give up the illusion that their neurotic defenses are justified and should be strengthened and encouraged rather than changed; and (7) cannot see how a bunch of neurotics can be of any possible help to them.

The well-trained therapist can allay these fears in prior individual private sessions that may number as few as one or two or continue for more than a year. The prospective group patient should be assured that he need not reveal any intimate material until he is ready to do so. He need not even tell his last name. The patient who wants the analyst to be exclusively his can be led gradually to the insight that this is an infantile demand for the possession of the isolated parent as represented by the analyst and that the way to maturity is to learn to undo the tie to the parental figure and make a more appropriate and reasonable relationship to people in and out of the group. Often, of course, some understanding is not achieved until the patient has been in group for some time. For those who fear the reincarnation of a nightmarish family, the therapist can promise and deliver a permissive protectiveness for a time, using his skill not to stifle other members of the group but to encourage ventilation of feelings, dreams, fantasies, and biographical material from the overfearful one, from the provocateur, and from the onlookers. So everyone in the group has a chance to be both participant and observer, helper and helped, each patient is encouraged to play a liberating, creative, expansive, and socializing role as he gives up his own repressive, destructive, and antisocial trends.

When the patient is ready to join the group, he may ask for and be given or not (depending on whether the therapist believes it to be necessary) brief, general, anonymous descriptions of the other members. The times of regular and alternate group meetings and the fee expected are discussed.

A heterogeneous group of eight to ten people is now ready to start therapeutic work. The heterogeneity of the group is a point that cannot be stressed too often, since that heterogeneity provides the structure that by its very nature promises greater reparative possibilities than could be afforded by a homogeneous group. It is worth repeating that the homogeneous group tends to defeat the individual patient, to force him into a conforming collusion that may be able to comfort him for a while, but will, in the end, betray him unless the therapist and patients struggle hard to uncover their latent heterogeneity. Every patient wishes, in some part, to justify and rationalize his neurotic maneuvers. If he is injected into an environment that largely mirrors his own disorder, or that demands identification and conformity, his resistance is fostered, and the goal of strengthening his differentiated resources is retarded.

Conversely, the heterogeneous group provides a structure that by its nature has greater reparative potential because it must stir the patient to change; it must stimulate, provoke, excite, and challenge him. Diversified interaction will elicit and promote multiple transferences and at the same time help break down the rigidity of the transferential reactions, while the variety of personalities to whom he assigns projected roles will more quickly highlight the discrepancy between his distortions and reality.

Despite this emphasis on heterogeneity, certain readily identifiable types are better treated individually or in homogeneous groups. Among these are manifestly exploitative psychopaths, severe alcoholics who cannot come to meetings sober, seriously disabled stutterers who can exhaust the patience of the other members, paranoids who are apt to include group members in their systematized delusions, intensely masochistic patients who manage always to seduce others into aggression, the senile who are too out of contact, the very depressed and suicidal who are too disturbed to tolerate interaction, the gravely autistic who cannot become involved, the rigidly obsessive-compulsive who are too preoccupied with their own rituals, the mental defectives who can burden a group, and the cardiac patient for whom the excitement and drama of group interaction might precipitate anginal spasm. The homosexual, who some therapists believe cannot be treated in a heterogeneous group, I have found to benefit enormously when included in a "general world atmosphere" and not limited to a homogeneous (homosexual) environment. And many of the types listed above can eventually be included in heterogeneous groups after individual treatment or after a homogeneous group experience. Only the cardiac patient who experiences anginal pain with affect should be kept out of any group, homogeneous or heterogeneous.

Although the hypothetical group I am describing here is one

that is newly formed, it is in no sense a closed group. From now on, to reinforce the principle of heterogeneity, this group will be ongoing and open-ended. If a member leaves, he is replaced by a new member. By the same token, if, for any reason, the group in its development becomes homogeneous in character, rigid, or over-confirming, it can be broken up and its members transferred to several other heterogeneous groups. To give an example of this, a homogeneous group, despite all efforts to establish a serious, working climate, prefers to act out verbally, to use banter as the prevailing tone of verbal interaction, and to use the alternate session primarily as a social activity. These same members, split up and placed in several other groups where the work of psychoanalysis is considered paramount, quickly adjust to the new level, since consciously at least they are suffering from their neurotic disturbance and really want therapeutic help.

But to get back to our newly formed group, they are now ready for their first meeting. As far as we are concerned, this is the only group meeting that can be called typical. No matter how well prepared the participants may be, practically everyone (including the therapist) experiences some anxiety at a first group meeting. Adequate preparation has enabled the group to gather, but all the rest of the experience still lies in the realm of the unknown, which is always somewhat anxiety-provoking. The patients usually meet outside in a waiting room and introduce themselves informally. When the therapist arrives, they all enter the meeting room and seat themselves in a circle. Someone may start the meeting by asking for clarification about the ground rules. Often, though, each member will wait for someone else to begin. It is at this point that the therapist may routinely be expected to get the interaction going (one of the most frequently asked questions about group psychotherapeutic technique). The therapist does this by asking the one question he can safely assume will be responded to by everyone: "Did anyone experience any anxiety about coming here today?" Someone or another is bound to answer, and the likelihood is that most will be willing and eager to discuss their mutual anxieties. From that point on we, at least, have generally not found it necessary to stimulate interaction, to get it going, to initiate or lead, or to direct group members. Such qualities or tendencies we reserve for the purpose of pursuing analytic interventions. And, as the members become more experienced and sophisticated in understanding latent content, we gradually encourage them to become more and more autonomous, intervening only when we believe it to be necessary and appropriate.

We believe that analytic work can begin in the very first session, usually with the ventilation of anxiety as just described. Once interaction has started, it is not at all unusual for a patient to recount a recent dream, a recurrent dream, or an old nightmare. Failing that, the analyst encourages the telling of daydreams, fantasies, and reveries. He asks members to avoid a censorship of fanciful speculation about one another's productions. In this way, the different personalities begin to emerge and the first steps are taken in the development of mutual rapport and antagonism. During these early meetings, the therapist plays a more active role, contributing his own spirit of warmth and optimism by a sympathetic, permissive attitude toward each patient's ventilating his frustrating problems, dreams, and aspirations.

Gradually, the sparking of interaction will be taken over by the members of the group and the therapist will sit back more and more, letting the interaction develop and the tensions build up. Every well-structured group usually contains one or more catalytic agents, ranging from the healthier patients – those who wish to do constructive work and get on with the process of mutual discovery and wholesome interrelatedness – to the more neurotically motivated provocateurs. Among the latter are (1) the exhibitionists, who do not hesitate to boast of their exceptional qualities and accomplishments; (2) the seducers, who are quick to inform about their sexual superiority; (3) the approval seekers, who continually stress their own infallibility or inadequacy and who collapse at the slightest breath of criticism; (4) the chronically anxious, who cannot bear a moment's silence; (5) the attention seekers, who cannot bear to be out of the spotlight for even one minute; (6) the habitually detached, who force themselves into desperate interaction or who remain dolefully silent; (7) the compulsive organizers, who must adhere to the same rigid structure and who cannot tolerate one minute of spontaneity; and (8) the compulsive socializers, who must keep the party going.

Even patients with slight psychopathic trends may provoke productive group reactions. While such members may try to exploit the group in order to express their irresponsibility, lack of discipline, and moral laxity, such behaviors tend to evoke vivid responses and to mobilize feelings in defense against it. Patients who chronically feel misused often carry their triggered fear into meetings, demanding their money's worth out of every session. Hypomanics are obviously a stimulant, while the schizoids are exceptionally facile with unconscious material. In fact, every person has some provocative tendencies, and the astute analyst will look for opportunities to bring these submerged catalysts to the surface.

If a patient persists in remaining silent, the analyst may leave him alone, refusing to indulge his silent provocation, and let the frustration build until he speaks because he must speak or burst. In other instances, the therapist may struggle to analyze a resistive silence or simply encourage the patient to speak. Those patients with weaker egos should be helped toward verbalization. Of these, the analyst may, at first, ask directly for a dream or fantasy, hopeful that the symbolic nature of the communication will serve as a defense against the anxiety of self-revelation. Failing that, and only as a last resort, the patient will be urged to discuss immediate or current problems of his life outside the group. With notable exceptions, most patients are too prone to compulsively recite and review their current difficulties or case histories, and it is just this form of resistance that successful group therapy tries to discourage.

The recounting of dreams, fantasies, and reveries and free association to these unconscious productions and tentative inter-pretations are among the first devices used to stimulate group interactions and to establish group rapport. The next step is to encourage free association of members to each other. Until recently, we used a technique we called "going around." Here a single member was asked to free associate about each other member of the group. Eventually, as patients became more sophisticated and appreciative of the power this artificially cen-tered position gave them, we noticed that there was never enough time, and before we knew it, each "going around" took up most of the regular session, naturally causing extreme frustration to some other members of the group. Today we use the device only rarely, and, when we do, we encourage immediate responses to the member "going around." We feel the same effect can be realized by promoting the free flow of interaction that inevitably gives rise to free association concerning group members and by constantly referring other free associations back to group members and familial antecedents. Let us give an example of how this might work hand in hand with other phases of analytic pursuit.

> Peter complained that he couldn't trust women. He free-associated to his mother and sister who were "always ready to jump on him." Kay, a group member, asked, "Does anyone here remind you of your mother or sister?" Peter answered, "Yes, Jane. You're like a tight spring," he tells Jane. "I'm afraid you'll suddenly uncoil and snap at me. What are you afraid of? Do you, any time you're approached, feel you're going to be raped?"
>
> Jane resented the association and the inference. She refused to accept any of it as valid for her, insisting that it revealed nothing but Peter's own projection. But that night she had a dream that uncovered her obsessional fear and concomitant wish for erotic contact with her father. At succeeding sessions, the deeper intracacies of erotic interest in and fear of her father were elaborated, and working through begun via analysis of her interaction with the men in the group.

This one example illustrates the use of basic psychoanalytic technique—free association, the use of dream material, the subsequent uncovering of repressed material, or transference and working through—all brought about by the interaction within the group.

ANALYSIS OF RESISTANCE AND TRANSFERENCE

The analysis of resistance is also greatly facilitated by the group setting and the group interaction. For example, as patients interact, the person rigidly blocked in erotic, transferential interest in the analyst is helped to insight by the other members of the group, who are quick to assert their own special investment in the authority figure, while at the same time resenting the lack of attention being given them by the therapist or their peers. The commonly seen resistances or acting out of a missionary spirit, martyrdom, scapegoatism, and so forth, are among others most easily exposed in the group for the neurotic commitments we know them to be. Another form of resistance, not so easily available for direct study in individual analysis but glaringly obvious in the group situation, is voyeurism in its more socially acceptable form of living through others. The injustice collector, the consistent diagnoser of other peoples' ills, the judgment dispenser, the hider of historical detail, all these and many other resistive manifestations are clarified in group interaction and are made available as they become familiar and characteristic operations of the individual.

The analysis of transference, closely allied to the analysis of resistance, is one of the most important and productive aspects of psychoanalysis in groups. The projection of parental and sibling images onto other group members are phenomena requiring exhaustive study, and the analysis of this transferential process is the largest single area of concentration of this particular method — except working through. Under the analyst's guidance, patients discover the extent to which they invest one another with early familiar qualities. In the group setting, in which a member may not only project a significant historical figure onto the analyst, but may also single out members of the group for the same purpose, the field for transference, in the formation and in working through, is appreciably extended.

At first, the analyst stresses certain truisms about the transference phenomenon. He explains that all of us carry a heritage out of childhood that impels us to endow the present with old forms, that we see ourselves and others in terms of our own circumscribed experiences, that this attributes to other qualities they may not actually possess and results in the distorted relationships that lead to the pain and self-defeat of all neuroses and that therapeutic help, if not cure, can be measured by the extent to which these distortions can be revised in the patient himself and tolerated when directed toward him by others. Patients are alerted to the general qualities of the transference reaction — such as irrelevance, compulsion, repetition, irrationality, overcompensation, and so forth, so that they can learn to spot these transferential reactions as they occur in themselves and others.

As we said before, we believe the discovery, analysis, and working through of transference to be the most important work of psychoanalysis in groups, since transference repeatedly interferes with the patient's true estimate of reality, and since by its nature it must prevade every area of the patient's life. In the group, it is possible to study this phenomenon in all its myriad mutations and to demonstrate over and over again its repetitive and all-pervading qualities. Once the patient has been alerted to these general qualities of transference, he is ready to observe and analyze its manifestations in interaction. Since, as we all know, the transferential response is unconscious, we must expect considerable resistance to its recognition. Here again the group can be of great help. Since there is a great variety of interaction, the endless calling of attention to transference need not become a mechanical bore. So, we are in a position to remind the patient time and again when he is reacting to a mask that exists largely in his mind, when his reactions are illogical, unreasonable, absurd, or at least archaic and when he exhibits affective disturbances or anxiety, extreme irritability, depression, fearfulness, or even panic and terror.

Other qualities of transference are more easily observable in group than in other treatment situations. Here we can see how rigid are the transferential patterns, how excessive, how helpless is the person in their grip, and see how inhibiting they are to projector and object alike. By examples and illustrative material presented at the moment of occurrence, the analyst repeatedly verifies these identifying features of transference, using every opportunity possible to clarify the particular response in terms of the present reality and the possible historical background of the response.

Sometimes a patient's transference is so rigid that he projects the same distortions on everyone, no matter how different the other personalities. These patients are easy enough to diagnose: they are often psychotic. But they are much more difficult to treat. Here again the group can be of immeasurable help, by provoking less threatening versions of the transference in the

form of less menacing peer personalities. Every group will contain some such less threatening figures and allow the emergence
of penumbral variations of response, which, later on, may make
it possible to reach the core transference problem with the
therapist.

For example, a patient rigidly fixed in transference gives a
complicated historical picture of a powerful, inimical family of
parents and siblings. In individual analysis, the patient may
project onto the therapist at one time or another all these images.
It is not always possible in the individual analytic situation to
pursue these multiple, volatile responses. Certainly, it is not
always possible to differentiate the source of the particular
projection. In group, the situation is reversed. "You are my sister,
brother, father, mother, aunt, or uncle," the patient may say at
one time or another to the analyst and group members. Or he
may say to each one, "You are my mother; everyone is like my
mother." In either case, his response remains the same. And the
group is bound to respond compulsively as well as spontaneously
to these irrational investments, dealing with them in the less-
threatening peer interaction until the rigidity of response is
worked through to more flexible and realistic alternatives. At this
point, it is easier for the therapist to start to deal with the thematic
or central transference, which is usually centered on him. Since
this is usually a reproduction of a relationship with a more
significant parent or authority figure with whom the patient was
most ambivalently and affectively bound, it must also of necessity
pose the greatest threat to the defenses of the patient. With the
groundwork of this laid beforehand in interaction and analysis of
peer relationships, penumbral transferences, and so on, the
threat is no longer so great. Now, hopefully, the door has been
opened to tackling a core problem that would have been too
painful to approach earlier or more directly.

In group, when transference is evoked, the patient is asked for
both the immediate provocation, so that the validity of his
response can be evaluated, and for the possible historical background for the response itself and for his estimate of the quality
of that response. Thus, the searching for historical data and for
the releasing of this data becomes not an obsessional maneuver to
evade reality, but rather a search specifically focused on clarifica-

tion of the transference as an opening door to reality. I believe that the therapist who can concentrate early in treatment on the analysis of transference can shorten the duration of treatment considerably and can more reasonably expect that the benefits gained from treatment will last.

We would like to cite here one example of this process, which highlights the totally different responses exhibited by a patient when in individual analysis and when transferred to a group.

In thirty preliminary sessions, Joe and the analyst got on famously. Joe was brilliant, serene, and exceptionally friendly; he made rapid progress. There seemed to be no obvious resistance. He interpreted a dream, and the therapist would add some additional points. Joe would accept these and perhaps add some modifications that seemed entirely appropriate to both of us. Suspicious as it might sound, there seemed to be no stumbling blocks. The whole relationship was simply too unneurotic, and the analyst began to wonder why Joe was in therapy at all. The therapist suggested that he join a group, so that we might have a chance to explore certain areas of his personality that individual analysis had not revealed. Joe agreed. The analyst was not able to detect any lack of enthusiasm toward the suggestion. But at the very first group session, Joe exhibited his first sign of negative transference. He was a changed man. Our harmonious relationship, his warm appreciation of what the analyst had done for him, his eager willingness to act reasonably, all vanished. Now, at this very first meeting, he challenged everything the group leader said. He used his fine intellect and keen intuition to analyze all his fellow group members, unconsciously managing to forestall or to belittle any contribution the analyst might dare to make. Whereas in the prior private sessions patient and therapist had had easy interchanges, in the group he would hardly allow the leader to open his mouth. He interrupted, he anticipated, and predicted—often accurately enough—everything the therapist was about to say. The group leader let this go on for some time. In fact, he let it go on until the group began to notice his compulsive behavior and began calling it to his attention. Joe could hardly believe his ears, and finally he turned to the analyst for confirmation. He remarked then on the sharp contrast between Joe's friendliness in individual sessions and his truculence toward the leader in the group. This time Joe was surprised and embarrassed. But he could see that what was said was true. And, almost immediately, he could allow repressed memories, which had not seemed appropriate in the individual situation, to come into consciousness. In subsequent sessions, Joe recalled with what pontifical dignity and Victorian strictness his father had held court at the dining room table when Joe was a child; how one had to tiptoe about the house when his father was napping; how he was not allowed to speak unless spoken to in his father's presence. His rage mounted as Joe recalled other indignities reaching back into early childhood as, for example, that his father could visit with his mother while she was taking a bath, while he, Joe, was excluded. As time went on, Joe's field of insight widened. He began to realize that he could relate freely and well with one person—so long as that contact was self limited and circumscribed. He then was able to recall that he could always talk with his mother when he was alone with her but that she was not too often available to him for any extended periods. In a group, however, he felt driven to excel, to be the genius of the living room. In other words, he discovered that in every social gathering, he habitually recreated the family milieu and automatically strove to become its guiding intellect. The group suggested and Joe agreed that what he was acting out was his father's role and that probably he had often fantasized as a child that he would one day successfully challenge his father in everything he said and did. Joe was then able to see how consistently he had been acting out this unconscious fantasy in his business and social lives, to his own self defeat, because, although he was relatively successful in both areas, he was far from reaching his full potential, a fact that had brought him into therapy. Now the group had given him the chance to act out the fantasy in a situation in which it could really be explored in depth.

It was then made clear that when Joe was in a one-to-one relationship of limited commitment, as he had been with the analyst, he could reproduce the pleasantries of his relationship with his mother. But that when the analyst was in the group, he became his father and the group his family. From this insight we were able to proceed more deeply into his oedipal conflict, his intense attachment to his mother, his repressed rivalry with his father and his compulsive replacement of his father in the regenerated family. Obviously, Joe's transfer to a group revived old family ghosts who would have appeared in individual analysis with difficulty but who had been almost immediately and spontaneously evoked in a group situation. What's more, they had been evoked with such undeniable drama and concreteness that insight had to be experienced by anyone not desperately ill. The group setting proved just as concretely helpful in the working through of the transference. And what held true in Joe's case has been observable in many other cases that heretofore were held to be unanalyzable. As his father transference was worked through, the analyst again became the preoedipal mother from whom he was ultimately able to separate himself.

As the foregoing indicates, we are still committed to the practice of psychoanalysis in groups with the modifications that necessarily must come with the change in settings. We believe that human behavior is largely determined by original provocation and the formation of early distortions. We do not believe that man functions accidentally, as a consequence of impulsivity or imagination that is initially self-generated and unrelated to causality or etiology. We believe rather, that a patient's behavior, his illness, and his health are also largely consequences of his history and that transference in the present is the repetition compulsion of an earlier relationship, which can be worked through, so that there is a gradual but radical displacement of the negative history in the course of treatment. The group analyst need not avoid or reject spontaneity, inspiration, choice, or accident. But neither does he give up trying to discover, at every turn, the patient's motivation, the original causes of his pathology, the development, and the laws that govern its present operation. While in early treatment, he allows spontaneous interaction to build up, he also consciously and expertly enters into the therapeutic relationship, always with the aim of facilitating freedom from compulsion by dispelling projective illusions. Gradually, he helps supplement the technique of spontaneous interaction with an encouragement to strive for conscious, methodical sifting and planning of verbalized responses in the best personal and mutual interests of the members of the group. This is always a process of intense struggle for the patient—struggle with his own transference reactions when they cannot be justified or condoned, when insight without acting on it cannot be tolerated, when character change must replace explaining, and when self and group discipline demands personal reconstruction. This struggle is how I see "working through." And, like all other struggles taking place in psychoanalysis, it runs throughout the course of treatment. When termination is near, however, it takes precedence over the other phases and in group is a generally rewarding phenomenon. When the other members begin to remark with pleasure on the changes in attitude, we know that the patient is on the way to termination.

One test of readiness for discharge is the patient's ability to analyze and dispose of his own transferences by choosing more realistic alternatives and his ability to recognize situations in which formerly he might have reacted in transference. Instead of acting out verbally his lateral transferences to other patients, he learns to respond more appropriately.

THE ROLE OF THE THERAPIST

All this calls for considerable skill on the part of the therapist. His role is complicated, much more complicated than that of the individual analyst. Therefore, it is also one of the most controversial topics of discussion among group therapists. There are some who see him as the most important patient in the group, participating on every level as the patient participates. Others liken him to the conductor of an orchestra or the director of a play. Others see him as a leader or conversely as a silent figure who represents leaderlessness and whose object is to build up the ultimate in frustration among group members.

Our view of the group therapist is much more conservative, conventional if you will. We believe the group therapist should be first and foremost a well-trained psychoanalyst. He should be trained in the principles of individual psychoanalysis, and then later specifically for psychoanalysis in groups. He must have self understanding and a capacity for empathy. These should be enhanced by study so that these endowments are under his conscious control and cease to be a source of wonder to him or to others. But above all, we believe he should have the ability to scrutinize and work through his own transferences and countertransferences. This is why he needs a thorough individual analysis and in addition a sustained heterogeneous group analytic experience. We are firm believers in postgraduate workshops in which the young and not-so-young therapists focus their attention on and continue to resolve their transferences and countertransferences to their patients.

We hold this point of view not only to protect the patient, which is our therapeutic responsibility, but also to protect the therapist himself. If he is really doing his job in the group, he must expect constant efforts to manipulate him; he cannot afford to be discouraged or thrown off balance by the intensity of interpersonal feeling that occasionally develops in meetings. He must even encourage the most timid to react to him, and he must support the angry or loving patient who will test him to the utmost. He must be strong enough to lead and to exercise control where control is in the patient's interest. He must be strong enough to acknowledge his errors and secure enough to relinquish the initiative to the group or to a patient as the situation of the moment demands, without feeling that his authority is being threatened. He must be able to control any tendency to play the proselytizing missionary or arbitrary dictator. He must remind himself at all times that the meaning of the interaction within the group is the significant focus of his attention and the jumping-off point for all analysis, and that, therefore, he must regard the patients in his group as partners in the analytic pursuit, while at the same time maintaining the reality position of the guiding expert—a position he can neither relinquish nor misuse if he abides by the reality principle established by the tenets of psychoanalysis.

This is by no means an easy position to maintain at all times and in all situations. Nevertheless, a conscious attempt should be made to find ways of doing so. I think there are two ways, among others, for the conscientious therapist to accomplish this. In the first place, it is of paramount importance that he check continually on the possibility of his own countertransferences interfering with his relationship to the patient. He must also look for ways to build the self confidence and ego strength of his patients, so that dependency on the authority is steadily decreased, and material that must be repressed or hidden from that authority is released.

THE ALTERNATE SESSION

It was in the service of this last principle that we introduced the formal concept of the alternate session, and our conviction as to its importance, theoretically and practically in any group therapy plan, has grown stronger with the passing years.

The alternate session, as we have indicated, is a scheduled meeting of a therapeutic group without the therapist being present. These sessions alternate with the regular sessions when, of course, the therapist is always present. Usually, alternate sessions take place in the homes of various members of the group, with the objective of utilizing a still more informal atmosphere, so that interaction and participation are further stimulated. We have rarely given formal rules as to how these alternate sessions are to be conducted. But experience with hundreds of patients has demonstrated that the alternate session usually becomes an extension of the regular session and tends to preserve the tone, form, and quality of the work done when the group is with the therapist.

The alternate session serves many purposes adjunctive to and helpful to the therapeutic picture in both the horizontal and vertical levels. On the horizontal level, it emphasizes the important role interaction with one's peers must play in therapy. Members learn they can disagree with each other and settle their differences without the intervention of the authority. In other words, they learn they can stand on their own two feet without running to Mama or Papa for protection. Many patients feel freer to interact at alternate meetings when transferences to the therapist are less threatening or less repressive. Some report they can experience, see, and define different transferences more easily in these circumstances, and others say that it is largely at the alternate session that they can really feel they are relating to their fellow members. Necessarily, these are also attitudes that need to be worked through. At the alternate meeting, the patient has a greater chance to learn how to ask for help from his peers, and conversely he can give help in circumstances he would ordinarily leave to the therapist to handle.

Another important function of the alternate session is that it gives members a chance to compare their behavior in the two climates. Anyone who has had experience in these different settings will tell you this is not a trivial factor in human relatedness. As far as we are concerned, it is one of the reasons we believe tape recordings of analytic sessions or watching through one-way mirrors is unsatisfactory and does not give a true picture of what actually goes on in such meetings. Since, ethically, the patient must be appraised of these mechanical interventions, they are naturally conscious of them, even if they themselves maintain it makes no difference in their behavior. The same contention is almost uniformly expressed by patients in the group. Almost to a man they deny there is even the slightest difference in their behavior between one meeting and the other. But continued verbalizations usually prove just the opposite. Rarely, the therapist may ask some questions about what happened at an alternate meeting, although we have found that usually this is not necessary and often unwise. The pertinent facts will be disclosed sooner or later. So we find out from one member or another that the patient who praises us to the skies in the regular meeting saves all his complaints about us for the alternate session. The therapist–patient who is a genial colleague at the regular session is an agent provocateur at the alternate, openly inciting the members to revolt against us or to quarreling among themselves. The conventional lady, compulsively conforming, may fantasize all kinds of escapades the mice might indulge in while the cat's away. The habitually silent member who waits for a chance to be able to get something said at a regular meeting, while the others are not busy vying for our attention or to get their money's worth, is allowed to speak only at alternate sessions. As we have said, the "alternate" material is introduced in regular sessions sooner or later. The following is an example.

Shortly after World War II, there was a therapist–patient in one of our groups who wanted to learn about group therapy as well as resolve his neurotic difficulties. He was an older man, experienced in individual psychoanalysis, with emotional problems of his own. In the group was also a younger man who had suffered the horrors of a Nazi concentration camp in his early adolescence. The therapist–member was not Jewish and had displayed latent hostility toward one of us as a father figure, but no feelings tainted with prejudice. At one regular session, the young Jewish man suddenly blurted out, "If anyone calls me 'dirty Jew,' I won't be responsible for what I will do." Everyone looked rather embarrassed, and he repeated his threat. The leader did not probe for clarification, because he was not certain how much the accusation had to do with reality and how much was a manifestation of his illness. He was also waiting for more background material. A week later, one of the women was angry with the therapist–member and accused him of deliberate taunting. "The way you kept needling Abe at the alternate, always asking him, 'What would you do now if someone called you dirty Jew?' " The occasion gave all members a chance to discuss their reluctance to be tattletales, although all were angry at the therapist–member. It gave the latter a chance really to get his teeth into his own transferential disturbance, and it gave Abe a chance to ventilate his pent-up violent feelings against those he felt had misused him so horrendously.

It would have taken a much longer time for this material to emerge if the group had met only in regular sessions. And we wonder sometimes if it would have come out at all. There is no doubt in our minds that for a clearer picture of the dynamics of any given patient the alternate session is invaluable. In the analyst's absence, members develop a relationship to each other on their own in which they can learn to assimilate and tolerate their own contradictory feelings, and this fact alone can often motivate a group to stay together as well as to engage each other. This is one reason why the alternate session is ego-demanding and therefore ego-building.

It would seem then that the alternate session should be an accepted part of all group therapy plans. This, however, is far from the case. Many therapists are still extremely fearful that the members of the group will become negatively involved in a way that would endanger not only their therapy but also the reputation of the therapist. Sexual acting out is usually given as a chief danger; physical violence ranks second among the fears; and emotional damage or disturbance because of inept, premature, and amateur interpretation and wild analysis is third.

We have never seen any figures, statistics, or case histories to substantiate these objections to the alternate session. And we, ourselves, have never seen anyone seriously hurt because of these sessions. Sexual acting out has occurred in our groups on rare occasions during our years of practice, but as far as we know there has also been this kind of acting out in the groups of therapists we are acquainted with who do not permit the alternate session in their therapy plan. Physical acting out of an aggressive nature is equally uncommon. So far no one has been seriously hurt. As for the third fear, we have found patients eminently able to defend themselves against premature insights. Either they do not hear what they are not ready to hear, or they remind the attacker of his resistances, that he too is sick, or they ask to see his permit to practice, or they call on the other members for support. If, in spite of these choices, too much anxiety does result, the analyst at the regular session is always available.

With so much positive evidence for the desirability of the alternate session and so little clinical evidence against it, the conclusion seems inescapable that the objecting therapist must find the reasons for his theoretical assumptions within himself and his relationship with his patients. As for ourselves, we continue to maintain that, since the relationship to authority and peers is one of the primary problems in mental disturbance, we are fortunate to have at our disposal a treatment scheme that enables us to deal with the problem practically and clinically. A group therapy plan that does this by reinforcing the individual's interactive relatedness with his peers, instead of encouraging and perpetuating the often neurotic patterns of rebelling or submitting to authority, is, we think, a realistic one for the patient without requiring the therapist to be in absolute surveillance. At the same time, the regular session provides a setting in which authority problems can be dealt with.

Having gone this far, we would like to elaborate a bit more on the alternate session, mainly to answer some of the more frequently asked questions.

When in the course of treatment does the group start having alternate sessions? As far as we are concerned, the first regular group sessions can be followed immediately by the first alternate session. If the therapist thinks the patients are too sick to gather by themselves, he may wait until he feels more secure. And we believe that if patients are well enough to function outside of a hospital and to be engaged in some sort of life outside of group, there is little reason for exaggerated fear that gathering with fellow patients will lead to some kind of disaster. We think it worth repeating that therapeutic groups have always in our experience set their own limits, and, if left to their own devices, will be able to control their acting out. Of course, if the therapist himself acts out and unconsciously encourages the group to do so, the problem becomes quite different. Irrationality can be infectious. But if the therapist can transmit his conviction that acting out retards therapy and demonstrates its resistive character, the extent to which the group goes along with him will not differ radically between regular and alternate sessions.

Another question that puzzles many is how the therapist can do his job when the patients know so much more about what is going on than he does.

The answer is that the therapist knows more than they do, not necessarily every detail, but more of the psychopathology and has more of a conscious plan for working through. Besides, the alternate meeting is part of a continuum. It does not exist in a vacuum, nor is it isolated from the regular session, so it is bound to come up at some regular session. But more importantly, the alternate meeting is there to help the patient, to get him to understand the nature of, let us say, the repetition compulsion, the all-pervading quality of transference, to raise questions about how he can resolve his frustration and to bring these problems back to the regular session until he can function more appropriately on his own.

Another common question is: Is it necessary to hold alternate meetings in the homes of members? No, of course not. We do, however, think it is desirable. Some of our groups cannot afford the extra time alternate evening meetings take, and so must meet in our offices. There is, of course, nothing we can do about these reality matters, if, for example, a member has a night job. But if these concessions are made, the therapist should be fully aware that certain drawbacks will be present. These meetings simply will not be as free, in breadth, depth, or relaxation. If, for one reason or another, they must be held in the analyst's office, we suggest that they be held after and not before the regular session. In the prior session, there is a strong tendency for many to withhold until the therapist arrives, and here is an example.

One of us had a patient who was generally accepted by the group and the therapist as being a hard and conscientious worker for his own therapy and that of others. We tended to forgive his temper tantrums when others, in his opinion, talked too much, as being part of his particular problem. This group had switched their alternate meetings from members' houses to prior sessions in the office. The therapist had not noticed that, whenever he entered the room for the regular session, this patient (let us call him Max) was always launched on some discussion or other, until one day, one of the women in the group took the bull by the horns and accused him of a plot. She pointed out that he was always very active with the other members of the group, flattering them with his attention and offers of help and sympathy, right until 2 minutes to one, when the regular session was scheduled to begin. Then, suddenly, as if a bell had been rung, he switched the subject to himself, and continued on it, as the therapist, entered and seated himself.

Max, naturally, denied any such plot, and, since none of the others had noticed this method of operation, he stood more or less group supported, and his accuser was seen as a projector. What happened thereafter, however, was most interesting. It was not too important to check on whether Max continued his maneuver. It was much more important to see that once the modus operandi had been exposed, all the other members thought it such a splendid idea that you couldn't get anyone to discuss anything more personal than the weather before the magic hour of one. Gradually, members started drifting in later and later. All attempts to analyze this, although interesting, did not solve the reality situation of the waste of the pre-session. The therapist ended switching the pre-session to a post-session with a full explanation of the reason for doing so and the expressed hope that meetings soon would be held again in members' homes. That summer when the therapist was on vacation, the meetings were resumed at the homes of the patients, and post-sessions at the office were never asked for again by that particular group.

This brings us to our last reason for sponsoring the concept of the alternate session as strongly as we do. It gives a continuity to the group life that most patients have missed in their own lives. During the long summer vacations, the struggle for realistic communication can still proceed. Life does not or need not stop just because the therapist goes away. This is especially necessary for the patient who literally thinks he dies when his analyst is gone. This type of patient will still suffer, but there is a chance of mitigating that pain when it can be discussed with the group in a relationship that already has a basis of operation without the therapist. In the same way, the alternate meeting can be an important part of any short-term group therapy plan. In short-term therapy, different levels of results can be hoped for or expected, but the idea of continuity and the possibility of holding the group together for a while longer through the alternate meeting plan can be very comforting to people who dread the end of help.

At present, we provide regular weekly sessions for 1½ hours with the analyst, alternate meetings once or twice a week without the therapist for 2 or 3 hours at a time, and selected individual sessions for three-quarters of an hour. This program provides for the exploration of peer and vertical vectors and shows the optimal usefulness of each procedural variation in the therapeutic field of operations.

COMBINED THERAPY

Some might say our stand on the alternate meeting is a far cry from traditional psychoanalysis. They might say the same about our attitude toward combined therapy, that is, the routine treatment of a patient in a group and simultaneous individual analysis. Our stand on this question is quite simple. We are neither for nor against combined therapy. What we are against is its routine use, except when absolutely necessary. There are certain things one must do routinely, but we don't think combined therapy is one of them. There are many patients we have treated who do not need individual therapy at all, others have had to have combined therapy throughout their group experience, and still others have not been able to take the group experience at all. Here, once again, a pet theory of the therapist can be a hollow one when placed against the needs of a particular patient. The needs of the particular patient at a particular time should determine whether or not combined therapy is indicated. It is as simple as that.

We seldom use regularly scheduled private sessions in addition to the group, except as indicated below.

Some patients need one-to-one experience with the maternal surrogate in the person of the analyst before they can join and interact with their siblings and peers. Others cannot avail themselves of the dyadic relationship with the therapist until they have had a liberating experience with their peers.

The group therapist who provides regular individual sessions has too little regard for the therapeutic effectiveness of treatment in a group. Individual hours are often promoted not out of the patients' real needs but out of the therapist's countertransference. Individual sessions are frequently rationalized as necessary in order to precipitate a transference neurosis as a step toward working it through, but such a requirement is unusual. For as resistances are analyzed in the group, pre-oedipal and nonverbal reactions emerge and can be resolved in the group setting.

Some group therapists provide individual hours on the assumption that if a patient is silent in the group or avoids a dyadic relationship with the analyst, he needs individual sessions to resolve one-to-one problems in the vertical vector. But it is a misunderstanding of group therapy to think that dyadic relationships do not exist in group interaction. One-to-one ties and connections develop in the group both in the horizontal and hierarchical vectors.

The regular use of individual hours often leads to an increase in resistance. Often the patient, certain of his routine and private access to the analyst, does not show in the group his responses to other members but saves them for exposure to the therapist alone. This leads to indirection and deviousness rather than working through to more straightforward responses. It also prevents the members from getting more immediate understanding of their mutually provocative behavior. It blocks reality testing and detailed on-the-spot and vigorous mutual investigation.

The belief that all patients at all times need combined treatment obscures differences among patients. It obscures the uniqueness of a patient's behavior in one context and another. It confuses the special value to the individual of the regular and alternate sessions. It muddies the differences of the members. It might be more relevant for the therapist to ask himself with each patient why he wants to offer private sessions just now. Would individual sessions promote the patient's resistance?

The patient may ask for individual hours in order to avoid participation in the group. Or he may misuse the group in order not to relate to the analyst. Or he may exhibit destructive behavior at group sessions and constructive behavior in individual interviews. Or the reverse may take place. Or he may resist telling the group what has taken place in individual treatment. Or the therapist's fear of the projected dangers of group members' interaction may lead the group to fall apart.

There are certain patients who ask for individual sessions, whose requests have to be denied and analyzed. Among these are the regressed psychotics in pre-oedipal attachment to a prior individual therapist or to the group analyst himself. The same caution needs to be exercised with the borderline psychotics. Others wish to control or seduce the therapist or to isolate him from the rest of the group. Such a maneuver may not be discovered until the analyst has seen the patient individually.

The generalized and nondiscriminative use of individual sessions parallel to group therapy tends to make treatment too leader-centered. The therapist's anxiety over the projected dangers of group interaction and acting out leads him inappropriately to provide too many overprotective individual hours. He invests group members with a helplessness and aggressivity that demand individual attention. As a result, patients are infantilized and subverted in their wholesome need to use their own resources in working through to a more maturating giving and taking with one another. Accordingly, we suggest only occasional rather than regular individual hours, when their use is appropriate and realistically necessary. Such sessions should be group-centered and the patient should be encouraged to tell the group what transpired in the individual meeting.

For many passive dependent patients, unless there is peer interaction, therapy does not take place. This has taught us in conducting individual analysis to promote the patients' interaction with other persons outside the therapeutic situation as well as in the treatment setting. Of course, with patients who are terrified of closeness, such deep anxiety proscribes interaction except in very small doses, built up slowly as treatment proceeds. Even these isolated individuals make no progress until they are drawn into interactional experience. Patients who are very passive, inactive, schizoid, or character-disordered profit enormously from the promotion of peer interaction with other group members.

We *treat* the patient in the group setting. Where transference involvement with the therapist is intense, individual private sessions may deepen the pathology. There are specific indications for providing adjunctive individual hours in certain circumstances and at certain times in the course of treatment. Psychoanalysis in groups does not exclude individual sessions where they are indicated. Each patient's treatment begins in individual sessions, and he is free to return to them, if they are in his best interest. Our concern is that the patient not be forced into an entrenchment of a transference neurosis or psychosis. His dependence on the group operates against such a hazard. We see the dangerous entrenchment of the pre-oedipal attachment all too often. Many of our patients come to us from overextended transference neurosis or psychosis to one or more individual analysts.

There have been some attempts to be discriminating in the selection or rejection of particular diagnostic categories of patients for combined therapy. However, in the hands of different therapists, the variety of patients includes the whole range of diagnostic possibilities. The criteria for selection, it appears, are not explicit. The problem remains unsolved. We need more adequate clinical experience and research.

It is possible, however, to be a bit more specific with regard to those patients who would benefit from associated individual sessions, where there is little danger of entrenching regression. Such patients have fairly intact egos. They are not pre-psychotic or psychotic. For them, regression is in the service of the ego. Others who benefit from associated individual sessions are the oldest, or nearly the oldest, siblings in a larger family who in childhood were prematurely forced to assume surrogate parental roles with the birth of each new sibling as the actual parents abdicated their parental responsibilities.

For some time analysts have been preoccupied with what harm the parents did the patient. More lately, analysts have attended to their own transferential and countertransferential roles in misusing the patient. Our group experience has taught us to reconsider this focus. Group members bring out what is done by the neurotic child in the patient, his provocative role. Group interaction clarifies not only what has been done to the patient but by him as well. We observe how a female member intrudes whenever another patient and the therapist interact, in order to exclude her sibling and have the mother in the therapist to herself. Behavior is interactive: bilateral, trilateral, quadratic, and so forth. The child psychiatrist tends to view the mother as hurtful to the child. But the mother does this in part because the father rejects her for her involvement with the child. This kind of triangular reenactment in group therapy illustrates the importance of understanding behavior in its multilaterality in individual analysis and recognizing that the behavior of the two persons changes with the addition of the third person, a fourth, and so on. In individual analysis, therefore, we look for the unseen third or fourth member in the manifest dyad of the patient and the therapist. For example, a male patient, who in his transference neurosis experiences the therapist as his mother and tries to escape her as he does all women, would take flight largely because the father is present in absentia, a castrated appendage with whom the patient identifies. In the dyad of the patient and ourselves, it is our dealing with his triadic and quadratic transferences, with the unseen group, as it were, that has enriched our individual analytic treatment.

Patients function differently in the dyad, in the regular group sessions, and at alternate meetings. The individual analyst who has had group therapy experience will explore the patients' fantasies about triadic and quadratic extensions of the therapeutic dyad. Our experience that the patient behaves differently in different social contexts than when with us alone leads us in individual treatment to ask him: "And who else was there?" The introduction through fantasy of a meaningful third or fourth person is commonly seen among individuals who conjure up different partners in the act of intercourse or who have, after intercourse, to go off and masturbate with a particular fantasy in mind. Group analytic experience enables the individual analyst to see the complexity of multiple relationships latent in the manifest dyad. There is a multiple psychology in operation, not just the dyadic psychology of mother and child or father and child. There is in operation the triadic psychology of mother, father, and child, the quadratic psychology of mother, father, sibling, and child.

III

APPLICATIONS

12

The Discriminating
Use of Feelings

Over the years and in numerous publications, we have demonstrated that good group therapy, like good individual therapy, must be firmly based both on a consistent theoretical foundation and on the reality of interpersonal relationships. In this chapter, we argue against the irrationality of those who believe in the indiscriminate use of feelings in group sessions. We see only danger in birdshot therapy that fires feelings in a broad pattern rather than aiming them at a significant and selective target.

There is so much that has happened in this century with the promise of stranger things to come, such as our flight to other planets, that most of us are prepared to expect the impossible. The mad science fiction of yesterday is becoming the space science of tomorrow. We hardly know what oddity will suddenly make sense. So many things that were preposterous in the past are routine today that it is hazardous to discredit what seems at first incredible.

Yet, what is clearly deluding is dangerous to endorse even today. In these suddenly changing times, the need for a reasonable respect for thoughtfulness, for logic, in psychotherapy must still be expected and assumed. Intemperately, sometimes fanatically, some of us join absurd or dangerous ventures in our field.

Very few seem piqued by the exaggerations and misinterpretations characteristic of the eccentric (to use the kindest word) whose glaring extravagance is the substance of their appeal. People look to misrepresentation and distortion as to a diverting experience. That may be all right, as long as it is clear that the peculiarity is manifest and the idiosyncracy fantastic. But the problem is that too many psychotherapists are being promoted in a sober spirit, replete with sweeping hyperbole, and that these methods are being accepted as reality and reality rejected as delusion. The extraordinary lengths to which some psychotherapy goes, devoid of good judgment and sense of reality, are appalling.

One cannot, for instance be for or against feeling, thinking, and acting, in or out of therapy. They are. They exist. They are part of the human condition. But feeling or thinking or acting may each, singly, be used in the service of resistance or of working through.

One of the problems of the inveterate emotionalists is their tendency to think in absolutes. In their view, a person thinks or feels. The therapist is either a feelingless thinking machine or he is a mindless but feelingful human being. This is a fractionated approach to a patient. Whatever the therapist says or does, even if it were possible to make a purely cognitive interpretation, is affectively experienced by the patient because he is in a transference relationship to the analyst. Besides, the therapist can never be purely rational. He cannot be exclusively intellectual or emotional. He is both. And no matter how the analyst intervenes, the patient will react affectively in transference. Any intervention or activity of the therapist has an emotional impact on the patient. It is more than likely that the analyst's immediate expression of his own affective state imposes too great a burden on the patient, often more than he can reasonably endure.

The question then is: Can the therapist be discriminating and reasonable enough to call upon his own emotional resources at certain times with certain patients and yet have enough conscious sensitivity and selectivity to withhold his feelings especially when it would be in the patient's best interest to do so?

The emotion-habitués among certain therapists reject thoughtfulness with the claim that insight so derived simply produces an awkward self consciousness that interferes with the development of natural health attainable only by the unrestrained expression of feeling. But maturity is achieved by learning at the mother's knee, at school, and then, hopefully, by independent pursuit of knowledge. If the mother was mentally disturbed and the teachers misinforming, then their victims recoil from the quest for enlightenment. In terms of their history of exposure to an irrational mother and poor schooling, their distrust of traditional and reasonable means seems quite natural. What is valuable in the traditional they perceive as derived from the nongiving, punitive parent or the heartless pedagogue and therefore misleading and unacceptable. Growing up, then, is not the exciting discovery of the good to be derived from accumulated wisdom but a tortuous burden to be endured and dismissed.

What is overlooked in such an approach is the important fact that the uncovering of the repressed past with an open-minded but expert analyst helps the patient to re-experience and transcend his damaging history and to search reasonably for ways in which he clings to misperception of the present as if it were the past. However, the therapist who rejects the past because he himself had disturbed parents and teachers acts out his compulsive rebellion against reason. He feels he was never understood and compulsively protests against intellect as irrational. He joins each new mystifying cult that grants him license to express his inappropriate and persistent feeling to revenge himself against his own damaging forbears.

The group therapist who dares to show his feelings in a group has been described as courageous for making his latent affect manifest. Such justification for a therapeutic intervention, as, say, a group leader's daring to scream out loud in the midst of the session, seems hardly a legitimate reason for using it. It is like a nonswimmer taking a job as a lifeguard merely because he is audacious.

The affect-committed therapist reacts with his subjective feelings to all the members of his group equally and indiscriminately. While it is conceivable that this might be productive for some few patients, I believe the therapist has to differentiate one patient from another and treat each one differently, because each has a personal history, a particular diagnosis, a unique psychopathology, and varying kinds of healthy resources and needs, a different kind of working out and working through. Otherwise, the therapist is homogenizing the group into one patient. Therapeutic groups are heterogeneous, and the individuals in them require discriminating interventions with regard to their different needs.

Emotion-possessed group therapists stimulate and enjoy group interaction and emotional expression without adequate intrapsychic exploration. For certain autistic and otherwise isolated patients, this may be a salutary diversion from their detached rumination. But even for these members, the nature of the interpersonal involvement achieved by encouragement to emotional interaction exhibits bizarre qualities, which in turn need to be understood and worked through. Even when encouragement to affective engagement has relevance, it cannot solve all the problems. Further steps are necessary. The whole canvas of pathology and potential for health can be laid bare only by promoting free association, fantasies and dreams, thinking and feeling, intrapsychic as well as interpersonal reactivity in order to see where, when, and under what circumstances resistance, transference, and acting out occur, so that working through may be undertaken with understanding and clarity in a realistically chosen direction and not blindly in another. This can be meaningfully experienced only in a climate of interested concern and understanding.

At first, for some patients, it may be timely to encourage the expression of feelings in order to promote the development of transference, one of its qualities being inappropriate affect. But if the therapist listens to dreams and fantasies, tries to understand and to help, he inevitably elicits transferences, so that it is not necessary to press for the ventilation of feelings. The over-intellectualized, emotion-denying patients, the obsessive-compulsives, and those rigidly limited to one kind of response, one intensity of feeling, need the conscious support of the therapist to give their expression of feeling more freeing variety. But for most it is more therapeutic to ask them for their associations. What the therapist asks and does then depends on the diagnosis, the nature of the difficulty. He needs to be discriminating, to make interventions based on a considered appraisal of who the person is and what he really needs.

It has been suggested by the affect-fomentors that the therapist should become emotionally absorbed by the immediate experience. If he becomes so absorbed, he gives up his ego and goes into oceanic unconsciousness. If the emotional here-and-now is so emphasized, what of the patient's history and our understanding the present disturbance in the light of that history? What of his future? What plans can be made for his future? An affective, here-and-now emphasis may be appropriate in the treatment of patients obsessed with the past or compulsively planning for a future that evades living in the present. But how about patients who are already committed impulsively or compulsively to an emotional experiencing of the here-and-now in repeated catharsis?

The affect-charged therapist claims that he has no choice, that he must willy-nilly be emotionally participant with his patient. If the therapist has no freedom, he is either impulse-ridden or compulsive. If he has no choice, he has no discrimination. It is not in the patient's best interest for the therapist to feel compelled always to be active and interactive. Is it never good practice for him simply to listen in silence? Are not the dimensions of introspection, free association, and the recovery of affect-bound, repressed history also relevant?

When a therapist says that emotional freedom reaches out to patients and at the same time elicits affective candor in return, we would ask: Can he not engage them by his reasonableness, interest, and warmth? Patients express their associations and feelings even to such overtures, if their resistances are analyzed.

It is possible for the therapist to use his emotional reactions to the patient constructively. But since everyone's responses, even the therapist's, are contaminated by transference elements, it is necessary for the therapist to explore for himself his own reactions in search of their distorted components. If he is able to do this, he may then use his responses appropriately so that both may better understand what is going on between them. But this is a far cry from the indiscriminate expression of feeling we have been discussing.

The affect-addicted group therapist claims that the patient's deepest feelings are not communicated to a therapist when interventions are planned and technical, because the patient sees through these tricks. The implication is that thoughtfulness on the patient's behalf is a feelingless, insincere, and cunning deception played upon him. It is important for the mother to plan to feed her child, to have a sense of time, to calculate in advance for the best possible future for her child. This, in and of itself is not a cold, detached attitude. It can be a considerate concern born of love. The over-emotional group therapist counsels us to value only our immediate, instantaneous affect that seizes us in dealing with patients. But such feelings dictated by chance or compulsion may pathologically gratify the patient's transferences with countertransference.

The emotion-bent therapist protests that his expression of feeling is in itself therapeutic by engaging and involving the patient. The spontaneous comment is desirable, for spontaneity is not disruptive or inappropriate. But instantaneity is. Spontaneity is not an automatic, indiscriminate expression of one's feelings. Spontaneity requires prior struggle, searching, study, commitment, and synthesis. The spontaneity of an artist does not arise out of, nor is it limited to, the moment.

It is the therapist's assumption of personal license to express anything he likes that traps the incautious. There is a covert promise here of immunity from any distress, custom, deliberation, or social demand. There need then be no concern with any of the basic requirements, the rules that enable is to live with one another. This philosophy permits the therapist to justify his disequilibrating feelings expressed toward patients as ruthless honesty. He need never justify his right to such ventilation, since, as he sees it, his candor is principled because it heartens the patient to do likewise. Any and every emotion, no matter what, may be enjoyed as a rousing sensation, to feel one's self excitedly alive, for without it one feels dead. So feelings must be experienced. Life must be manic or depressed. Tomorrow or the very next moment may mean death or what amounts to the same thing; a killing cerebration. Let us live, then, in the here-and-now.

The emotionalists claim a pure and exclusive contact with the inner essence of man that the rest of us lack. They pretend to an honesty of heart with sudden access to the depths of feeling in their patients that inevitably leads to instant therapy. The promise of a shared relief from all control has enormous appeal. Freud used free association to gain access to repressed conflict and hitherto unavailable affect. The emotionalists use affective limitlessness as a way of life. Freud used analysis of pathological behavior as a means to achieve a rational and loving commitment and responsibility. They use emotional regression to attain a more irrational irresponsibility. They engage the patient with abandoned relish to induce in him the same response. Unknowingly, they use their psychopathology to tumble the patient's ego into his overwhelming unconsciousness.

The affective school of therapy is essentially mystical. No amount of intellectual endeavor can save a man. Only his wholehearted faith in God can assure him of security and eternal life. And only the patient's fervent devotion to the therapist fired by inspiration and revelation can redeem him. The patient has been dirtied by thought and guilt-ridden for wanting to know. He has tasted of the devilish fruit of the tree of knowledge. The therapist will cleanse him and remake him, like himself, pure in heart. If only the patient will submit, he will become as grandiose as the therapist.

The emotionally embroiled group therapist believes that in order to help his patients, he must start where the patient is lost, in his residual reason. Before coming to the therapist, the patient has unfortunately some capacity for reflection. Otherwise, he would not have to be saved. Therefore, if the dedicated healer is to cure such a miserably erring fellow, the therapist must be ready to join the patient in unreason, to wallow with him in irrationality. He must share the burden of enduring the horrors. After all, was not Jesus Himself eager to debase Himself by joining mankind in order to save men? Can the group therapist do less? Did not Jesus, through His glory-giving tenderness for man become a man in order that we might become Him? Ought the group therapist to do less? It is not the work of the mind but only the patient's faith in the therapist's goodness of the heart that can save him. And because the patient's pride and arrogance of mind can be made to yield only before the therapist's benevolence or wrath, the therapist's consuming capacity to feel is never the basis for bravado but for supreme humility. It is only the operations of the mind that are given to mean and shallow pretensions and heroics. Therefore, patients need to humble themselves before the fervid therapist who will exalt them by making them one with him in ecstasy and agony.

How do we know the therapist's unconscious interaction is therapeutic, particularly when by the unconscious self is meant the pathological, nonrational self? The assumption seems to be that the "right feeling" and involvement on the part of the therapist is therapeutic for the patient, and the "wrong thought" is hurtful to him. How does one know when one has the "right feeling" or the "wrong thought?" What makes them "right" or "wrong?" Only God and a group of His archangelic therapists seem to know. If they have the "feeling," it is "right." One would think a reasonable therapist would have some self-doubt as to the magical appropriateness of his magically expressed affect. The therapist who is so certain he always has the right therapeutic feeling has unresolved problems of grandiosity. He has available homeopathic doses of love that he dispenses in exact and proper amounts to meet each patient's need. He has a phallic sincero-meter, and he believes he can give one to each of his patients.

The affect-dedicated therapist is blind to the differences between himself and the patient. He uses his feelings as a way of denying differences. He makes a virtue of being sicker than the patient who is seen as healthier than the therapist.

By a curious, inverted thinking, the sicker therapist makes the patient equally disturbed, thereby introducing him to the nirvana of sick-health where the therapist is enthroned. But has not the patient the need and the right to expect reasonable expertise and constructive leadership in the therapist? There seems here to be a denial of differences between the therapist and patient and between the divergent needs of various patients. There is also a denial of the therapist's status. Is there no difference between child and parent, between wife and husband, between patient and therapist? If a child throws a temper tantrum, should the parent do so as well? If the patient behaves inappropriately, should the therapist do so as well?

I know of at least one group therapist whose compassionate devotion to his patients is felt most keenly by him when he is asleep in the group and, as he says, dreaming of his charges. He therefore frequently dozes off in order to maintain his tender contact with patients. Such dedication is usually rewarded by group members who show their appreciation of the work-weary projected mother or father in the therapist by whispering to one another in order not to wake him up. So any emotional interchange has to be conducted in a more subdued way while mother or father has a nap. In this exchange of roles, the group becomes the mothering parent and the therapist the needy child. At other times, there is a fusion of mother and child and frequent reversal of mutually irresponsible roles. This acting out of primitive and touching-feeling enables, distinguishes, and consolidates the group. For what is more elevating and moving to the human spirit than the sight or experience of being a mother and child? How gratifying it must be to keep re-experiencing the mother at the breast or the completely helpless suckling. No wonder patient and therapist want to remain forever in the ecstasy of "treatment."

It might be said of the critics of the emotionalists that we show our own immaturity in taking the affectivists too seriously. After all, children should be allowed to play. It is, in fact, destructive not to let them divert themselves. But the analogy to play does not hold. We are not against child's play for children and adult play for adults. However, should the presumedly responsible therapist play house with his patients? It might be said of us that we are opposed to constructive flights of creative imagination, trying coldly to bury the soaring mind in brutal reality. It is not so. We are merely wary of child's play that may damage the child or the adult, or of adult play that is only a facade for unconscious child play to the extent that it destroys freedom and growth.

The over-emotional therapist who wishes similarly to engage his patients is fundamentally disregardful of those to whom he should be responsible. He is egocentric but hides these characteristics under a screen of seeming interest in the patient's right to find and express his feelings. If this is not true, and in some instances it seems unfair to charge the affectivists with such cruel and conscious judgment, then it would seem as if they are quite irrational. They are, then, childlike dictators who try and succeed mostly in winning the devotion of patients by the artless practice of remaining children. But the child is as yet incapable of being the carrier of the best that psychotherapy has to offer. Until he has acquired those assets, he usually resists or rejects the burden of minding his elders. "Minding" is an interesting word in this connection. He rebelliously and with great feeling (like many patients) refuses to heed the reasoned counsel of more experienced adults. As a child, he makes the adult his enemy, as an employee his boss, as a patient his therapist, as an emotionalist reason. The child is unprincipled without an adequate superego or good judgment. It is only in play that the child can in phallic illusion assume the fantastic authority he would realize. But such a group therapist sits at the head of a series of patients and plays out his game.

In working through, the therapist is aware that at an unconscious level the patient does not as in infancy distinguish between himself and the projectively maternal therapist. And as in infancy, the patient looks on the therapist as an extension of himself who will fulfill his archaic feelings as, in his expectations, a good mother should. Since the therapist frustrates these longings, the patient re-experiences with him the pre-oedipal, conflicting feelings of love and hate. It is only when the patient can relinquish these exorbitant demands and experience the pleasures of more mature satisfactions that he appreciates the therapist's denying him the gratification of his immature longings. But this requires hard work, struggle. The affect-infatuated therapist does not want to do this hard work any more than the patient does. He does not experience work, a major part of the life of the adult, as pleasurable. Only nonwork, only play, only instantaneity are fun. So like the child he is, he engages the patient in endless mudpie-making in the shifting sandcastles of affective egoboundlessness.

The emotionally intoxicated therapist or patient cannot describe the "experience" of treatment without thereby being deprived of the exquisite sensation of being in it. It is as if the mere attempt to articulate the ecstasy eradicates it. He cannot say, "I love you," without interfering with the rapture of orgasm. Any intellectual abstraction checks the pervading passion. To speak is to think, and no thought can describe or fathom the nature of feeling. Feeling, like psychosis, must be experienced, because feeling cannot be represented in speech. Feeling is feeling is feeling. . . .

Can it be that the activists are in revolt against a dry, cold phallic grandiosity among the supra-rationalists who reject the unconscious and the expression of affect as inappropriate? But the supra-rationalists are irrational and rejective of intellect. They only believe themselves to be rational. It may be that the affectivists are in compulsive revolt against the oppressive control and domination of puritanical intellectualism. They would burn down the dry, mummifying braininess of tradition, which, as they see it, petrifies creativity. But neither extreme serves our purpose. The oppressive intellectuals are killers of the dream, the poem, the feeling, and the professional rebels of the heart are killers of the mind.

The exercise of intellect incites feeling. Man is characterized by consciousness, by the struggle to know himself and his world, by his endless curiosity and expanding comprehension. In the pursuit of knowing himself and others, he has achieved heights of pleasure not available to lesser animals of lesser mind. When certain cynics about mankind point to the dog as capable of greater love than man, one is inclined to note that when dogs grow up in the wilderness apart from man they are as brutish as wolves. It is only in their domestication by man that animals subdue their primitive instincts and demonstrate some of his socialized virtues such as constancy and loyalty. So, it is my impression that the forerunner—indeed, the prerequisite—for the capacity to be aware of the needs of the other, to care for or to love the other, is intellect, a component of consciousness.

I think it is a puristic view of orthodox analysis to regard the analyst as a detached observer, unfeeling in his attitudes toward the patient. Freud was unorthodox enough to take a walk with Gustav Mahler for several hours and relieve him of his impotence in one extended session. Whereas a warm regard for the patient is important, it is of as much use as compassionate tears for a person suffering from acute appendicitis. Just as a surgical case needs the application of surgical skill, the mentally disturbed patient requires psychoanalytic expertise. Insights are not cold, detached, unrelated dirty words. If the patient experiences the analyst as nonaffectively abstract, it may or may not be so. If the therapist is, in fact, a cold, detached, unfeeling person, the patient would be well advised to seek help elsewhere.

The analyst is not neutral because he is aware that activity may be destructive to the patient. The analyst's nonreactivity is consciously used to sponsor regression, to foster frustration, thereby increasing the patient's feelings, anger, and archaic responses in order to work them through. Freud believed that the analyst should be inactive until the patient developed a transference neurosis, that is, became obsessed with the analyst as a parental figure. Patients who were frustrated and regressed by his neutrality expressed their anger toward him but also loved him and wanted to crawl into his lap. The analyst's neutrality may well encourage the patient's distortions and anxiety, but the therapist purposely wants to elicit the pathology in order to resolve it. Is the analyst always isolated, remote, hostile, nonempathic, unrelated? For some patients, the therapist's neutral listening is an acceptance of them that is the most therapeutic part of the experience.

The intellectual search and development of Freud's genius in the pursuit of unconscious processes is an enduringly thrilling story. So, too, is the experience of any psychoanalyst in the rational pursuit and unraveling of a patient's psychopathology and the struggle with him to work it through. The traditional psychoanalytic aim is calculated and far sighted because in the exactitude of its pursuit of repressed feelings it adds an artistic awareness of the science itself. Thus, the analyst and patient enjoy a dual return for their effort that we do not get from a mystical or merely tactical approach; the satisfaction of a shared undertaking; the patient in the telling, the analyst in observing the increasingly reasonable effect of what he tells.

Group therapists want to know the nature of psychodynamics and psychopathology and the means to work through, in order to become experts in their field, for the pleasure of grasping the unknown and passing this insight along to their patients. The therapist needs to respect his own intellectual growth if he is to convey to the patient a similar value. The extent to which we make our lives fulfilling depends on the extent to which we invest also in the reflective. The uses of reason enrich our potential for making our life span a gratifying experience. An aim of treatment is to free the patient's mind from neurotic boredom. The passion to know and understand needs to be felt by the therapist to reconcile his own life, to make his own intrapsychic and inter-personal living agreeable. His dedication to this value helps him to demonstrate its importance to the patient.

The understanding that the therapist has and believes he has communicated to the patient is only vaguely perceived. He interprets the insight offered in a way that fits in with the preservation of his primitive feelings and fantasies. The patient's commitment is emotional and fantastic; the therapist's is intellec-tual and realistic. The process of working through requires repeated, well-thought-out confrontations with reality. This does not mean the patient is thereby being denied an emotional existence by a cold, machine-like therapist. The therapist is, in fact, offering the patient a release from infantile and compulsive feeling to more mature and gratifying uses of affect.

I do not think it either possible or necessary to "love" the patient, as some affect-fanciers claim. Rather, I believe the ther-apist needs to have a proper regard for the patient's interests, free as possible of exploitative transferential and countertransferential attitudes. The therapist's ventilation of "loving" affect with a patient is characterized by distortions that are inconsistent with appropriate regard for him.

It is only the neurotic or psychotic component in the patient's character that hopes to win the therapist's love or is fearful of it. The rational side in the patient does not at all wish to seduce the therapist into loving him. The patient may try to induce in the therapist the kind of love he received from his parents or he may wish to experience from the therapist a love free of the damaging "love" of his parents. But the therapist cannot love all his patients. Understanding them in depth and his wish to help them resolve their problems until they can do so themselves enable him to experience the satisfaction of being an expert, a specialist whose years spent in study prove their usefulness in healing. If the therapist "loves" his patients, he is in countertransference and hurtful to them. The therapist must care for and have regard and respect for his patients or he should not treat them. With what healthy resources he has, the patient hopes the therapist is competent, a master of his art.

It would seem that a profound inconsistency in the affect-devotee is his wish to retain and experience his love for his mother and his displacements of this compulsion onto her multiple surrogates among his patients. For it is inconceivable to experience love, the privilege of man, without consciousness. But the therapist in quest of his "love" wants to lose his awareness, his mindfulness, himself, in the beloved object. And a "lover" without consciousness is no longer a lover, a sentient human being, a self. He is a fantasy, a dream of a therapist.

At a recent meeting of a large group-therapy association, a therapist presented a paper that emphasized the importance of the "humanity" of the therapist's emotional involvement in treatment. As an invited discussant, I had prepared a more reasonable statement of my reactions, but the speaker, whom we shall call Dr. Truelove, was so poetic, so passionate, and so inspired that he stirred in me an equally excited, disequilibrated, and uncontrollable desire to recite. So unthinkingly, I abandoned my carefully readied statement. I was neither as lyrical nor as dramatic as he, but, inspired by him and my repressed, childish longings out of a remote past, I seized the occasion to express my secret inclination to be both poet and actor. I asked the audience to indulge me while that impulsive instantaneity, stimulated by the speaker's eloquence, compelled me to act out, despite my detachment, neutrality, cold reason, and unfeeling inattention, no doubt developed by too long years behind the couch. Some members of the audience were so stirred by my remarks that they have induced me to write them down in the belief that such eloquence might move others to a return to reason. Therefore, with apologies to lovers of Shakespeare, to Shakespeare himself, and to lovers everywhere, I herewith set down my recitation of that evening:

Friends, New Yorkers, fellow therapists, lend me your third ears;
I come not to bury Reason but to praise him.
The mistakes Reason made live after him;
The good is oft interred with his bones;
So let it be with Reason, The noble speaker Truelove
Hath told you that Reason is cold;
If it were so, it is a grievous fault;
And grievously hath Reason answer'd it.
Here, under the leaves of a lover of man, and the rest

(For Truelove is a feelingful man;
So are they all, all feelingful men),
Come I to speak for Reason undone.
Reason was my friend, faithful and just to me;
And Truelove says Reason was too rational;
And Truelove is a feelingful man —
I speak not to disprove what a lover spoke,
But here I am to speak what I do know.
You all did love Reason once, not without cause;
What cause withholds you, then, to mourn for him?
O, judgment, thou art fled to primary process,
And men have lost their minds! — Bear with me,
My heart is in the coffin there with Reason,
And I must pause till it come back with me —
But yesterday, the word of Reason might
Have stood against the world; now he lies there
And none so poor to do him reverence.
Oh, friends! If I were disposed to stir
Your hearts and minds to dissent and anger,
I would do Truelove wrong, and his lovers wrong,
Who, you all know, are kind and tender men;
I will not do them wrong; I rather choose
To wrong good judgment, to wrong myself, and you,
Then I will wrong such devoted and ardent men.
But here's a parchment, with the seal of Reason,
I found it in his closet, 'tis his will;
Let but group therapists hear this testament
(Which, pardon me, I do not mean to read).
And they would go and kiss Reason's wounds,
And dip their notebooks in his sacred blood;
Yea, beg a hair of him for memory,
And, dying, mention it within their wills,
Bequeathing it, as a rich legacy,
Unto their patients —
But wait, gentle therapists, I must not read the will;
It is not meant you know how Reason loved you.
You are not wood, you are not stones, but men;
and, being men, hearing the will of Reason,
It will inflame you, it will make you mad;
'Tis good you know not that you are his heirs;
For if you should, O, what would come of it —
Will you be the patient? Will you stay a while?

I have o'ershot myself to tell you of it.
I fear I wrong the earnest and fervent men
Whose daggers have stabb'd Reason; I do fear it.

You will compel me then to read the will?
Then make a ring about the wounds of Reason,
And let me show you the mind that made the will.

You all do know Reason; I remember
The first time ever Man embraced him;
'Twas on a summer's evening, in his lair;
That day he overcame Unreason; —
Look! In this place ran Feeling's dagger through,
No doubt to teach the loving value of pain.
See, what a rent Unthinking Suddenness made;
Through this, the well-beloved Truelove stabb'd;
And, as he plucked his passionate steel away,
Mark how the blood of Reason follow's it,
As rushing out of doors, to be resolved
If Truelove so unkindly knocks, or no;
For Truelove, as you know, was Reason's angel;
Judge, O, you gods, how dearly Reason loved him!
This was the most unkindest cut of all;
For when noble Reason saw him stab,
Ingratitude, more strong than traitors' arms,
Quite vanquished him; then burst his mighty heart;
And, in a mantle muffling up his face
Even at the base of Freud's statue,
Which all the while ran blood, great Reason fell,
O, what a fall was there, my group therapists:
Then I, and you, and all of us fell, down
Whilst Unreason flourish'd over us.
O, now you weep; and I perceive you feel
The dint of pity; these are gracious drops.
Kind souls, what, weep you, when you but behold
Our Reason's vesture wounded? Look you here.
Here is Reason himself, marr'd, as you see, by Impulse.
Good friends, sweet friends, let me not stir you
To such a sudden flood of feeling
They that have done this deed are loving men;
What private griefs they have, alas! I know not

That made them do it; they are human and benevolent;
And will, no doubt, with feeling answer you.
I come not, friends, to steal away your hearts;
I am no orator, as Truelove is;
But as you know me all, a plain blunt man,
That loves the Mind; and that they know full well
That invited me here to speak of it.
For I have neither wit, nor words, nor worth,
Action, nor utterance, nor the power of speech
To stir men's blood; I only speak right on;
I tell you that which you yourselves do know;
Show you sweet Reason's wounds, poor, poor, dumb mouths,
And bid them speak for me; but were I Truelove,
And Truelove Wolf, there were a Wolf
Would ruffle up your spirits, and put a tongue
In every wound of Reason, that should move
The hearts of therapists to rise and protest.
Why, friends, you go to do you know not what;
Wherein hath Reason thus deserved your loves?
Alas, you know not—I must tell you then;—
You have forgot the will I told you of.
Here is the will, and under Freud's seal.
To every psychotherapist he gives
This heritage of Learning:
That he who cares in the moment—cares not,
But he who thoughtfully and planfully
Teaches him who does not know
To value the past, present and future,
Who cherishes not just this ecstatic moment
But pauses to reflect,
More than cares, he heals.

13

Dealing with the Roots of Aggression

The problem of aggression and how to deal with it has vexed mankind for centuries. In a letter to Sigmund Freud on July 30, 1932, Albert Einstein posed the most insistent of all the problems civilization has to face: "Is there any way of delivering mankind from the menace of war?" Freud's reply was characteristically shocking: "Conflicts of interest between men are settled by the use of violence." We are still hard-pressed, 50 years later, to answer adequately the question posed by Einstein. However, the phenomenon of aggressive behavior has been the focus of scientific study (see Kutash et al. 1978), and it is the mission of this chapter to present the view of the practitioners of psychoanalysis in groups.

In our therapeutic sanctuaries, mental health professionals attempt to return the aggressive, the violent, and the murderous to more peaceful means to achieve their ends. We have been asked by some and asked ourselves how we can extend our professional skills from the treatment chamber to resolve violence in the family, between ethnic and nationalistic groups, among terrorists and tyrants, between street gangs, and between warring factions (see Wolf and Schwartz 1969). Others have preceded us in offering guidelines and solutions. The following pages represent still another attempt to tell what we believe to be a step in the same direction.

It is necessary to recognize the importance of any individual's right to feel and in appropriate contexts to express anger. It is only the impulsive or compulsive aspects of anger and aggression and acting out on these feelings against one another in violence that we would endeavor to understand and work through. Anxiety, fear, and guilt are the sources of much aggression. It is, therefore, not so much the aggression that needs to be dealt with directly as it is the underlying concerns, uncertainties, tensions, phobias, and self-blame at the root.

All of us, members of the mental health profession, are interpreters of the human condition, whether intrapsychic or interpersonal. We see and understand and interpret one another according to our various subjective lights and hopefully increasingly realistic perception. To the extent that we cannot truly understand one another or to the degree we misinterpret one another's motives for good or ill, we may ascribe malevolent intentions toward those who could be our friends. It is our belief after conducting psychoanalysis in groups over many years (see Kutash and Wolf 1982; Wolf 1949; Wolf and Schwartz 1962) that we need leaders among our parents, siblings, psychotherapists, teachers, friends, and representatives in governing us who can interpret for those of us in contention the hidden motives for our differences and keep us talking to each other in discussion. These mediators can thereby intercept our antagonism and resolve our conflicts through negotiation by promoting honest and straightforward communication. For us this method in clinical practice has been the most productive means for resolving our mutual distrust, fear of one another, prejudice, and hatred. In the following pages, then, the functions of the psychoanalyst and patients in a therapeutic group will be described in part in order to clarify the ways to resolve aggressive interaction that occurs among members. The aim in providing this discussion is to offer it to other negotiators who may find it useful in dealing with acting out, violence, and aggression.

An oversimplified definition of psychoanalysis in groups is that it is a small assemblage of patients who try, with the help of a negotiating expert, to continue their warfare by increasingly less aggressive and more peaceful means until they are able to achieve greater degrees of harmonious interaction in and out of a therapeutic group.

The analyst in a group is a strategist, a sympathetic steward who serves his patients with loyalty and fidelity to enable them to pull together rather than move apart. He devotes himself to the solution of hostile exchanges among patients by analytically mediating for increments of appropriate mutual concessions. More often than not he is the only member to urge patients in standoff aggression to attempt to be more reasonable. In this effort, he needs to be imaginative, inventive, warm, sanguine, and bold; dependable and constant; protective and supportive; not highhanded nor domineering; not dictatorial but encouraging when there are divergent points of view; not imposing compliance and homogeneity but sponsoring individuality and independence. Finally, he must admit to his fallibility.

Not just the social offender but all of us are bewildered to some degree about the significance of our communication. Not infrequently, the very same expression is employed in various contexts to express different meanings. The mental health professional is committed, by offering interpretation, to achieving mutual understanding in order to enable the confused and biased to cope reasonably with their anxiety rather than release it in inappropriate action. The mental health interpreter is likewise entrusted to demonstrate the relationship between what is manifest and latent, archaic and relevant, intrapsychic and interpersonal, fantasy and actuality, and activity inside and outside the therapeutic setting.

All of us, not just the social deviant, need to be understood. We translate from one tongue to another to help each other to grasp what we would communicate. Even Shakespeare and the Bible have had thousands of interpreters and Freud nearly as many. Our mothers steadily interpreted for us as children the nature of maturating transactions, of existence, so that we gradually learned what was happening to and around us. We thereby discover the means to use our own perceptions and resources, our own knowledge and reasoning powers, and we define our own affairs on the basis of our past history. We believe the socially destructive deviant will have, in each instance, to live through with a mental health professional a healthier surrogate than his mother or father, the successive stages that the infant requires in order to achieve the status of a socialized human being.

When there is discord, anger, or violence in a marital or family relationship, in a therapeutic group, in a community, among ethnic groups, or between nations, a neutral observer, a specialist, an arbitrator, a mental health professional, or the United Nations may be called upon to see if the contestants can be moved to greater accord, mutual agreement, and tolerance for one another's differences. This is in part the commitment of the counselor, the psychotherapist, the minister, the attorney, the instructor, the family member, and the friend. It is likewise the role of the parent who explains to the child the behavior of the spouse, of a sibling, of a classmate, of a neighbor. The analyst is merely one of a series of negotiators and interpreters in the life of his patients. The other group members play similar but less expert roles. Negotiation and interpretation are fundamental aspects of human conduct. It is their use in dealing with angry people that can humanize them.

A common source of frustration and consequent aggression lies in the feeling of going unheard. In group analytic therapy, the leader promotes communication by facilitating interaction in the process uncovering bilateral transferential distortion, which prevents us from understanding one another until, through interpretation, mediation, and negotiation we learn gradually, by listening in greater depth not to gratify each other's archaic longings and to become increasingly more responsive to our mutual needs and struggle for growth and maturity.

From psychoanalysis in groups, we learn that the antagonism among members is frequently a consequence of a failure to understand one another. Here the group leader acts as an expert in facilitating, promoting, and maintaining verbal interaction and understanding. He not only resuscitates communication, but, by providing insight, he also enables the antagonists to listen to one another, an essential precursor to ultimate harmony in conflicts. The interpreting analyst must try not to fail to sense the subtle shading in a phrase, the subjective, the spontaneous, the creative, the affective, the spirit, the nonverbal that lies underneath what is said. The analyst in a therapeutic group tries to convey, when a patient's communication is unclear, the meaning and the mood of the speaker. In so doing, he attempts to transmit the reality, the essence of the spoken word with its literate, intellectual, emotional, manifest, and latent content. The therapist is not merely paraphrastic; he is a humanistic diplomat. He endeavors to convey to the listening members the richness of his intimation with its many facets. Or, he may do the opposite; tell in a word or phrase the hidden core of what the communicant's struggling to say but cannot. For us this is where the angry man needs the most help—an ally who will help him say what he is unable to communicate. It is just this frustration that leads him to act out his aggression. Once—and then again and again—experiencing and re-experiencing the interest and caring of such an interpretating ally, his anger is allayed and nonaggressive and self-expressive urges replace it.

The language the analyst uses in coping with angry group members in mutual negative transference may have little effect on them. What does cause a bitter exchange of feeling is his identification with one or the other. His positive attitude toward member A and his negative view of member B seriously distorts his perception of the problem between them and serves no good purpose, unless he becomes aware of his distorting bias and is able to resolve it. Not infrequently, other observing group members themselves not so directly involved in the contention confront him with his misperception and enable him to become more relevantly interpretive. The interpreter's neutrality, his nonpartisanship in bringing antagonists to mutual understanding and harmonious compromise, is essential in attaining a working through of aggression.

The analyst as interpreter and negotiator is in trouble when one of the parties in contention regards negotiation as a form of self humiliation, when one of the contestants has a compulsive need to win every argument and to prove himself right no matter what occurs, or when a member rejects communication and instead acts out his aggression against his assumed enemy to silence or destroy him. Under such circumstances, negotiation is hardly possible. This means that if negotiation and interpretation are to go on, the participants need, at the very least, to agree to talk rather than take inappropriate verbal or physical action.

The group leader needs to be careful to note whether an adversary only manifestly complies with the necessity to communicate freely and honestly but merely pretends to or compulsively pursues a role as a co-interpreter behind which facade he rigidly maintains a cold anger. Some such members are masterful at inspecting others with genuine or seeming appropriateness, and then use their acute observing powers to hurt and provoke the opposition to still further aggression. From the vantage point of their insulation and the merely assumed exterior of interpreter, they misuse their resourcefulness to promote rather than prevent the resolution of bilateral eruption.

Certain aggressive patients, competitive with the parental figure in the person of the therapist, conceal their rivalry with him by acting as co-therapists, volunteering interpretation sometimes with considerable effectiveness. The analyst, overly pleased by the actual help provided him, may overlook such a screened attack when, in fact, it requires exposure and analysis. What the patient is expressing is that the group leader is unable to speak for himself or is so inadequate that he depends on the patient for clarification. If the therapist yields repeatedly to such reduction in status, he not only fails to do responsible analytic work, he feeds the patient's competitiveness and grandiosity.

The group member in negative transference to the group leader usually cannot make out what the therapist is trying to convey to enable the patient to gain insight. The analyst frustrates him, makes no sense to him, or angers him. Not infrequently, a co-patient toward whom he feels more positive is able effectively to translate what the therapist is saying so that it has a more favorable impact. Members of groups grasp communication from individuals whose understanding is offered without malice and with genuine friendliness and misunderstand alternative proposals expressed in anger.

A group leader or a group member may unconsciously, in the spirit of trying to help opponents negotiate more amicably, actually be more latently intent on deepening their hostilities toward one another. He may try still further to disrupt the negatively engaged who may, in some degree, be making feeble attempts to understand one another in similarity and difference. In the guise of a mediator and intercessor, he steps between contending members to sabotage their striving for whatever positive collaboration there may be. He tries to subvert negotiation, to maneuver the members to respond exclusively to him and through him as a central exchange of intercourse between them, if he permits them any interaction at all. If the group leader plays such a part, he breaks up interaction among the members and makes the group largely leader-centered. He imposes his authority destructively and demands that interaction take place only via his interception, a frustrating and enraging imposition of power. The analyst may himself then be in rejective and offensive countertransference to a patient. When he is so misled by his distorted perception, surely whatever "help" he offers the analyst will go unheard and will provoke withdrawal, hurt, and counter-offense.

The members of the group are inclined to respond too hastily or immediately to the individual trying to say what he means. There is too much prejudice against a view foreign to our own, too much inflexibility in the necessity to face the new and the divergent. There is in almost every group a latent pressure for compliance and concession to authority. This domination may emanate from a member, from the group, the leader, or a prevailing group theme. This demand for homogeneity and conformity does not allow the individual to express himself freely. Unless the leader points out and resolves this common problem in the group, frustration, irritability, depression, and anger are sure to follow.

The overly enterprising group leader may also be too ready to interpret the members to one another. He may thereby be prematurely informative, expecting them to be too precipitously knowledgeable about one another. This can meddlesomely interrupt the privilege of members to exchange thoughts and feelings freely with one another, to acquire the freedom and knowledge so that they can mediate more and more without his intervention. Each member discovers, as his ego grows, that he has the need and privilege to talk for himself.

Qualification, therefore, for the role of negotiator among mutually misunderstood and therefore angry people can be met only by adequate training. Otherwise, the group leader may dominate rather than resolve, manipulate rather than encourage, interfere rather than mediate, prevail over rather than promote more reasonable exchange. His training and long experience enable him to convey to antagonists the basis for their difference and opposition and to make their divergence both more understandable and acceptable to one another.

The need for high-level skills among negotiators is so great in the resolution of aggression that it is important to note that no matter how similar the training may be when applied to the development of mediating skills, all negotiators differ remarkably from one another in personality and in the application of their distinctive artistry. The mark, the essence of his individual style, becomes manifest in the way he plays his role. To the extent his training as a negotiator is good, to that degree will he make constructive use of his creative self among contenders. Group leaders become more skillful with training, and their virtuosity has an important function as a consequence of this competence. Members of the group who have become more expert with the passage of time also become increasingly deft as negotiators between hostile others.

The effectiveness of the analyst depends to a large degree on the extent to which he can be relied upon if the patient truly reveals himself. Otherwise, genuine communication will be interrupted and discomfiture and aggression will follow. If the patient trusts his analyst, resolving conflicts, daring to be friendly, and taking chances to collaborate rather than compulsively oppose are more likely to ensue. The more forbidding the leader or a co-patient is, the more the members will reciprocate with threats.

The emphasis in these observations has been on the necessity to promote communication in the conviction that freedom of speech reduces the necessity to take aggressive action. We have tried to demonstrate ways to help the speechless speak, the unheard be heard, the misunderstood be understood, the unspeakable become speakable, and the covert become overt. It is only in such an atmosphere that aggression can give way to cooperation based on trust, mutual esteem, and a return to reason.

14

Pathological Motivation

This chapter attempts to discuss pathological motivations that impel patient as well as therapist to choose individual analysis or psychoanalysis in groups as a therapeutic medium. There are, of course, also reasonable motives that guide both patient and analyst alike to choose the individual or group setting in which to function, but these more appropriate considerations will not be addressed at this time.

PATHOLOGICAL MOTIVATION IN THE PATIENT

Whenever a patient enters a group motivated by pathological reasons undetected by the analyst prior to admission to the group, it may be said that such a member has in most instances been introduced prematurely, which may jeopardize his treatment, unless his inappropriate motives are discovered and replaced by more reasonable considerations. Sometimes this change can be brought about in the group. In other cases, it may be wiser to work through the unsuitable promptings that attract patients to a group before they join it, so that they may enter it more appropriately motivated. While a patient may be admitted to a group despite his abnormal motives, effective therapy requires a thorough analysis and working through of his pathological attraction to the group. It may be discovered that, when his neurotic reason for choosing treatment in common with others is exposed, individual therapy for a considerable period is indicated before he can return to the group with more rational considerations for exploring himself in relation to others.

A fair number of applicants come to group therapy after an unhappy experience in individual treatment, whether it be their insuperable resistances, the therapist's having acted out, the high cost of individual care, or some other difficulty. However, a good many candidates are constructively motivated to begin with their honest need for more wholesome and realistic interpersonal contact and an earnest wish to work through their distortions in the group setting.

Occasionally, a patient will apply for group membership in the wish to escape deep analysis, to avoid exposure of basic trends, to maintain resistive defenses, to preserve lifelong facades, or somehow to make his neurotic maneuvers work to his greater advantage. He unconsciously selects psychotherapy in a group in the hope of hiding out there. The aim is not to be seen. Perhaps, he hopes, the analyst will direct his attention to the other members, and they too will let him be. He cannot, of course, conceal himself for long in a group without exciting the curiosity and interest of other patients who begin to ask provocative questions about him and to react to his detachment with stronger demands for involvement.

An applicant may say, "I don't want intensive analysis; I just want group therapy." Such a patient who seeks a group to act out his resistance to treatment in the belief that he does not require much help or that his problems are not deep may apply for therapy on his own. More frequently, he is referred by an analyst, sometimes even a group therapist, in the illusion that the group can offer him only superficial treatment. When analytic means are applied in the group therapy, the patient is soon disabused of notions with reference to its shallowness and then must choose to stay with us or take resistive flight from our intensive searching.

There is a type of patient who cannot endure the dyadic

relationship confined exclusively to that with the analyst. Successively he moves from one therapist to another until he discovers group therapy. In individual treatment, the analyst inevitably assumes the projected character of an unconsciously hated and/or beloved parent, who elicits such resistive, transferential, or other intolerable intrapsychic pathology that the patient inevitably abandons therapy in disappointment and frustration. The patient may take flight from private therapy in a homosexual panic seeking security in the group's numbers from being alone with his feelings about a man. Or he may choose analysis in a group because he was so severely rejected by his parents that he feels hopeless about reaching their surrogates in any therapist. Or he is a person who has been so severely traumatized by a parent as not to be able to withstand a one-to-one relationship with an authority figure, but whose sibling or peer contact was more benign, so that the horizontal associations provided in group therapy are more satisfying. Together with other patients he is placed in the position where he can share the guilt of his aggression and love for the parental surrogate he has held at a distance. In the angry and tender example and joint expressions of affect toward the therapist, the patient is encouraged to face, experience, and work through his alienation from the parent in the person of the leader. It is vital that such an individual, a common applicant for group psychotherapy, not be permitted to evade a thorough exploration of his problems with the authority figure. For his easier rapport with group members may be so beguiling as to obscure his problems in the hierarchical vector. While for many, these difficulties may be resolved in the group as long as the therapist pushes for responses to him, there are some who require combined treatment and still others who may have to return to individual therapy for an extended period, depending on how much they shun the analyst.

Several years ago a woman presented herself to one of us (A. W.) with the request for individual analysis. She was, however, so anxious during the initial consultation that it was suspected she might not return for a succeeding visit. So she was asked directly if she cared to make another appointment. She said she was too uncomfortable with the therapist and preferred not to. It was then suggested that she might be interested in group therapy. She accepted the proposal with considerable relief. It was only after some time in the group that we discovered that in our first interview she had made an immediate father transference, so full of anxiously erotic and conflictual affect, that the offer of the group as an alternative was a welcome escape from her unbearable nervousness alone with the therapist.

A patient might take refuge in a group if he perceives help coming from an authority figure as humiliating. He may find it too distressing to be isolated in individual treatment with an analyst projected as a superior, contemptuous, arrogant, controlling, or benevolently patronizing parent or older sibling. Even if the therapist feels himself on a par with the patient and gives no real cause to elicit the distortion, the mere fact that the relationship is always helper to helped makes the situation an intolerable one to the analysand. His abasement and frustration at the hands of a seemingly helpful parent is so traumatic for him that he misperceives all interest on the part of the expert as irritatingly patronizing. Under these circumstances, he finds it more satisfying to accept interventions on his behalf from his peers. So the group becomes for him a welcome relief from the therapist. But no adequate working through of his problem in the authority vector is possible until he has faced and resolved his difficulties with the leader.

Occasionally, an applicant for therapy will join a group to evade an inquiry into his own psychodynamics and spend his time listening to and analyzing other people's troubles. Actually, he may thereby be indicating his underlying contempt for those to whom he offers insight, refusing at all costs to put himself in the same abject position. His agility with the other members may win him their esteem, but if they do not before long catch on to his resistive assumption of an exclusively intellectual and analytic role, it is the function of the analyst to point out his fugitive measures as circumventions operating to his disadvantage. Not infrequently, his activity may represent an indirect form of competition with the therapist in conducting, or, as the patient sees it, manipulating the group. As a matter of fact, he may have joined the group to try to manipulate it in a way the therapist will not permit himself to be misused.

Patients who were raised in institutions like orphanages, who had little experience of family life or parental care, may apply for treatment in a group, but often require an extensive dyadic therapeutic relationship as well, as a precursor to their becoming able to enjoy a happy one-to-one intimacy in their own lives.

The therapeutic group may attract both the exhibitionist and the voyeur, although it is surprising how infrequently these types present themselves in pure form. Although the therapist, in choosing to practice psychoanalysis in a group, underwrites, within certain limits, the concept of deeply sharing our intimate mutual concerns, which involve seeing and being seen, hearing and being heard, feeling and being felt, he does not sponsor a spurious self display or voyeurism, except insofar as these appear spontaneously, in which case they are simply regarded as symptoms that must ultimately yield to a healthier adaptation. Here the therapist distinguishes between compulsively seductive self exposure and its complementary salacious observation on the one hand, and that wholesome exchange whose purpose in bilateral unfolding is to make destructive characteristics yield to sounder ones. The therapist discriminates between the kind of obsessive preoccupation with eavesdropping and ostentatious publicity excited by certain newspapers and magazines and the profound communication that insures genuine human regard. He differentiates between our need to share our inner strengths and weaknesses and our right to privacy within the group. He recognizes the neurotic quality of the exhibitionist's and the voyeur's participation, for their self parade and peeping extend beyond the therapeutic group.

Related to the voyeur's pleasure in looking without direct participation is the problem of the patient who cannot love or feel himself loved, but who is emotionally moved to tenderness or passion when he is witness to another couple's amorous engagement. He says, "I wish I could feel and be felt directly, but I can't. The only time I am moved is when I see others in love." He is deeply devoted to the theater, movies, and romantic novels. His interest in the group is motivated by the emotional stirrings he experiences when any two members of the group express their affectionate or erotic attachment to one another.

Sometimes the analyst discovers that a patient has joined one of his groups, not out of personal choice or preference, but in obedience to the therapist's wish. The patient has merely acted out one of his problems, in compulsively submitting to an authority in order to please, to be liked. Occasionally, this disclosure may lead to insight and struggle against obsessive ingratiation in the course of the patient's stay in the group. In other instances, no therapeutic progress is possible until the patient's basic preference for individual treatment is analyzed and group therapy abandoned or postponed until a more advanced phase of treatment has been reached.

When the group analyst encounters a passive, dependent, or borderline patient who has been referred by another therapist for treatment in a group, it is useful to explore the degree to which the applicant is merely acting in extension of the referring therapist's will and the extent to which the candidate is voluntarily choosing group therapy. It may be discovered, for example, that the referring analyst was hostile to the patient or to the group analyst, contemptuous of the presumed superficiality of therapy in groups, or hopeless about, indifferent to, or irresponsible toward the patient. In such instances, the compliant patient does not know he is being dumped but obediently follows prescriptions. While the group may serve such a patient well, a thorough analysis of the submissiveness that led him to the group in the first place is in order.

The patient who is seeking to act out his particular psychopathology may join a group to find foils for his neurotic destructiveness. There he may try to exercise his sado-masochistic, controlling, monopolistic, or dominating inclination, trying to give rein to whatever unhealthy impulses move him. He may try to indulge regressive sexual urges and attempt to excite other group members into sensuous acting out. He may seek to make sexual conquests in the group rationalized as looking for love.

Just as certain bizarre or eccentric persons seek their own kind to act out their pathology in concert in a sheltered, abnormal subculture, which, apart from the more normal mainstream of society, sanctions irrationality in bohemia, some patients approach the therapeutic group setting with a similar purpose in mind, namely to indulge impulsive and unreasonable impulses seeking gratification. One therapist mentioned, for example, a group of obese patients, who after commiserating with one another during a meeting over their excess weight, would retire to an ice cream parlor afterwards for double banana splits. This is one of the dangers of organizing homogeneous groups, which lack the divergent character structures that act as a corrective check on one another. The homogeneous group also tends to foster a conflictual generalized tolerance for and resentment of the narcissistically shared problem, body image, or personality. But even the homogeneous group eventually sets limits to its pathological acting out.

A good many years ago we introduced a woman to a group who, after her first meeting with the other patients, protested to us privately that they were too naive and immature for her tastes and inquired whether we did not have a more worldly and sophisticated group that, she believed, would suit her better. At her suggestion, we managed to organize about her a meeting she found more congenial, persons like her in fact, witty, facile in shallow repartee, arrogant, egocentric, clever, sharp, or contemptuous of all unlike them. It soon became apparent that they all used their talents to maintain a resistive, superficial banter that precluded genuine communication and deep analysis. Any tentative attempt to present a dream or other profoundly personal material was met with a humiliating badinage that soon discouraged further faltering ventures in this direction. It was only after we dispersed the membership into other groups that these patients were able in a therapeutically oriented climate to essay a more serious investigation of themselves. This experience illustrates the danger of unthinkingly catering to the neurotic motivation of certain applicants for psychoanalysis in groups. Here the patient's aim was to provide herself with an environment that would enable her to preserve those resistive maneuvers that operated against any deep or genuine human contact. This experience illustrates further an unfortunate consequence of organizing a homogeneous group, in which the membership tolerates only its own kind of pathology to the point of misperceiving it as a virtue and leading to its entrenchment rather than eradication. A group planned around such a coincidence of trends, which in failing to provide heterogeneous challenges to the individual's narcissism by the absence of personalities different from his own, merely cultivates the illusion of the fitness of his self image by surrounding him with a subculture in kind.

Compulsive talkers who drive the listener away in impatience or exhaustion may choose a group to share the burden of their loquacity. By turning their effusion to successively new members as the prior auditors become weary, the group offers more assurance against the anxiety of having no attentive audience available at all.

Occasionally, a patient may be encountered who is looking for a group resistively practiced in homogeneously reciting the intricate dynamics of their respective disorders with no intention or plan for overcoming this. These recitals have replaced and are equivalent to certain hypochondriacally obsessive reviews of bodily complaints without genuine insight. Unable any longer to find extra-group listeners to their interminable absorption in the psychological significance of everything, they come to group to pursue their substitute for living. The alert analyst will expose such an activity as a compulsive defense against repressed material and more wholesome interpersonal relations.

Psychoanalysis in groups may attract patients so masochistically disturbed or so guilty over their presumed or real transgressions that they seek semi-public confessional and exposure to invite multiple punishment and aggression against themselves.

The group is a magnet for patients who have been trained since childhood to look upon all self-interested activity as egocentric, selfish, and unethical. Such individuals feel it is immorally self indulgent to spend time and money for a purely personal analysis, when the world is so sadly full of disturbed persons more seriously in need of help than they are. What better way in good conscience to serve the larger interest than to share with these sufferers the good offices of psychotherapy.

One such man consistently antagonized his group with his devotions to them. When he reported to us that his magnanimity extended to his girlfriend on whose behalf he exercised himself at times for an hour in vain attempts to help her achieve an orgasm, some of his observant peers in the group pointed out the parallel between his industry with them and with her. They encouraged him to try to relinquish his generosity on both fronts and to seek to gratify his own needs more directly than through the antecedent intermediation of their or her pleasure. Despite many protests that this would be too self centered, he was in time gradually induced more flexibly to permit himself the luxury of personal pleasure without seeing first that his associates were enjoying themselves. Interestingly enough, the group became more positively disposed toward him and his girlfriend more sensually responsive, as they no longer were oppressed by his overworked self denial.

Another such patient, equally self effacing when it came to the needs of other people, proposed to us that he be permitted to bring all the members of his original family—they needed professional help he said—to treatment so that he and his kin would constitute a therapeutic group. Since for some time we had been eager to work with a whole family together, we quickly acceded without knowing at the time how pathological his motivation was. And so we proceeded, seven young adult siblings and their parents, to embark on an exploration of their difficulties. Before very long, when it came to the payment of fees, the family insisted that the original patient who had proposed family therapy assume the full burden of financial obligation. He seemed quite ready to do this. The therapist was the only one to protest that such an arrangement seemed unfair and requested that we consider why a more equitable sharing of responsibility was not warranted. This led to considerable wrangling, an inability to work through the more equalized liability, and a definite refusal to share the payment of fees. As a result the group broke up, but we learned in the process that the patient, who had organized it, had been trained as the eldest son to assume most financial responsibility for the entire family since childhood, a role that parents and siblings exploited and to which he all to readily acceded. We then made the further mistake of placing him in another group of strangers, where he proceeded just as uniformly to distinguish himself by dedication to the problems of the other members. It was only after we removed him from the group that the therapist was able to interrupt his compulsive consecration to the need of familial surrogates and uncover his own frustrated and angry dependency. After an extended period in individual analysis, he was able to return to a group free of the pathological motivation that originally impelled him to join one.

PATHOLOGICAL MOTIVATION IN THE THERAPIST

In a time of social and personal turmoil when the need for psychotherapy is on the increase and the growing demand for group therapists is attracting sizeable numbers of inadequately trained practitioners to engage in the practice of group therapy, we are bound to raise questions with regard to the reasons why some of these aspirants have evinced special interest in this form of treatment. In this review of the therapist's possible neurotic motivation in preferring to do group psychotherapy, the number and variety of his pathological temptations must not give the impression that the majority of group therapists are so animated. For in the main the larger body of professionals now engaged in the treatment of patients in groups are induced to undertake their work out of more reasonable springs of action. In the course of supervising a number of student group psychotherapists, ample opportunity was provided to explore their motivation for undertaking the practice of group therapy. In the main, supervisees were attracted to the field for constructive reasons like the wish to learn a new therapeutic technique that had proved useful in other hands, the desire to make treatment available to patients of lesser income, or the hope of providing psychotherapy for larger numbers of patients. Other students who were led to explore group therapeutic practice revealed mixed promptings, some of which betrayed evidence of intrapsychic pathology as motivating factors.

Sometimes a preference for group therapy as a medium in which to undertake treatment is inspired largely by a calculated plan to earn more money. If the therapist is stimulated by a personal need to perform before an audience, his exhibitionism may find captive witnesses in the group. One therapist in supervision admitted that the patients he liked he kept in individual treatment and the ones he disliked he placed in groups! On one occasion, a homosexual therapist consulted me with a request for supervision of a group of homosexual patients he planned to organize. I felt that in all fairness to his patients it would be more in their interest to have a heterosexually oriented analyst. I felt too that they would profit more from a heterogeneously and heterosexually organized group. I also suspected he was selecting the membership out of his own unresolved pathology. I dissuaded him, therefore, from this particular project.

The group therapist may have strong ethical convictions about the democratic ideal that moves him to practice psychoanalysis in a group. There is a danger of applying valuable principles from the field of social economy to the field of group psychotherapy, in which they may have little or no relevance. The group therapist's devotion to the image of fraternity may blind him to the patient's need to uncover and work through the pathology of his one-to-one relationships. The group therapist may then deny the patient individual sessions when they are really indicated and inappropriately limit him to group meetings. Also, at group sessions the leader may be so dedicated to group trends, group process, group mores, and group prejudices that he neglects the significance of bilateral interaction between any two patients, between any one patient and himself, or the exploration of intrapsychic conflict. The conflict of social cooperation, compulsively applied to the treatment of a group, may induce the therapist nondiscriminately to proscribe private consultations with him. Here is an instance in which the therapist's absorption in a social ethic may provide the patient with the ability to establish good communal relations but leave him at sea with his inner conflicts and inept in association with a single person.

Occasionally, a therapist, whose personal individual analysis proved to be an inadequate experience, rejects the one-to-one setting for all his analysands as likely to be equally deficient and expresses his protest against traditional dyadic treatment by nondiscriminately consigning all his patients to group therapy. A therapist who has undergone a successful personal individual analysis and who, as a result, feels relatively secure in most one-to-one relationships, may find himself nevertheless somewhat ill-at-ease in a group of any kind. Instead of joining a therapeutic group as a patient in order to explore and work through his discomfiture in company, he may choose to treat a group of patients with the undisclosed purpose of overcoming his own social disease.

It has been our experience that group therapy in many instances provokes countertransferences and other evidence of intrapsychic pathology that were not in evidence or were unresolved in the therapist's prior one-to-one analytic training. In some instances, while his earlier didactic treatment worked through his dyadic difficulties, his triadic, quadratic, and multilateral problems lay dormant, to emerge only in the course of his therapeutic efforts with groups. Under these circumstances, many of these men have joined a therapeutic group to participate there as patients, succeeding only in coping effectively with the newly discovered internal disorder elicited by the group and in turn becoming thereby more expert in dealing rationally with their own assembled patients.

Occasionally, a student in group therapy will make it clear in the course of supervision that one of his unconscious purposes in conducting a group is to ensconce himself in the position of a nonparticipant voyeur who enjoys observing the cast of patients acting out their respective roles on the stage before him. Here the therapist has forgotten the pursuit for which he was engaged and rather chooses to indulge in gratifying predetermined demands to be a detached witness to the interaction of others. Whether their involvement represents a reenactment of the primal scene or some other historic transaction of the therapist's past varies with his intrapsychic dynamics.

Sometimes the therapist is impelled to employ the group to express attitudes that he is reluctant to declare. He may fear that if he openly says what he thinks, he may be disliked or rejected, an eventuality too distressing to bear. He may be inordinately afraid of counteraggression if he exposes a patient's hidden motives. The therapist may hesitate to speak up in anxiety lest his own distortions be thereby made manifest. Accordingly, immobilized and increasingly detached, he may secretly resent the members' freedom in self expression and derive secret pleasure from their aggression or sexuality with one another, activities that he covertly sponsors and identifies with, an indirect participant in acting out to which he has no right.

The therapist, in fear of exposing his countertransference reactions to a patient, may persuade him to join a group. Or, in his inappropriate concern that any affective reaction on his part has no place in treatment, the therapist may find it easier to ward off the patient, who provocatively seeks emotional involvement, by putting him in a group. Here, the leader's anxiety over responding to the patient disposes him to introduce one patient to the next so that they can interact while the therapist maintains a defensive disconnection. The therapeutic group setting, however, proves to be no place where the leader can sustain a retiring disposition for very long without careful scrutiny of his behavior by the group. The membership soon demands from him a participation as a therapist and as a relatively normal human being that it has every right to expect, as long as that involvement serves therapeutic ends.

We have encountered a therapist who was so prone to becoming seriously involved with his patients in individual treatment that his temptations were consigned to groups in order to control the therapist's sexual acting out. Here, the motive for doing group therapy was not directly on the patients' behalf, although their interests were served indirectly insofar as they were, in the group at least, protected from the therapist's physical self indulgence. Not infrequently, such a leader will unconsciously continue by one means or another to attempt to seduce the patients even while in group, but commonly the fear of exposure acts to curtail any literal sexual acting out.

The therapist may be motivated to do group therapy by his mounting anxiety in individual treatment in the face the patient's criticism, aggression, or frightening relapse into regression or suicidal depression. He may not be able to tolerate the threat of the patients' unfolding psychopathology and take flight from therapeutic responsibility by shifting the burden to other members in a group.

If the therapist prefers to indulge his unhealthy trends and is unable to or rejects the exercise of a more wholesome relationship with his patients, but recognizes the need for more constructive give and take, he may ask them to join one another in a group in order to find a more positive climate for the evolution of their good potentials. Here he uses the power to provide each other with the healthy relationship he himself is incapable of having. He may then extol the virtues of group therapy with vague references to the inherent salutary mystique of group-as-a-whole treatment whose healing powers are employed to conceal his own detachment, his fear of realistic interpersonal involvement, and his inability to relate.

The student therapist may choose to practice group therapy, if he is provoked by patients' pathology in individual treatment into disturbing countertransference reactions. His hope then is to escape the provocatively disordered behavior of the patient by placing him in a group. The therapist's expectation here is that the patient will direct his overpowering feeling toward other members and thereby permit the leader to escape the unpleasantness of experiencing his own intrapsychic morbidity. In such a maneuver, the therapist tries to hide out in the group, exploits the membership as foils against one another, and generally assumes a position of guarded detachment. As a result, problems that patients have with authority figures tend to be ignored and inadequately worked through. The therapist also finds to his dismay that the group is no sanctuary in which he can escape his countertransference problems. For inevitably the peers in interaction mobilize sufficient ego resources to respond to his evasiveness and demand more participation and therapeutic responsibility from him. The only constructive way to deal with this issue is for the leader to return to therapy for further resolution of his own projections and to didactic supervision for instruction in coping with and working through his patient's psychological disorder.

While it is easier in individual treatment for the therapist to maintain a leader-centered, egocentric authority if he is so inclined, there are some therapists who are more disposed to elicit veneration from a whole entourage, for which the group may provide a medium. Under these circumstances, the leader's role is largely a repressive, inspirational one, while the patients stand in awe and admiration of his Alexandrine pronouncements, which screen his subtle contempt for them. However, it is not possible for long for a patient, particularly when he is reinforced by others, to withstand such an assumption of infallibility. Members, one by one, begin to drop out of the group or to challenge the therapist's arrogance.

If the therapist has not resolved his own neurotic need for supremacy, he may inappropriately exercise in the group a compulsive drive to fragment the membership, sabotage positive peer relations among them, and cultivate each patient's abnormal dependency on him. Or, impelled by the pleasure derived from being witness to the members' aggression against one another, he may sponsor discordant sallies among them as a rationalization for needing to bring hostility out of repression. Such a group soon deteriorates into a battleground for acting out, until one member after another leaves in frustration and more entrenched psychopathology.

An authoritarian therapist who imagines that all reparative forces emanate from himself and that few, if any, patients can exercise constructive resources with one another, may occasionally so organize the treatment process as to limit peer interaction. He does this by providing each member with one or two individual interviews a week, limiting the frequency of group meetings and excluding alternate sessions in which the group meets without the analyst. Accordingly, patients become bound to and dependent on the therapist in the vertical vector and fail to resolve their problems with authority figures at the same time as they are prevented from exploring and working through their difficulties in the horizontal vector.

An authoritarian therapist who imagines that all reparative forces emanate from patients and that few, if any, professionals can exercise therapeutic functions with patients, and who believes further that the expression and development of psychopathology is the high road to recovery may make the group the instrument of "treatment." His authoritarianism manifests itself in his persistent urge to drive the patients into irrational and impulsive pursuits. His rationale for using the group is based on the fact that patients are better able to provide in one another cross-currents of disturbance that are in themselves assumed to be therapeutic. As a result, the group atmosphere becomes charged with increasingly irrational outbursts until a "therapeutic psychosis" takes place, unless the patient is sufficiently in possession of his wits to escape from such treatment. In this climate, alternate meetings are encouraged but misused to entrench a tyranny of unreason.

The irrational psychotherapist, in revolt against consciousness, reason, and tradition, may choose the group to perpetuate a rebellious subculture, no matter how bizarre and eccentric, so long as it is antagonistic to intellection. This dedication to unconsciousness and pathology may find some ready adherents among certain group members who join the assault on understanding by zestful acting out. But the mainspring for initiating and maintaining the noxious disorder is the therapist's investment in it.

One group therapist we know terminated his didactic analysis prematurely to protest over his analyst's reluctance to respond to him with the intensity of feeling the analysand demanded. He found successive individual therapists all lacking in depth of their emotional response to him. None of them could match his own affect. It was discovered in supervision with me that he had turned to doing group therapy to find there, among patients, the kind of feelingful reactions he could not elicit elsewhere. But he valued only that emotion that permitted him to ventilate his intrapsychic pathology in acting out his resentment against his original family, his father in particular, for their failure to respond to him affectively and to allow him the privilege of expressing his irrational feelings. Unable then to find the climate in individual analysis suitable to the cultivation of his unreasonable passion, he chose a group milieu to provide a subculture in which to provoke and attempt to maintain his irrationality.

One therapist admitted to his preference for the group milieu in desperation over his confusion as to the technique of working through with those patients he has in individual treatment. Apparently he was assigning to them the responsibilities of the therapist. They would treat each other, while he abdicated his role. Here they were not merely auxiliary therapists, as members of groups are sometimes inappropriately referred to, but expected to be *the* therapist, while the presumed leader played an auxiliary role.

The therapist who is irrationally disposed to disregard the necessity to value past history or to make plans for the future and is obsessed primarily with gratification in the present moment may choose the group to afford him the pleasure of yielding to fascinations in the here-and-now. The membership itself to begin with, too often victimized by such a bent, may provide a fertile field further to excite immediate impulsivity. The therapist's indifference to the past, to the future, to consequences and his refusal or inability to think or plan for the patient's constructive development result in a chaotic interaction in which no therapeutic outcome is possible. This is, of course, not to say that a discriminative emphasis on the value of current gratification is not in order for those patients who are obsessed only with history or the future.

If the therapist is in serious countertransference, he may project the group as his original family. There he may set out whatever role his unconscious demands impose on him, whether to submit passively to projected family figures or to control and dictate to them. If he tamely gives way to the group, he relinquishes conscious leadership that is essential for him to conduct responsible treatment. If he dominates the group, he vertically imposes a hierarchical authority that interferes with salutary peer interaction. In countertransference, he may act out in the group competitive behavior with a father or brother figure and attempt to isolate him in winning a mother or sister surrogate's affection.

A therapist may inappropriately exercise in a group a role that had its inception in his childhood, when one parent assigned him the task of acting as protector to the family against the cruelty of the other parent. In the group, the leader acts out this traditional function by unreasonably converting most interactions among patients into projected contests between one member inevitably judged to be unkind and the other benign. Or the group is intrusively overprotected by the therapist from the presumed ill-will of the patient misperceived as malicious, while the rest of the membership, cast as frightened siblings and the victimized parent, is shielded beyond its real need. Or, the leader may act out his earlier role as champion against a dominating sibling by contesting the supposed tyranny of a patient who is merely beginning to put to constructive practice his right to assert himself. If the therapist in his own past jealously came between the parents' affection for one another, he may in the group

improperly subvert the demonstration of warmth between patients because he feels left out again. If he was inclined in his own
history to be isolated by one familial figure and to seek an ally in
another against the aggressor, he is likely to set up the same
operation in the group. These practices are bound to create
dissension and confusion among patients already beset with their
own difficulties.

If the therapist's original family was loveless and quarrelsome,
he may find any hostile interaction in the group intolerable and
anxiously and prematurely demand positive expressions of feeling. If he was made to experience his own family as generally
benevolent and extrafamilial influences as inimical, he may
convey to the patients the illusion that the group offers them the
only secure fortress in a hostile society. If in his early life, there
was no safe anchorage within the home and he constantly sought
escape in the world outside, he may find himself ridden with
tension during group sessions and turning with relief to the end
of a day spent with successive groups. He may then convey to the
patients his pervading anxiety to which they contagiously respond with their respective intrapsychic pathology.

The therapist who has not resolved his own oedipal problems
may unconsciously choose the group as a forum to continue to act
out his contest with the father for the mother, using group
members as surrogates. Or he may, having denied the existence
of his oedipal conflict, and taken flight from it in his own analysis,
proscribe its emergence from repression by catering to patient
resistances in the group.

A therapist in a group who is consumed with his devotions to
the membership may on occasion be discovered to be acting out
his neurotic overprotection. His missionary spirit may be a
rationalization for unconscious resentment and guilt toward the
patients to whom he is so dedicated. Such a therapist will not
infrequently work himself to exhaustion in his consecration to the
group inducing in the membership a sense of obligation, guilt,
and resentment at his self sacrifice. His self-effacing benevolence
is too remindful of their own sadomasochistic parents and elicits
and consolidates their transferences.

Sometimes the therapist's preference for the particular size of a
group is a reflection not so much of rational considerations that

would serve each patient's improvement but a countertransferential maneuver based on the therapist's projective need. For example, he may feel that a group of three or four is the ideal number, if his original family was made up of three or four members. Or, he may just as firmly believe that the standard should be eight or ten patients, if his family constellation was so constituted. In such an operation, he is projectively intent on re-animating his original familial circle governed by his own predetermined needs. Or, if his compulsion would escape a reproduction of his earlier relationship, he may just as vigorously maintain that a group of some other size than that of his family is the therapeutic model to be followed. The number he then advocates may have been determined by the gang he played with as a boy, a band that represented his release and rebellion against familial restraint. Or, he may unconsciously select a particular number of patient-surrogates that corresponds exactly to the size of the idealized family that lived next door during childhood.

There has been some inclination among a few therapists to extend their interest from the treatment of small groups to high-flown fantasies of mass psychotherapy. In these instances, the grandiose role in which the therapist casts himself gives his visions of leading the misguided multitudes to a better way of life. So proposals have been made for therapeutizing whole cabinets, congresses, houses of parliament, and government leaders en masse with the group therapist masterminding the whole scene. Psychotherapy in this ecstasy of castle-building is extended from the individual to small groups to whole nations and the masses of mankind. While no one can object to a reasonable extension of the legitimate uses of the benefits to be derived from group therapy to ever-widening circles of patients who really need treatment, these florid daydreams have little to do with reality. They suggest rather that the therapist who is preoccupied with them is more the victim of a flamboyant imagination than grounded in the limitations of practical psychotherapy. The therapist so affected would do better to distinguish between the fields of professional operation leaving some social problems to other collegial experts among the sociologists, anthropologists, philosophers, and politicians. Otherwise, he is embarrassingly suspect of making his interest in the masses look like an ornament to his grandiosity.

INDIVIDUAL ANALYSIS: PATHOLOGICAL
MOTIVATIONS IN THE PATIENT

One pathological motivation in the patient that induces him to seek out individual analysis rather than psychoanalysis in a group is concerned with the problem of privacy, isolation, and exposure. While we are living in a time when the individual's right to privacy is being seriously encroached upon from all sides, and we recognize his right not to incriminate himself, and gross public intrusion on personal reserve is made to seem a national virtue, group therapy must be distinguished from these abuses of justifiable privileges against self exposure. For treatment in a group has not the same objective of baring the person with a view to stigmatizing or homogenizing him. Its aim, among others, is to overcome his *abnormal* isolation, his *exclusive* quest for privacy, and his *nondiscriminating* anxiety lest he be seen. In fact, many patients who have "concluded" their personal, individual analysis are then referred by their therapist for treatment in a group because of a residual inability to enter freely into social relations. It is often just this type of patient who is most in need of analysis in a group, who instead resistively applies for private treatment. To accept him in a dyadic relationship may at first be a necessary concession to his exaggerated fear of wider communication, but to keep him in individual therapy interminably is an inadmissible yielding to his pathological demands. While it may truly be said that the very fact that the detached patient has entered any treatment situation at all, even individual therapy, is already a step toward overcoming his fragile sense of relatedness, such a person can more generally profit from a group experience to test and solidify his expanding interrelation.

If his fear is that the group, unlike the analyst who is bound by ethical practices to keep what is told to him secret, might expose him to outsiders, he can be reassured by the therapist as to the actual rarity of such disclosures in a large clinical experience and the general preservation of anonymity to outsiders. He can be told that group rapport, mutual regard, moral obligations, the fear of retaliation and the analysis of any tendency to gossip, all operate as safeguards.

Sometimes a patient will object to psychoanalysis in a group on the grounds that it is quite possible he may discover there someone he knows socially. While he can be assured that this is unlikely, since the membership is selected from a large city, and that, if he does meet a patient of his acquaintance, he can always take his leave, it might be more appropriate to analyze in individual sessions his concern over such a likelihood. Not infrequently his anxiety can be traced to an earlier fear that his behavior will be discovered or his thoughts discerned by an intrusive or lurking parent or sibling. He can be confronted with the increasingly satisfactory experience in the group therapy of psychoanalysts who knew each other in advance of their assembling or of families together or husbands and wives together.

The patient who is fearful of exposing his sexual problems to a group may choose individual analysis. Or he may avoid a group in the apprehension that it may contain homosexuals who might seduce him. More commonly than not, the patient discovers that he can more easily share sexual disclosures with the peers in the group than with the therapist, who stands somewhat apart without baring his own sexual life as patients do and therefore does not so readily invite intimate confessions. Generally, the applicant who selects private care in his anxiety about revealing his sexual difficulties in a group is equally if not more resistive to uncovering them secluded with the therapist. The same observations could be made with reference to a generalized shyness or reluctance to expose oneself in all areas.

There is the patient who says, "I just wouldn't be able to talk in a group. I wouldn't know what to say." But such a man may be silent for interminable hours on the couch. Even if he manages at last to become verbal in individual analysis but cannot get at the root of or overcome his social silence, a group therapeutic experience may be indicated to study in group interaction the psychodynamics of his muteness. Such a patient is often referred for psychoanalysis in a group after an extended effort in private analysis has failed to correct his speechlessness. He may be the sort of person who demands of himself blueprinted speech before he utters a word, a compulsive preparation to check spontaneous or unconscious responses, a guardedness that overcomes him particularly before more than an audience of one.

The patient may say, "I don't want to listen to other people's troubles; I have enough of my own." While this may seem like a reasonable objection to group therapy, it should not be too easily bypassed as such, for it may be grounded in historically based distortions. If the patient was trained to meet the neurotic demands, originally family-imposed and then incorporated, of other people, he may wish to handle his compulsion by simply escaping their executions instead of learning to acquire the right to discriminate with whom, when, and to which expectations he chooses to respond in the common interest. Or, it may be discovered that he is contemptuous of people in adversity, himself included. Or, he may be attempting to isolate himself in a protective superindependence that rejects the offer of help. Or, he may be too humiliated at the prospect of exposing any personal limitation or weakness to his peers.

Occasionally, the preference for individual treatment over therapy in a group is based on a wish for exclusive possession of the projected parent in the person of the analyst. While for the patient deprived of an early wholesome dependency on the parent, such initial security with the therapist alone may be indicated, there comes a time with the patient, as with the growing child, when his development requires a tolerance for sharing the longed-for parent with his siblings and a more equitable access to the authority figure among the peers. Otherwise, an extended stay in isolation with the analyst may cultivate an unsound dependence that becomes ever more difficult to break to the point where the patient resists all attempts to introduce him to the group and makes analysis interminable.

We saw one patient some time ago who had spent many years in individual analysis clinging to her therapist projected as the protective mother figure. The role she unconsciously assigned to him and that he apparently accepted was to guard her from discovering her erotic interest in and fear of her father. To keep this conflict in repression, she renounced all sexual gratification with her husband and nurtured an ever-growing, childlike dependency on her analyst. As a result, her helplessness increased and she withdrew and denied her own resources in the search for maternal support.

The patient who neurotically demanded the exclusive attention of a parent and tried to exclude the siblings from their share of familial consideration may seize the opportunity in individual analysis to act out the abnormal fulfillment of this aspiration. The trouble is that, since this is a predetermined and compulsive activity, its accomplishment in therapy by no means fully satisfies the patient who still finds himself frustrated in the same expectation in the world at large. The protest that in group he can hope to get only a fraction of the analytic attention he needs is to put too high a premium on the therapeutic powers of the expert and too low a premium on the reparative resources of his peers. The group offers many more receptive, sensitive, and intuitive faculties to attend him than the analyst alone.

An applicant for treatment may choose individual rather than group therapy in fear of encountering there again the projected original family with all its anxiety-provoking discord, rivalry, domination, and mutual exploitation. He may prefer the objective calm of being with the analyst alone to the threatening climate of contending group members who merely revive his repressed difficulties with parents and siblings. While there is something to be said for his embracing the more peaceful engagement with the analyst, the transferences elicited by the group are more vividly reproduced in action and offer the patient a more practical testing ground in reality for working through his distortions than the unprovocative tranquility of the therapist. The group also plays its part in being an intermediate tryout for the patient's ultimate dealings with all people beyond its confines.

One patient reported a dream that took place before her entry into therapy. She said, "In the dream, I blew the group up, killed them all and myself too. I got rid of you, my parents, my family." In association, she remarked that she was reserved and evasive, that in childhood she was obsessed with destructive fantasies directed against family figures, because they might discover her "bad" secrets. Other patients, similarly fearful of and hostile to the group as projected family, may choose individual treatment to avoid the painful re-experiencing of self-destructive affect and other affect as well.

Rarely does one encounter a patient for whom the prospect of joining a therapeutic group feels like the threat of entombment. Such a patient usually felt himself a prisoner in his original family but was unable to leave it, repressed his death wishes against his parents, and devoted his life compulsively and guiltily to serving them in every way possible. For him, then, the idea of getting trapped in a projected family again renders him claustrophobic to group therapy. He shuns the suggestion of group and chooses individual treatment. It may be necessary to treat him individually. If at a later time he can tolerate a group, combined therapy may be indicated with liberal doses of private sessions whenever he feels caught in the group. Finally, the group experience becomes a vital part of his therapy to work through his compulsive devotion, resentment, and guilt toward his family and its surrogates.

If group members are projected by the applicant for treatment as substitutes for terrifying nonfamilial strangers of childhood or the distasteful unruly gang he was always fearful of joining, while he clung anxiously to his mother, he may welcome individual analytic care to escape the illusory threat of therapy in a group. Here the choice of private treatment is largely an acting out in the hope of insuring a renewal of maternal overprotection, which is liable to intensify his already serious withdrawal from extrafamilial and peer relations, unless the analyst is so aware of this maneuver that he repeatedly strives to counteract the patient's neurotic dependency at the same time as he guides him to explore the unfamiliar world. Even so, the therapeutic group makes available to both therapist and patient a readier social instrument for such testing.

The patient may resist entry into a group out of successive social experiences in which he finds that his personality is so controlling that his associates become immobilized in his presence, an emotional paralysis that is embarrassing to him and impels him to take flight from group situations. He may even understand that his blocking others is related to his own inability to let go of his own restraints. He may also have some insights into the historical basis for his dilemma in his early training, which required the incorporation of rigid self-discipline against emotional exchanges of any kind, if he was to be accepted. Such a man may choose individual therapy to act out his prohibitions and to protect himself from the anxiety that the affective give and take of analysis in a group may provoke.

The patient who is afraid to stir strong feelings in others or in himself may choose individual rather than group therapy. He may have a preconceived notion that emotional outbursts get beyond control in a group and that members have difficulty recovering reasonable restraints. Or, he may be so unnerved by criticism or aggression directed at him that one manifestation of his problem is his flight into insularity. He may be so embarrassed by a show of warmth or affection that he prefers the relative segregation of the couch to the precarious involvement of multiple face-to-face relations. He may be so threatened by strong rivalry feelings in himself or in competitors that he evades a group setting because it would surely elicit those feelings. He instead embraces a one-to-one relationship, which offers more assurance that the analyst, at least, is on his side. Catering to his predilection for individual treatment may help him to evade facing and working through problems in order to achieve the healthy affective give and take that is characteristic of group therapy.

If the candidate for treatment selects individual therapy because he thinks that the group might attack his defenses with a cruelty of which the analyst would be incapable, he is projecting a generalized sadism onto the group that is uncharacteristic of it. While some patients may treat him with an undue harshness that reflects their own intrapsychic pathology and that is unwarranted by his behavior, he can certainly expect and receive considerate treatment from the larger body. Besides, unless the therapist organizes a homogeneous group of sadomasochists, a structure we believe to be contraindicated, the group is so heterogeneously planned as to assure each member such a variety of responses to him that he can always depend on support from one quarter or another. His anxiety about the extent of the aggression against him suggests a personal problem other than objective reality. His preconceived notions about his fragility and others' cruel intent might be more appropriately tested in a group than in the benign seclusion with the analyst. The patient may misuse the therapist's benevolence to serve a resistive avoidance of critical appraisal that would more vigorously demand constructive change. If this maneuver escapes the analyst, it becomes his problem, usually one of overprotection. In one instance after another, we have discovered how often a patient welcomes assertive and direct responses from his peers, when the therapist had anticipated anxious collapse and was about to intervene on his behalf to shield him beyond his need.

A patient may select individual analysis rather than psycho-analysis in a group in the belief that an analyst would tolerate his neuroticism more readily than a group. Or, he may feel that the therapist would be more indulgent of him in his awkwardness or stupidity, whereas the group might laugh at or ridicule him in his or their ignorance. This permissiveness varies with the analyst and the group and varies with each member of the group. What one patient sanctions, another may find disagreeable. But the group offers every one in it a small cross-section of society whose varied responses to each individual are both sanctioning and critical. Where the group is intolerant, the patient is rendered the opportunity to discover his protective role in terms of how his psychopathology elicits negative reactions. Sometimes the thera-pist's nondiscriminative tolerance becomes as much of a trap as parents' permissiveness. The group more often than not provides a good consensual check on the patient's inordinate demand that his every abnormality be allowed and on the therapist's unmea-sured allowing, if it occurs. Whenever a patient selects individual as opposed to group therapy with visions of limitlessness, he is acting out a pathological fantasy.

The patient may hold himself in such little esteem and project any prospective group as so intelligent or advanced in analytic procedure as to feel that he would be left far behind, confused and lost in the group and accordingly requests individual treat-ment. To allow him, under these circumstances, to escape the group is to contribute to his self-effacing illusion and to prevent him from discovering and developing his real equality or stature. He may protest with the remark, "I am sicker than any of the others could be. How then can I show myself to them? They will despise me." Analyzing his self derogation is often not enough to erase it. Often, only a direct testing experience with his peers convinces him that he is neither the most afflicted nor the most contemptible member as a prelude to a more ego-sustaining self perception.

The patient may feel that the group may not meet his intellec-tual requirements, that he is more sophisticated, that his knowledge of analysis in which he is widely read and his superior mental gifts would outclass a group, which might then deter his progress. Such an applicant is likely to choose individual analysis. And the therapist who yields to this preference, even if there is some basis in fact for the patient's conception of himself, endorses an egocentricity, a defensiveness, a rationalization, a grandiosity, a separateness and withdrawal, and an underestimation and contempt for others that is certainly pathological. The analyst, by the way, even those who practice group therapy, may share with the patient the belief that the group experience is not so intensive a therapeutic process as individual analysis. If this is the expert's opinion, no doubt with such an analyst the applicant would do better in private therapy. But if the leader has had experience in applying psychoanalytic techniques in the group and has not misused individual sessions to serve the patient's resistance, he will with more certainty be able to assure the patient of depth therapy in a group.

A man who in public life is in a position of real or imagined leadership, a role he has always pursued obsessively but with underlying doubts and apprehension, may resist group therapy in fear that his mask of command may be removed and his uncertainty and bewilderment stand revealed. He may be afraid too, now that his mounting anxiety has so shaken his sense of pre-eminence as to force him to consider therapy, that the group will further undermine his assumed rank. He may, therefore, in selecting individual rather than group therapy be acting out the preservation of internal, inexorable demands for authority that are not consonant with more realistic sharing of this role nor discriminating as to the particular areas in which he can truly offer leadership.

In rejecting a group for individual treatment, the patient may be acting out a contempt for his peers. His disdain for the group may find expression in his refusal to ally himself "with a bunch of neurotics," betraying in the remark his derisive attitude toward himself as well. If his evasion of the group is contaminated by distrust and grandiosity, the therapist may suspect a paranoid constellation.

The applicant for individual analysis to the exclusion of the group may reject treatment in common with others on the grounds that a group might curb the emergence of his unique individuality. This is indeed a danger, if the therapist tries to treat the group-as-a-whole, if he is more preoccupied with group process, group values, and group prejudices than with the individual in interaction. It is also a danger, if the leader organizes the group so homogeneously as to obscure personal differences among the members. But one of the aims of realistically oriented group therapy is to constitute the membership so heterogeneously as to sharpen the unfolding of original, personal resources. It is, however, to be kept in mind, that not infrequently the contentious objection to all analysis is that it might smother the patient's creative identity. Sometimes the candidate for treatment who makes this protest exhibits an anomalous eccentricity masquerading as constructive individuality.

In a society that prides itself on a tradition of individual enterprise, it is a wonder that patients in such numbers seek out any therapy at all, let alone group therapy. While the group therapist is eager to encourage the evolution of the patient's untapped potentials, he believes these can neither be realized by exclusively isolated endeavor nor by totally dependent ventures. He distinguishes between the obsessive and astringent straining for complete success on one's own that characterizes the ascendant individual in our culture and the need, if treatment is to be effective, to sow the seeds for the development of more creative resources that require some dependence on and synthesis of wholesome traditional and currently discriminating values. At the same time, he is equally sensitive to the danger that the average patient today is also the servant of many fruitless arbitrary concepts to which he so utterly subscribes and rebels that he is distrustful of any new dependency. Accordingly, the analyst strives to achieve for his patients an interchange that liberates their independent and original competence in a reciprocal climate. He recognizes the pathology inherent in the fantasy of absolute independence or dependence and endeavors in the group therapeutic process so to facilitate communication and complementary individuality as to bring out in each participant his mature interdependence and constructively unique differentiation. Despite this aim, the compulsively individual entrepreneur may look upon psychoanalysis in a group as a threat to his independence. He may, therefore, select private therapy as more harmonious with his contemporary phallic philosophy of derring-do.

INDIVIDUAL ANALYSIS: PATHOLOGICAL MOTIVATION IN THE THERAPIST

The analyst may reject group therapy in the conviction that a group cannot provide the patient with a treatment experience of adequate intensity or depth. Illustrative of this attitude is the experience of a group therapist colleague at a psychiatric clinic who asked his apparently cooperative professional associates, all individual analysts, to suggest to each new candidate for therapy that he consider joining a group. In a large series of consultations, no applicants were found willing to enter group therapy. When, then, the group therapist reinterviewed each of these patients once more, he found nine out of ten willing to join the group. Their response was some evidence that the candidates were sensitive to both the individual analyst's resistance to psychoanalysis in a group and the group analyst's enthusiasm for it. When a therapist has had any sizeable clinical experience in which extensively regressive psychopathology was uncovered and worked through in a group through the application of psychoanalytic means, he can only regard the confirmed and nondiscriminative adherence to private treatment under all circumstances as an indication of rigid orthodoxy, a stubborn clinging to traditional forms and methods, which exclude a flexible willingness to experiment, to try the new and different.

If, in a group situation, the analyst is inclined to reanimate projected familial figures when he re-experiences with anxiety, it is possible that he might select a less provocative bilateral treatment setting than the painful multilateral stimulation of a group. Here the preference for individual analysis is not so much a rational choice as acting out a countertransferential flight from the group.

While the traditional position of the analyst behind the couch enables him to maintain a somewhat detached yet participating observing role, on occasion the therapist is more motivated by his fear of being seen and his resistance to any kind of involvement in mutual interaction than responsible cooperative endeavor. This is a perversion of his obligation to be a watchful collaborator into becoming a mere isolated spectator. Individual treatment may offer him a fine refuge in which to rationalize his anxiety about exposing countertransference problems into justifications for withdrawing to the safe shadows behind the reclining patient in his interest. If the therapist is so unnerved at the possibility of facing a single patient, he is more than likely to be even more ill at ease at the prospect of sitting in a circle in a group. Here the preference for individual analysis reflects a problem of the therapist and has little basis in reality for being the most appropriate means to deal with the patient.

The individual analyst may justify his own approach to treatment by citing the inhibiting effect of multiple negative transferences directed at any given patient in a group in contrast to the therapist's benevolent approach. But the fact is that each patient is the target of positive transferences as well and the recipient of nonpathologically considerate, realistic, supportive, and critical appraisals at the same time. And even when these are in short supply, the leader is still available to exercise his therapeutic functions. As for the patient's emergence in the group, more often than not a larger canvas of his psychopathology and dormant capacity is uncovered by the multiple affective provocation of other members than by the traditional therapist's comparatively passive, relatively nonparticipant, and occasionally bromidic, role.

It may not be only the patient with whom the therapist is concerned. The analyst himself may be agitated and enervated by expressions of hostility directed toward him that he finds difficult enough to cope with in private without subjecting himself to concerted attacks from a group. If he finds himself so disturbed, he may maneuver the patient into repressing negative affect that really needs to be verbalized. This is more easily accomplished in the dyadic relationship than in a group, where the members ally themselves to mobilize the strength to air their feelings about the authority figure. To protect himself, then, against the painful emergence of aggression, the therapist in countertransference may elect the one-to-one relationship to serve his own rather than the patient's needs.

We once had a patient who came primarily for group therapy. He had undergone 3 years of individual analysis with little success. In the course of our work together, he discovered his repressed resentment against his former therapist and elaborated the analyst's interventions to demonstrate how subtly they prevented him from coming upon his legitimate and illegitimate anger. In these revelations, and the ventilation and working through of his animosity toward his first therapist, his present therapist, and his father, group members were his ready, if not indispensable, partisans.

If the analyst has not worked through his own neurotic need for the exclusive possession of a familial figure, he may act out his problem by monopolizing each patient in a one-to-one relationship. He may also reject the feasibility of psychoanalysis in a group as a realistically therapeutic procedure while he rationalizes his irrationally based preference for individual treatment.

The analyst who believes that his function in therapy is to be the good parental surrogate may be motivated by some reasonable considerations, but the assumption of a father or mother role tends to infantilize the patient. Occasionally, the analyst may be governed by his own need to win the patient's regard by being the exemplary parent. This course can be more easily pursued in individual rather than group therapy, where sibling rivalries and contradictory demands for various sources force the leader to assume positions not equally satisfactory to all at any given time. In private treatment, by contrast, if the therapist is given to extract the patient's approval, he can pursue this course without concern over jeopardizing appreciation from other patients.

The nondiscriminatory preference for individual analysis may on occasion express the therapist's lack of confidence in people, his cynicism about their being able to get together and work cooperatively in their mutual interest. He may even, if he is more disturbed, be actually opposed to their constructive engagement in common. Even though he may be doing group therapy, he may organize his group so homogeneously as to try to treat them as a massed individual and thereby indicate his underlying opposition to a democratic heterogeneous group in which complementary individuality can flourish and his basic preference for private treatment. His skepticism about patients having any positive resources or responsibility in their dealings with one another may lead him to an unbalanced overprotective attitude that excludes his permitting them to make adequate contact with each other.

The analyst working year in and year out with patients who continually invest him with exaggerated powers for good and evil is dangerously inclined to accept these projections as real. Instead of limiting himself to the achievement of more expertness, he is liable in his frailty to bask in their impressions of him. He may then come to overestimate his judgment and ability and under-value those of others. Certainly, he would tend to regard the therapeutic gifts of patients as distinctly limited. But patients are not required or asked to be auxiliary therapists in a group, and the analyst is always in fact, or should be, the expert. But it is through their multiple interaction and reparative rather than therapeutic activity that group members play a constructive part. So, in isolating each patient in private analysis, the therapist says in effect, "Only I am able to elicit a deep emotional response in the patient." Anyone who has had an experience of psychoanalysis in a group can testify to the grandiosity of such a notion. An interesting side effect of the group therapist who encourages the development and expression of patients' feelings and ideas is his increasing humility and regard for their perceptive powers.

A group is much more difficult to control or dominate than an individual. A group manages more effectively than one person alone to pool its healthy and neurotic protest against any one who tries to dictate to it, whether he be patient or therapist. The group, therefore, is more threatening than the isolated patient to a therapist who has not overcome his authoritarian trends, his need to intimidate, control, and master the other. The analyst, may, therefore, prefer to work with the patient alone where he yields more tractably to command than in a group. If such a therapist does practice group therapy, he is likely to limit the frequency of meetings, deny the membership the right to alter-nate sessions without him, and routinely prescribe regular indi-vidual consultations for all.

For a number of years, we have been conducting groups

limited to student analysts in training, some of whom are still undergoing individual analysis. On one occasion, such an analysand, himself eager to join a group, was warned by his therapist not to become involved with us, for in his opinion there was no professional group more given to destructive back-biting than our own kind. Accordingly, he sought to protect his patient from the disappointment and frustration that were bound to follow such a hazardous venture. The analysand, however, had been overprotected by a mother who denied him access to his peers and had progressed now in treatment to the point where he was ready to rebel against its duplication by the therapist. So he joined the group despite the therapist's anxiety and worked through for himself, and to some extent for his therapist, toward a larger security in the horizontal vector with his equals. The therapist who nondiscriminately projects the patient's environment as noxious and only his own influence as benign is likely to nurse the patient along into segregated dependency. The therapist who misperceives assembled patients as promiscuously incapable of having any restorative influence on one another but bent primarily on acting out their pathology is in countertransference.

If the analyst is not given to try a new method until it has proven its value many times over in the past, he might be regarded as a careful and dependable scientist, who has the patient's interests at heart. But, at times, it may be that the therapist is so obsessed with the need for a blueprint in procedure, so timid about a less-tried venture, that he postpones what could be an experimental advance for by now possibly outmoded orthodoxy.

Analytic crisis and therapeutic interventions in individual treatment have been rather thoroughly studied and systematized by now so that the therapist knows pretty much in advance successive procedures to follow. Psychoanalysis in groups is not so well ordered and may never be, in view of the multiplicity of possible interactions. For an analyst who has to know in advance everything that is going to happen, a group may be too unpredictable. He may then choose to practice individual analysis in fear of the unforeseen, the unknown, and the uncharted. This is not to say that his reasonable caution is not better than irresponsible impetuosity. But when traditional forms and methods deteriorate into rigid prescriptions and procedures that exclude the experimental evaluation of new possibilities, his conventional practice may be suspected of secreting a pathological conformance to precedent. For such a therapist, the challenge of bringing order and integration into what must seem to him like chaotic interaction in a group constituted of multiple personalities in different stages of regression and progress may be, in the face of this anxiety, too much for him.

15

Creativity and the Submerged Personality Disorder

We have found the use of psychoanalysis in groups to be particularly applicable to patients we characterize as having submerged ego disorders (Kutash 1984, Wolf 1957, 1980, and Wolf and Kutash 1984, 1985) and see this as of increasing importance in future applications as growth of these disorders is further fostered by present conditions in society and the family. We have found this as extremely important to the freeing of creative potential in the submerged egos of our patients.

The freedom to be selective is inherent in the presence of eight to ten patients. The multiplicity of persons demands and provokes and elicits more selective responses. Every member has wider choice to select with whom he will interact and to whom he will or will not respond. He has numerous alternatives. In dyadic analysis, he has less freedom. He can react only to his therapist— without the freedom to choose or select an alternative figure. The analyst too has more freedom in the group to choose flexibly with whom to respond and with what interaction or situation, or to what person it is most appropriate to provide insight. Everyone in the group has the liberty to shift attention.

The core of unfreedom in submerged personality disorders is the persistence of ambivalence as a result of the incorporated dual pseudoegos. A patient's responses to fellow members are less intense, because they are less influenced by the controlling mother figure than is the analyst. Comparing each patient's differing perceptions of co-patients and the analyst offers a striking study in contrasts and offers all the participants the freedom to choose where and when to resolve their distortions. The group's meetings, especially the alternate sessions, support the right to be free of the projected parent in the group leader. The absence of the analyst gives all the members that distance from the suppressing parent invested in the leader that liberates them to question his authority as well as the imposing internalized authority of their own pseudoegos. The group member is free to consider what the therapist offers and yet make room discriminatingly to dismiss it for his own perception or those of his fellow patients. The meetings with and without the analyst help the patient to work through his maternal transference on him as well as liberating his creative ego from his internalized, maternally derived pseudoegos. The alternate session promotes ego autonomy, independence, and reciprocal interdependence based on reality. The presence of other patients and the alternate sessions displace control from the external and internal authority to the members and to the emerging self, so that each patient directs his own life and encourages every other to do the same in complementary creative difference.

The first milestone for the patient with a submerged personality disorder comes when he is able to accept the insight that he has spent so much of his life utilizing most of his energy either conforming or rebelling around introjected parental values and has never truly found himself. At this point, the submerged personality needs psychoanalysis in groups to create new parental transferences and discover further his complying with and rebelling against them, so he can ultimately resist either side of this coin and be himself. The patient's transference to the therapist can become sufficiently diluted in the group to enable him to accept interpretations about his ambivalating within the group.

In general, the patient in individual analysis is under constant scrutiny in his therapeutic hours, whereas, in the group, attention shifts from him from time to time, giving him the freedom from such "oppressive" examination, a time to explore his own responses, time to evaluate what *he* thinks and feels, time to be "alone," to be creatively active in secondary rather than in primary process. Peers in group free the patient from the projected parental parent in the analyst as does also the alternate session. He is free at times to be silent in the group. The individual analyst intrudes if the patient is silent when he says, "What are you thinking or feeling?" This is more accepted from a group peer.

One of us (I. L.K.) has been experimenting with something we call the mini-group (see Kutash 1988b). Since some individuals feel lost even in a group as small as eight because they were neglected in a family, an experience in a group setting where the leader can assure them a prominent role can provide a new constructive experience. Several people who had previously found themselves overwhelmed in large groups were placed in a group with three or four individuals. The smaller size of the group was never mentioned as the reason for the invitation to these groups. These patients found themselves participating more and feeling a unique freedom. They were at last in a setting without overpowering mother, father, or sibling figures, while simultaneously not feeling lost in a crowd. At a later date, additional members were added including less passive potential transferential mothers or fathers. At this point, their egos were more secure from their previous experience with the leader as a "good parent." They felt his respect for their participation and the regard of siblings who were not perceived as overpowering or parental favorites. The larger group then became the arena for their further growth.

An adaptation of this was tried in a group solely for treating submerged personalities. The group was composed so as not to include overpowering mother, father, or sibling figures and only at a later date were less ambivalent potential transferential mothers or fathers added. At this point, their egos were more secure from their previous experience with the leader as a "neutral parent." The analyst in this group placed his faith in recovering the integrity of the suppressed ego and was convinced that this was possible not only by disincorporating the pseudoegos but by bypassing as well any dominating group member or process. The patient came to feel respect for their participation and the regard of siblings who were not perceived as overpowering or parental favorites. Initially, all being submerged personalities, they could count on resistance to whatever they interpreted to others, but it soon became apparent to them that all they needed to do was to switch sides to bring out the opposite point of view in their antagonist. This left all feelings safe; not being locked into complying and rebelling against any fixed parental positions. Furthermore, on any issues, they found a pro person for every con person or vice versa and again felt safe in the evenly divided numbers their submerged personalities created. The analyst in the group—and before long the patients as well—observed what was going on in the group and knew that behind this manifest performance something quite different was going on. This allowed many members to get past their initial fear of being overpowered by a parent or the therapist and allowed many group members to safely let their own submerged egos emerge. It should be cautioned that, while all patients were submerged personalities, the group was heterogeneous in other regards.

CREATIVITY IN SUBMERGED PERSONALITY DISORDERS

Submerged personality disorders develop before the age of 2 under the influence of a controlling and domineering parent, usually a mother who does not see the infant as an individual, separate and different from herself. The infant, seeking her approval, if not love, and fearful of her disapproval if he or she does not submit to her will, denies his own perceptions and abides by her judgment. To the extent that the infant submits to mother's persistence, he suppresses his own ego and incorporates her views as a negative pseudoego against which he repeatedly and compulsively rebels with an equally protesting pseudoego. Thereafter, the child, and later the adult with these two superimposed pseudoegos, separate from his own real self and, oppositional to each other, is ambivalent about any suggestions of another person, projecting on him or her the original mother or parenting figure. This ambivalating between complying and rebelling leaves little time or energy for the expression of an individual's own genuine ego, own perceptions, judgments, appreciation of reality, and his or her own creativity. Eventually, the submerged personality's struggle is not with his parents or their projected surrogates; it is with himself, with his incorporated parents, with their persistence in him, with his compulsive submission and rebellion against their incorporation. It is only when the battle is seen as an internal contest that the submerged personality can be free enough to yield to the artist within. It is only when the implanted parental seed dies that the creative ego can bear fruit. In order to be his real self, he needs to pass beyond his obsessive pseudoselves.

How is it then that men and women of genius exhibit both submerged maneuvers and at the same time are able to achieve extraordinary creative production? This phenomenon inspired a study of the dual pseudoegos in the lives and works of Shakespeare, Freud, and Einstein (Wolf 1980). Shakespeare, in fact, gave us in *Hamlet* the clearest clinical description of submergence up to the present time. Hamlet, in the split between his pseudoegos and between these pseudoegos and his true submerged ego, "fluctuates between love and hate, between submission and rebellion, between inhibition and impulsivity, between depression and aggression, between heterosexuality and homosexuality" (Wolf 1980, p. 216). Wolf (1980) said Freud vacillated between

> liberalism and authoritarianism, his wish to "know" women genitally and his wish to return to infantile grandiosity. . . . He was a "naive positivist" and "unscientific idealist," biologist and psychologist, mystic and materialist, revolutionary and reactionary, cosmopolitan and provincial, a believer in the progressive psychodynamic changeability of man and a believer in the immutability of instinct. . . . His preoccupation with the Oedipus complex, profound a discovery as it was, was nevertheless in some degree a displacement of his hostility from the more imposing mother to the less threatening father, a set of circumstances encountered in the creative genius, the homosexual and the di-egophrenic. [p. 220]

According to Wolf (1980), Einstein's ambivalence was between a longing for isolation and a sense of social responsibility. He vacillated between being

> a Jew and a non-Jew, a Zionist and non-Zionist, a German and non-German, a child and an adult, a profound thinker and a gullible boy, decisive and indecisive, stubborn and yielding, impractical idealist and practical realist, political and apolitical, ingenious and profound, confident and self-doubting, a pacifist who helped develop the atomic bomb. [p. 219]

In a dialogue between the two authors, Wolf suggested that all submerged personalities have some positive experience with the primary, nurturant mother, which promotes the development of a substantial ego before she becomes the secondary ego-denying mother, when the child begins to express his independence and separateness at about 2 years of age. Wolf further assumed that it was this beneficent experience with the primary mother that led to the growth in the infant of the substantial, creative ego, which was only partially and temporarily overwhelmed by the destructive secondary mother, which led in turn to split pseudoego maneuvers and submergence. Why then is genius more often associated with submergence when it appears to develop despite it? Here Kutash suggested two types of creativity. One is of the nihilistic nature — in trying to rebel or oppose what is, the submerged creates what isn't — something new. We term this *ego alien* or *oppositional* creativity. When the suppressed ego itself is liberated and creativity results, we term this *ego syntonic* creativity, and it is what we strive for in psychoanalysis in groups. The former is the product of tortured geniuses, the latter the product of actualized ones, able to create and be themselves. Furthermore, the former is limited to creating what is new and opposite; the latter can create what is new — period.

The rebellious component of the split pseudoego plays the lesser part in the creative process (1) because it is simply too obstructively responsive or reactive to the imposing submerged parent and her surrogate in the incorporated pseudoegos and (2) because its reactions are too immediate and compulsive to have as much creative quality. When, in the course of treatment, both pseudoegos are disincorporated, and the patient's previously suppressed ego is liberated, the ego becomes free to exercise its creative functions more fully. Furthermore, this liberating process enables the ego, formerly in suppression, to tap previously unconscious primary process material that can be used and integrated through secondary process along creative channels.

In combining these conjectures, the authors concluded that for the submerged to progress from ego alien or oppositional to ego syntonic creativity, he or she must have had a good primary mother. In therapy, techniques must be applied to free the ego submerged by the bad secondary mother. The creative ego can survive by submission to external necessity, to external pressure, to fate, if you will, but it is inflexibly unyielding to the abandonment of its artistic core.

We were led to the work with liberating creativity through psychoanalysis in groups, not only because genius was so often associated with submergence, but also because we found that among our nongenius patients, a similar, if less magnificent, creative evolution occurred once the submerged ego was liberated in those with submergence problems. A quote from Flaubert (Brombert 1967) gives a picture of the premorbid submerged personality and presents some evidence of his submergence and suppressed ego and their relation to his genius:

> Since I did not use existence, existence used me: my dreams wearied me more than great labors. A whole creative, motionless, unrevealed to itself, lived mute below my life. I was sleeping chaos of a thousand fertile elements which knew not how to manifest themselves nor what to be, sucking their form and awaiting their mold.

We shall attempt to illustrate this process, first by presenting what creativity is, then by discussing how to encourage its emergence in the submerged personality.

CREATIVE PROCESS

First and foremost, it is proposed that individuality needs to be fostered if creative potential is to be promoted. The bad secondary mother cannot tolerate individuality in her child. In the first weeks of life, the infant has no reason to rebel. As a consequence, he elicits a wholesome, nurturant support and affirmation from the good primary mother. When he begins to show autonomous functions, the infant brings out in the mother latent secondary maternal qualities. The neurotic mother demands of the infant homogeneity with her misperceptions. She is herself symbiotically attached to him. As long as he needs her, she can cling to him. As long as he complies, she is nurturant. When he strives for autonomy, she experiences his struggle for independence as separation from her. Her own dependent needs are threatened. In her fear of losing his symbolic support, she demands homogeneity from him and thereby becomes the bad secondary mother.

A danger for the submerged personality in group psychotherapy is that he may simply continue to submit and rebel in the face of group pressures, of group process dynamics, or under the influence of members who are more outspokenly forceful. He may join the aggressor, idealize his bondage, and see it as liberating, when it is not. As Dr. Zhivago says (Pasternak 1958),

> Health is ruined by the system's duplicity, forced on people if you say the opposite of what you feel, if you grovel before what you dislike and rejoice at what brings you nothing but misfortune. Your nervous system isn't a fiction, it's a fact of your physical body and your soul exists in space and is inside you like the teeth in your head. You can't keep isolating it with impunity. I found it painful to listen to you, Nicky, when you told how you were re-educated and grew up in jail. It was like listening to a circus horse describing how it broke itself in.

So, the submerged personality needs to resist neutralization by a prevailing group and listen to his inward drummer, as must the therapist with him. The artist–patient treasures in himself this most precious jewel of creative selfhood. He recognizes in the powers-that-be an illusion of genuine character and originality. He knows that with the loss of the privilege of power, they have no independence of thought and genuineness. The group-as-a-whole devalues personal opinion. Everyone must join the chorus, sing the same tune, or be condemned as a renegade. The so-called deviant is a treasure who prefers to be natural and spontaneous, instead of homogeneously dull. If he or she is overpowered by the group-as-a-whole, submits in guilt at his deviance, and renounces his freedom and artistry, he becomes submergently masochistic.

Additional essential ingredients necessary to the promotion of the individual's ego syntonic creative potential are his or her: freedom, originality, curiosity, and organization—the search for the whole in a new synthesis rather than the disordered parts (Wolf and Schwartz 1964). To achieve freedom, the availability of choice is necessary as well as the capacity to be selective, to see nature in a new way. The submerged personality is bound to unfreedom by his ambivalently compulsive pseudoegos. He is limited by lack of a freed ego that would enable him to choose, to be selective. A liberated ego would help him to examine what he has been told, appraise it, then create a new perception. He would have the autonomy, the strength, to go beyond the given to propose an independent view. In analytic group, he is encouraged to free associate, to fantasize, to dream, to have regard for his own intuition, to be open to his thoughts, feelings, perceptions, and not to resist saying what is on his mind. He is supported in his right to have access to his suppressed self and to allow himself and the other members similar privilege. To this end, he is encouraged to take the risk, despite his anxiety, of exploring the unknown in himself and in the other patients. In the process, he gets ego-promoting confirmation from the group members. They as a result of their identification, their interaction, and the general encouragement to associate freely, give more and more mutual support to imaginative processes, which, with the help of the therapist as well as their own increasing resourcefulness, fosters greater understanding and opens up new possibilities for an emerging self independent of the compulsive ambivalence of the superimposed, split pseudoegos.

Group members alternate between free association and conscious appraisal of what they have spontaneously said, just as they tell a dream, freely associate to it, then try to gain insight into its meaning. Verbal disinhibition is encouraged, followed by thoughtful examination of their psychodynamics and psychopathology. Group members' anxiety about giving up defenses and exploring unconscious material is relieved by seeing other patients return safely from primary to secondary process. It is often easier to free associate among one's peers than in the hierarchical vector with the analyst. There are enough egos and superegos available among the group members to pull any one patient back to reality. Dreams and daydreams are associated to multilaterally and then consciously examined in secondary process for insight. The creative ego is given potential to emerge and thrive by dipping into primary process, then examining the material in secondary process. Mutual exposure reduces defenses in multilateral catalysis.

This is further enhanced by promoting the alternate session. The therapist thereby is saying to the patients: "I trust you and respect you. I have confidence you will not act out in my absence but rather interact with each other reasonably within limits." The analyst's conviction that group members can, independently, exercise their creative, resourceful egos, impels them to do so. His belief that he can rely on their mutual responsibility to one another supports their growing, creative autonomy. Every submerged personality has had some positive, nurturant experience with the primary, ego-promoting mother. The analyst's conviction that his creative treasure can be liberated by regard for the patient's unused potential helps the wholesome ego to blossom. Group members, supported by the analyst's stance, develop increasing regard for themselves and one another.

The submerged personality needs to hear his or her internal messages, with the therapist alongside, and not those of any dogmatic and despotic other. He needs to heed his own imaginings and dreams, and the therapist needs to listen to him. It is only when his own ego is liberated that he can heed others, then freely choose, from what is offered, the useful, creative, growth-promoting, realistic, and imaginative, and reject what is stifling. The freeing of the suppressed ego is experienced by the submerged personality as a personal and liberating revolution. Before he was carrying, as a compulsive private burden, the defensive and useless core of parentally invested pseudoegos, a false self; now he can operate with his genuine self.

Besides individuality and freedom, a third quality characterizes the creative process: originality. To achieve this end, the therapist encourages new and different perceptions. Group members, tired of each others' static ambivalence, appreciate a novel perception, which adds refreshing insight into external and internal reality and unreality. Everyone is stirred by a patient who, previously oppressed by his pseudoegos, manages to go beyond the compulsive given to achieve a fresh outlook. It is original, creative, imaginative, unique, ego-building. It is heedful of intuition and refreshingly perceptive. The analyst's position is that the compulsive search for unconscious psychodynamics and psychopathology is not creative. The creative patient needs to dip into primary process, then reflectively organize his exploration with secondary process, with ego functions, in the way a dream has to be analyzed to provide insight, a creative process. While a patient cannot go beyond his history with his mother and his incorporation of her perceptions unless he examines what has happened to him in the past, he may be just as obsessively limited and overcome with rigidity and uncreativity by a too exclusive preoccupation with history. However, if he explores his family history, then goes beyond it, he taps his creative ego.

Psychoanalysis in a group facilitates the emergence of the creative ego of each member. A heterogeneous group provides a setting of unique individuals so that stereotyping is broken through to a flexible newness. Because the multiple stimuli are so diverse, the analytic group is especially stimulating to the emergence of the creatively new. Group interaction provides new qualities, new responses not previously seen. Fresh material shows itself because of the pressure to interact. The shifting attention from patient to patient is in keeping with the need for alternating periods of activity and relaxation, attention and inattention, so necessary for the creative ego to grow. The analyst, by providing meetings with and without himself, is judiciously heedful and judiciously disregardful, which also fosters the emergence of more creative egos.

A fourth facet of the creative ego is curiosity, which spurs the individual to solve problems and reach a realistic goal. The improving patient develops a clearer view of reality, which was formerly obscured by illusion. He becomes more engaged in the search for insight, due to an animating curiosity about himself and the other patients. He joins more avidly in pursuit of an ego-building reality, formerly buried by the old split pseudoegos. In the analytic group, there are more anchors to reality, more appeals to reason, more demands on each member to relinquish inappropriate commitments and assume more reasonable ones. He is urged to examine his unconsciously provocative role in eliciting the sort of reactions he gets from other patients. He is encouraged to consider the possible reality in their responses. He is confronted by the realities around him: other members' provocation, stimuli, reactions, demands, difficulties, and recommendations for his choosing more legitimate alternatives to his pathology. Awareness of multiple realities grows because having a number of patients helps to avoid resistive neurotic or psychotic distortions. The patient is impelled to react more appropriately, because he is less isolated, because anonymity is not neurotically overvalued, because the inner and outer realities are analyzed.

A fifth component of the creative ego is organization—the movement from concentration on details to a more organized whole, the relinquishing of a more limited view for a more inclusive, better-organized, larger view. A new perception of the organizing principle clarifies the relatedness of the parts. The patient's insight into the history of his submergence makes him an eager collaborator with the analyst and other patients in the recovery of his suppressed ego. He becomes creatively involved in obtaining an insight, in evaluating it, in elaborating it, and in developing it. The analyst, in his struggle to replace disorder with order, confusion with clarity, chaos with method, and confusion with analysis, leads the group members to pursue a similar course.

Organization is one of the fundamental qualities of the creative ego. In the analytic group, the intrapsychic is integrated with the interpersonal, the authority with the peer, the real with the fantastic, the alternate with the regular meeting, the patient with the other group members, treatment with life. The goals and results of combined therapy with submerged personalities will now be described in more detail.

TREATMENT

Bellak and Faithorn (1978) list twelve major ego functions: (1) reality testing; (2) judgment; (3) sense of reality of the world and of the self; (4) regulation and control of drives, affects, and impulses; (5) object (or interpersonal) relationships; (6) thought processes; (7) adaptive regression in the service of the ego; (8) defenses; (9) stimulus barrier; (10) autonomy; (11) synthesis and integration; and (12) mastery and competence. Since the first aim in the treatment of submergence is to promote the recovery and growth of the creative ego, it is of interest to examine the way in which each of these ego functions can be enhanced in the therapy of patients with split pseudoego difficulties.

1. In reality testing, the patient needs to distinguish between inner and outer stimuli. The submerged is relatively unaware of his inner self, his suppressed ego, and operates largely by incorporating and rejecting the views and judgment of every other person, as he formerly did those of the pathological parent. He is overly sensitive to outer stimuli. He has little available inner self. He is a pseudoself buffeted about, submissive, and restrictive to every outer stimulus. The other stimulus is immediately incorporated and expelled by his two pseudoegos, respectively. His perceptions are inaccurate, because they are too seldom his own. His perceptions are those of everyone else, even while he denies their validity. He has too little psychological-mindedness or awareness of his inner state, because he has too little reflective capacity with which to operate. If he is severely ill, he vacillates between neurosis and normality. In psychotic episode, he may hallucinate, suffer delusions, and be grossly distortive in perceptual functions. If he is less disturbed, he does not hallucinate, is not deluded, but has various illusions. In the most serious or the mildest states, the submerged compulsively projects onto others his introjected, oppressive pseudoego, against which he rebels with his other pseudoego. This is the nature of his transference, which he compulsively projects on everyone with characteristic ambivalence. He is the victim of every outer stimulus and has little of the gratification that comes from the experience of creative ego resources. Not having an available inner self, being the victim of every external attitude, he is confused about his own identity.

In the course of treatment, as he begins to recover his own ego, he is better able to distinguish between inner and outer stimuli. He becomes freer of the compulsive necessity to be homogeneous with all others and of his equally compulsive need to deviate. He becomes more able to operate with his own perception and judgment, even to synthesize a new creative perception of reality. He becomes more able to distinguish between his own perceptions and those of others. He is no longer so needful of approval from others. Formerly, when he elicited approval, he could not trust it or believe it because of his submission. In his paranoid state, his latent rebellion, his sadomasochism, or his ambivalence, he subverted any reliable or ongoing acceptance that he so desperately sought. As he becomes better, he no longer compulsively seeks such appreciation. He is content in his own self-regard and in his regard for others. Formerly, he had no sense of belonging. He felt dishonest, undeserving, unloving, and unloved. He felt deeply wounded by any negative appraisal, and, feeling derided, he nurtured a private or open everlasting fantasy of revenge. Improving, he becomes more aware of and has more insight into his internal reality, and is equally appreciative of external reality without suppressing his creative ego functions.

2. The exercise of good judgment is an important aim in promoting the development of the creative ego. The patient with a split ego needs ultimately, but not too early in treatment, to become aware of the appropriateness and possible results of what he intends to say and do. Too early an emphasis by the therapist on such an aim is liable to inhibit the patient in his free association hunt for his buried self. To the extent that he lacks judgment, he is liable to serious acting out.

3. The patient's sense of reality of the outer world and of the self are significant ego functions. The extent to which he allows himself to be manipulated by external influences and allows them to intrude upon and be incorporated by his split pseudoegos, versus a healthier sense that events to a large degree can be determined by the exercise of the creative resources of his own ego, measure, respectively, the extent to which he is ill or improving. If he is developing a personal authentic self, a right to be different from others, and self-regard, as well as enjoying the same privilege in others, he is on the way to becoming well. He

is well to the degree to which he is less symbiotically and compulsively attached to his incorporated pseudoegos and their projection onto others, permitting himself and the others separate and disparate individuality.

4. Another ego function worth exploring in submergence concerns the regulation and control of drives, affects, and impulses. Involved here is the direct expression of impulses, the discriminating exercise of delay, frustration tolerance, and the movement from primary to secondary process by thoughtful evaluation, emotional communication, and appropriate behavior. The submerged tends to act out split pseudoego functions such as ambivalence, sadomasochism, paranoia, and bisexual behavior. To the extent his ego functions are less available, he tolerates analysis, cannot understand or accept insight, and may act out.

5. Still another creative ego function is concerned with the nature of the patient's object or interpersonal relations. The submerged tends to alternate between symbiotic attachment and withdrawal, to cling yet fear to be close, to want to swallow the other and vomit him up. He has no sense of adult mutuality and reciprocity. He is always in search of the nurturant, good, primary mother in her surrogate, but soon discovers in her the disappointing, demanding, rejecting, bad secondary mother, from whom he withdraws in repeated cycles. He is trapped in the fruitless and frustrating archaic views of childhood instead of pursuing more relevant, serviceable, and gratifying adult goals. Due to symbiotic attachments in the submerged parent and her stand-ins, others are used largely for incorporative and discorporative purposes. He has no adequate ego to see himself and the others as separate and distinct individuals. He cannot sustain an ongoing relationship. He cannot tolerate the actual presence, or absence, of any other. He longs for and misses the other but finds her, on resumption of the relation, too flawed to stand for long. He suffers from separation anxiety, but shortly after re-establishment of any symbiotic tie, is revolted by the inadequacy of his previously sought-after parental substitute. The therapist is at first idealized, but soon found to have clay feet. It is only when, in the course of treatment, the patient can relinquish his symbiotic tie, separate, and individuate, that he can abandon all ambivalence for an ongoing, mature relationship.

6. Thought processes are a significant ego function. Since the seriously ill submerged personality is subject to alternations of psychosis and neurosis, it is necessary for the analyst not to encourage unlimited free association but to intervene frequently with suggestions that some thought be given by the patient to what he has just said. Nor should the patient immerse himself in dreams or fantasies without thinking about them. Primary process material must not be allowed to go on for long without pursuit of secondary process. A distinction must be made between encouraging primary process and encouraging the development of ego functions.

The therapist needs to observe and value the patient's thought processes, the capacity to pay thoughtful attention to himself, to concentrate, to form his own concepts, to retain his discoveries about himself session after session. The therapist needs to be alert to the extent to which the patient's thinking is inappropriate, makes no sense or is disconnected, so that he or she can gently affirm when it is appropriate, reasonable, and sequential, instead of pointing out when the patient is irrational, unreasonable, or too loose in his thinking.

7. Adaptive regression in the service of the ego is useful with mildly or moderately submerged patients who may be subject only to submergent maneuvers. It is not appropriate to use such means with patients with severely split pseudoegos, because of their tendency to psychotic episodes. Here again, the therapist needs to distinguish primary process from suppression of ego functions. While he cannot easily encourage primary process, the therapist needs to endorse as covertly as possible every creative ego function. When sufficient ego functions begin to emerge and become more substantial, the therapist can then support the emergence of unconscious process—free association, fantasy, dreams—and support the patient's thoughtful examination of his unconscious communication via secondary process. If the patient has developed enough of an ego and has expressed his unambivalent hostility toward the analyst, the analyst can more securely encourage adaptive regression in the service of the ego and safely offer insight, without concern that the patient might, as formerly, simply feel ambivalent about anything the analyst said.

8. Defenses are also aspects of ego functions. The infant or

child's incorporation of the pathological parent's misconceptions and demands are both defensively adaptive and maladaptive. They are adaptive as a way of coping with the harmful parent and in secreting the creative ego from harm. They are maladaptive in distorting the victim's thought processes and behavior. The tendency of the submerged to misperceive his ambivalence and other inappropriate responses as being provoked by others rather than as internal problems, the results of his split pseudoegos, leads to the defense mechanisms of denial and projection.

9. The stimulus barrier is another ego function. The submerged is overly sensitive to external stimuli, to which he responds by incorporation and disincorporation. This response is both compulsive and disorganizing. He comes close and avoids. He welcomes and withdraws. These are his coping devices. The patient needs at first to withdraw from external pressure in order to focus on the recovery of the suppressed ego functions rather than focus on what others say, do, or require of him. If his stimulus barrier is low, he is too much distracted by the members of the therapeutic group and requires the quiet, silent affirmation of the listening and ego-supporting therapist.

10. The development of autonomy is yet another ego function. The submerged has little autonomy. He is an angry prisoner in a cage built for him by a parent, who still governs him through his split pseudoegos. His freedom and autonomy are impaired. He sees and does not see. He hears but cannot listen. He intends to comply yet will not. He wants to study but cannot. He hopes to remember and forgets. He wants to learn but cannot. He tries to develop athletic or graceful skills but is too awkward. He wants to speak but stutters. He has habits that he breaks, returns to, and breaks again in cycles. He diets, loses weight, goes off his diet, regains his weight. He makes resolutions that he breaks. He gives up smoking and returns to it. He learns and forgets complex skills. He establishes and breaks his work routines. He tackles problems with resolve, then procrastinates. He is enthusiastic about a new interest, a hobby, but quickly loses his appetite for it. He is anorectic and overeats at intervals. He eats too much and vomits in the course of treatment, as he develops autonomous ego functions, increases his own perceptivity, attends to his own thoughts, feelings and judgments, gains more capacity to ex-

amine thoughtfully his unconscious material, and obtains a greater facility in recalling the past. He becomes ready for analytic therapy.

11. Synthesis and integration are ego functions. Only a creative ego can reconcile and integrate seemingly discrepant or contradictory attitudes, values, feelings, and conduct, and dispel the false for the genuine self. Only a creative ego can energetically integrate intrapsychic process and conduct. Only a creative ego can perceive the relevance of history to the here-and-now, of feeling to thought, of perception to experience. Because of the relative unavailability of this ego function in submergence, insight cannot be used early in treatment. The analyst cannot lend his or her own synthesizing capacity to the patient until the patient takes on the job on his own. The patient would feel ambivalent about the therapist's effort to undertake a task the patient needs gradually to assume on his own.

12. Mastery and competence are also ego functions. These functions are reflected in the patient's ability to interact appropriately, and cope effectively with others. They are also reflected in the degree to which he feels adequate and able. These functions are seriously limited in the submerged. It is only when he has recovered his own ego that he has a stable sense of self, a valued image of himself, and independence from what others think of him, an inner identity and continuity of experience. These, then, are the goals of psychoanalysis and psychoanalysis in groups with submerged personalities.

We will conclude by describing a group one of us (I. L. K.) has been experimentally working with composed solely of submerged personalities with suppressed creative potential or ego-alien creativity. Overpowering mother, father, or sibling figures were not included, and only at a later date were less ambivalent potentially transferential mothers or fathers added. The members consisted of a man who works for his father as an accountant, who had earlier studied fine arts but flunked out of school, and who paints on and off as a hobby; a woman who is currently a teacher like both her parents, who had been into the drug culture as a college student with sexual acting out, who could write, while on speed, publishable songs and poetry of an angry, antisocial nature, but who hadn't written since getting off drugs;

a photographer who would work two days a week doing photography and three days a week on a job the family approved of (particularly his wife, who had taken over for his father), who put together double-exposure images of good and bad, God and devil, and who, although quite talented, never made good commercial deals for his work; a professional artist who is a commercial success with his light art, who is less recognized for his truly creative work, which he does for himself but is bitter over its lack of acceptance and sometimes loves it himself and sometimes hates it. The other members are also submerged personalities but are not in the creative arts per se. Nonetheless, they are also conflicted and have difficulty with the emergence of their creative production from their submerged egos.

All being submerged, the group members initially could count on resistance to whatever they interpreted to others, but it soon became apparent to them that all they needed to do was switch sides to bring out the opposite point of view in their antagonist. This left all feeling safe, not being locked into complying with or rebelling against any fixed parental positions. Furthermore, on any issue they found a person who was in favor for every person who was against, or vice versa, and again felt safe in the even division submergence created. The analyst in the group, and before long the patients as well, observed what was going on in the group and knew that something quite different was happening behind this manifest performance. This allowed many patients to get past their initial fear of being overpowered by a parent, or the therapist, and encouraged members to let their own submerged egos emerge. This was combined with individual therapy—for some the one was an adjunct to the other.

The results to date include the following: The accountant is painting more and has become more assertive in the business with his father. The teacher–poet is again working, but without drugs. Her anger toward society remains intact, but she has decided to marry the man she lives with, concluding, "This is not to comply with my parents but because I want to." The group had encouraged her to follow her own feelings and did not themselves try to persuade her one way or the other, demonstrating their evolving understanding of the others' needs. The photographer is no longer producing his images of good and evil. His

work is less objectively creative, but he is doing better commer-
cially. His ego-syntonic creativity is more conventional than his
conflict-ridden productions, but he is more content. The painter is
doing more creative noncommercial work and finding more
success with it, as he believes in it more. The other members are
progressing as well. In fact, one computer programmer has added
some creative hobbies, including art. The group has had only one
casualty—a man who could not be helped, as yet, not to see the
group-as-whole as the parents he complies with and rebels
against. His solution was to split off his anger to the group and
his compliance to his home, and he quit group. He has, however,
not abandoned therapy altogether, and it is hoped that eventually
his group experience will be integrated differently.

In summary, the submerged needs the therapeutic process to
recover his or her suppressed ego and free it from the ambivalence of subordination and revolt inherent in his prevailing
pseudoegos. The submerged is afraid of success. He might lose
the goodwill of the parent, be unloved, hated, killed. So the
submerged maneuver is a defensive maneuver in the service of
survival. The secondary mother and father might vengefully
destroy him if he takes personal liberties to achieve creative
fulfillment. The sadness of the submerged state is that the patient
cannot reveal himself. He does not know himself. He believes he
is an impostor, a thief as yet uncaught, hiding in a thicket of
ambivalence. He is tortured and torturing, self- and other-
destructive, self condemning, and intolerant of others. It is the
primary task of the analyst to assist the patient in working
through the domination of his incorporated split pseudoegos
toward the liberation of his creative but suppressed ego. With the
emergence of his genuine self, the patient can relax and concentrate, can rest, then dedicatedly pursue his own perceptions. He
can contemplate the traditional, yet come to a new way of dealing
with it. He can have the patience to struggle appropriately to
produce a novel formulation instead of being mired in vacillation.
He can be more inventive autonomously, personally, enthusiastically, industriously. He can use his intellectual functions more
creatively than before. Complexities now interest and engage him
rather than frustrate him. He feels enriched by his therapeutic
experiences. He is more perceptive. He is able to suspend

judgment temporarily for intuition. He is more flexible, skillful, accurate, and interested in interaction. Instead of submitting and rebelling, he now respects tradition, but radically changes it for something better.

For the creative powers of the submerged to become available, the suppressed ego needs to be enabled to emerge. It is only then that the patient can permit himself to have his own experience and be guided by it rather than be obsessively governed by his incorporated pseudoegos. As the submerged recovers, he develops, through his now available ego functions, a clearer understanding of what he wants to do and he does it. He can allow his recollections and his previously suppressed ego to grow and give shape to his creative undertakings. The breaking through of the suppressed ego is itself a creative process.

16

The Future

What is the future of psychoanalysis in groups? Having no crystal ball or the "I predict" conviction of certain television personalities, our prediction is made up of one part hope, one part fantasy, and one part just plain ignorance.

There are some things we all know, however, whatever our professional or personal daily pursuits may be. We know we live in a world where racial, national, economic, and political pressures are increasing daily. We know we are being called upon to adapt at a moment's notice to shifting policies of racial integration, war and peace, taxation, rising living costs, problems of housing, traffic, juvenile delinquency, and increased criminality on our streets. We are seeing established authority being challenged around the world and the cop on the corner being shot with his own gun. And, most of all, the threat of extinction from atomic, chemical, or germ warfare hovers over us all.

A philosophic way out of this bewildering state of affairs could be suggested. It could be suggested that we try to reevaluate our needs, our beliefs, our passions, and our purpose, so that we can find the firm ground to be flexible without falling over, that we strive to find the courage to discard what is old and no longer usable, and the greater courage to receive the new and strange and make it workable.

Or, an even easier way out would be to spin happy fantasies about many gimmicks that might conceivably become part of the practice of psychotherapy in the space age we are entering. Certainly a lot of pills will be concocted that will be useful in inducing any physical or emotional state, from a sleep that is hibernation to the ecstasy of orgasm. But there will always be some of us who will prefer the old-fashioned methods already known to us with experimentally based modifications to achieve similar results. There will certainly be machines invented to diagnose and possibly treat the mental ills of mankind. But here there will be many of us who will feel that their greatest need is for human contact and human interaction, and who will insist on finding ways to get it. This is where I think psychoanalysis in groups will play its greatest role and deliver its greatest service. For the search to understand the thoughts, feelings, and behavior of people will never lose its fascination as long as humanity exists. That fascination will die when humanity dies, and humanity will die if the search for mutual understanding dies.

How can that search be kept alive? By communication, by learning to know what makes us tick, what makes the other fellow tick, and how he affects us and we him. And the more "other fellows" we know and who know us, the more we will communicate and, hopefully, the more we will understand. Psychoanalysis in groups in the future will try to understand and treat the individual and will direct its efforts to the end that he be able to adapt to the world in which he lives and also to change it, and to the end that he be able to communicate with and respond constructively to others by word and action. The standard for mental health will be in terms of the widening of the boundaries of one's active and interactive life rather than simply the solution of personal problems.

Considering the situation in the world today, in this context alone, psychoanalysis in groups cannot wait. It must become psychoanalysis for today, or there will be no future. Patients must get off their couches between sessions and analysts must get out from behind their couches between sessions and join people everywhere, especially when national and international crises are to be faced. Why, for example, should we all not be doing something, committing ourselves in some way or other, on the question of atomic testing and atomic bombing? If we do not, there will be no life with which to pursue liberty and no happiness to be sought with the help of psychoanalytic means. And those of us who are too persistently dedicated to the couch may, one day before long, find there is a sudden and dreadful peace from which no human being will escape.

It is part of the analyst's credo to be committed to the value of reason and against unreason; to consciousness, not unconsciousness; to reality, not unreality; to sanity, not insanity. How realistic, sane, conscious, and reasonable is he, pursuing the subtleties of repressed conflict in the individual patient over long years, when hovering over him and all of us is the possibility of sudden and total extinction? His dedication to mental health is an illusory pursuit, unless he also does all he can to mobilize himself and others in effective relationships and activity in the world about him with its demands, its problems, and its responsibilities. To pursue mental health, we need first to be certain that we keep our bodies and brains very much alive. Of course, to avert something like atomic catastrophe, analysts and their patients are not enough. Only all of mankind will do. But we must make a start—by coming out from behind our soundproof doors and joining with others, emerging out of bomb shelters, out of hiding, out of the passivity that waits to see what may happen and try to do something about it no matter how small.

Scientists are often too neutral. Atomic physicists have, with some notable exceptions, devoted themselves to the discovery and uses and misuses of atomic energy with an alarming neutrality with regard to its application. Psychoanalysts also suspend judgment in dealing, let us say, with a patient. They do this in order to allow the repressed to emerge during the course of treatment. But this suspension of judgment is sometimes unreasonably applied—just as it is by parents who yield to every whim of their children or make their children yield to every whim of theirs or by people who feel they must yield to the impulses or misjudgments of their leaders.

While psychoanalysis cannot solve the problems of the world, still the theories of Freud and those psychoanalysts who followed him have affected our society profoundly. Extensions of psycho-analytic thinking are evident everywhere: in the study of psycho-somatic medicine, anthropology, sociology, philosophy; in liter-ature, theater, painting, and criticism. Psychoanalysis in groups is a technical extension of those theories particularly suited to the needs of our times. And it, in turn, will create its own extensions in our professional, creative, and personal lives.

It is worth underlining the trend in group therapy away from the concept that the patient can be helped by only one person— God, the father, the mother, the analyst—or by only one kind of analysis. This is especially important for us today, when pater-nalism on the one hand is being fostered and encouraged by the "organizational man" structure and on the other is being violently rebelled against by a large part of the world. Analysis in group directs the patient away from the idea that there is only one source of help, only one omnipotent source for sustenance and development.

Some people have already learned this lesson, whether through experience in groups or not, but somewhere, somehow, the idea has caught on. Some years ago, a letter written by a psychologist in Stockbridge, Massachusetts, was passed on to one of us (A. W.) and we are going to present parts of it here, because it is such a splendid and moving example of how people's getting together in groups can be extended beyond the treatment of mental illness.

The letter begins by describing concern about the world crisis, with its threat to all of us. It describes the personal and long-unexpressed fears of the writer and his feelings of utter helpless-ness. Then he goes on to say:

> We have discovered the beginning of hope—a hope born of desperation and of a stubborn belief that it is better to do than not to do—that it is better to face the awesome enormity of our peril than to comfort ourselves by denying that peril and all its impli-cations. We have begun to share our loneliness, our fears, our anguish and our sense of helplessness about the perilous world situation. . . . At first we were afraid to let each other know of the dread we have locked in our hearts. . . . But then one of us timidly and tentatively let escape a hint of our deeply buried sense of burden and anguish. . . . And then the other of us, somewhat less

timidly but still with much discomfort and embarrassment allowed himself to say he, too, had been similarly burdened. And subsequently these two spoke to a third and a fourth and each time the effect was the same. We began to share our deep distress. We began to say so more openly. We began to discover that to talk and to share feelings and concerns that even the sheer act of doing something, even if it was only talking, somehow was helping us.

We began in a clumsy way—awkward in our self-consciousness. None of us knew any answers, least of all question—what can we do? Then we began one by one to talk and to ventilate our thoughts and feelings. And as we listened to each other in his turn, we saw ourselves. His words may have been different, and perhaps his thoughts and the course of action he advocated also were different—even alien. But in his sense of common peril, he was all of us.

The letter goes on to say that, as this small social group continued to meet, they began soon to speak of specific things: some argued for shelters, some against, others wondered how medical supplies and uncontaminated water could be provided, let alone distributed. And, to quote the letter again: "A strange thing happened. We started to feel less alone. We began to feel better. The sheer fact of talking to each other, and sharing loneliness with each other was helping us."

The original group split off into sections, each to form its own groups, oriented to the same purposes, until most of the town was included, and every shade of opinion was being aired. Later, there was communication on a wider level, through newspapers, radio, and television. So grass-root movements have been started before and so may this become one.

But to get back to our point. This letter describes very well one level of experience in psychoanalysis in groups. It is not easy to describe. Some people are afraid it might smack of the public confessional, the revival meeting, but it is not that at all. Psychoanalysis in a group or out, past, present, or future, has always tried to get the patient to know himself, to look his true thoughts and feelings in the face, and thereby improve his attitude toward himself and his relations with others.

Malraux is reported to have said that portraiture in modern art is practically nonexistent, because mankind has committed so many crimes in our era, it dares not look itself in the face. Group interaction is usually effective in trying to bring that very thing about. It is not easy for analyst or patient. It is only human nature for all of us to resist those who insist we put the mirror up to ourselves. In other interaction, we usually employ face-saving devices. To keep social interaction going we are apt, more often than not, to conceal the truth of our judgments and feelings. But for psychoanalysis to work, these face-saving devices need to be exposed and then analyzed. One of the things the analyst tries to show the patient is that it is possible to have a good relationship with him, at least, even if the truth is revealed. And he keeps trying, no matter how the patient resists, ambivalates, projects, and distorts in his struggle against knowing the reality.

In group, this situation is heightened and dramatized, because a member may refuse a relationship with fellow members who challenge him by letting down their face-saving masks. He may even vilify the analyst for allowing it. There are some who cannot tolerate the truth about themselves and who insist that others remain bound by the same chains. But there are others who take heart from seeing the struggle to ferret out the real from the illusory and who gain courage thereby to continue their own fight for mental health. The letter cited proves one thing, at least, that this level of interaction happens, that it is good to have happen, and that it makes the specific analytic treatment of the individual less isolated, less self-absorbed, and more in contact with humanity—and therefore all the more clearly experienced.

The reader may ask, if groups can take care of so many more patients, if such treatment is less expensive, if there is a shortage of analysts, and if analysis in groups can be so effective, why are so many analysts resistive to it?

One reason is that they have not had the experience of analysis in groups themselves. Another possibility is that analysis in groups can be hard on the analyst, who has been trained to sit with one patient at a time and usually behind the patient, where the analyst's actions and reactions are not under such scrutiny, and where he is in less danger of being challenged for his interpretations and reactions. The analyst in a group is called on by others, if not by himself, to examine his own reactions.

More and more analysts are, however, welcoming this trend

toward examining their own reactions, not only because it is in tune with the positive trends of our time, but also because giving up their godlike role spares them much of the iconoclastic malice they are subjected to in the popular press and humor magazines. Not that we do not deserve some of it or that we should not be able to take a little ribbing now and then. But there are enough pitfalls to being an analyst without having people demand that he always be perfectly healthy with a perfectly healthy wife and children, that he be omniscient, all-powerful, and magically able to solve all difficulties.

It is true that some few analysts believe their own publicity and try earnestly to live out their patient's image of them. But most of us understand that these jokes and attacks have a deeper origin in resentment that the analyst does not live up to these demands of perfection, that he does, indeed, have feet of clay.

In a group, the analyst who does understand has a chance to practice what he preaches: to show in his own conduct of the group and his own interaction with its members that he is not a god or a miracle worker but a human being with certain skills and certain professional training, human enough to make some mistakes. He is capable of learning something new just like any other person. What is more, such a situation is healthy, for how else are we to get new insights into human problems and behavior?

We will say more of psychoanalysis in groups, because in the immediate future, at least, psychoanalysis is moving in that direction. Perhaps analysis may, one day, be incorporated, like Newton's theory, into a much larger and more appropriate theory. Today we have moved from Newtonian to Einsteinian physics, from earth space to outer space science. Perhaps one day, psychoanalysis will move to a larger view of the minds of men, in a grander, more realistic understanding. Perhaps one area of research will be the question of why we are so fearful of knowing ourselves and of being seen and how to deal with our need to hide. The analyst needs to know that himself as well as the patient. There would not be so many schools of psychoanalysis and so much acrimonious debate about different methods if analysts themselves were readier to welcome knowledge from outside their particular spheres and biases.

In a symposium of analysts from a certain school we call, for want of a better name, "orthodox," a lecturer had been invited from another school, who spoke fervently of the need to revive, in our professional vocabulary, such words as "faith," "hope," "ideals," and so on, as positive facets of an integrated human being.

His audience was polite but over coffee in the cafeteria later, faintly derisive. What kind of nonsense was he talking, it was asked? Did he really think you could apply those words to science?

Nevertheless, one of them continued to press for some kind of integration, some meeting ground where the guest and they could join and understand each other. And suddenly he had it! "I know," he exclaimed, "you can hope you'll kill your father! You can have faith you'll sleep with your mother!" and so on.

BROADER TRAINING NEEDS

Unorthodoxy is like the weather. We all talk about it, but very few of us do anything about it—in the sense of fostering and welcoming it (unorthodoxy, not the weather). What we badly need in analysis is a United Methods Institute, a UM of Psychoanalysis, evolving from the many dissident groups existing today, where unorthodoxy and flexibility will be seen as desirable and as a healthy manifestation of mature minds engaged in a mutual search, rather than as an excuse for flight, splinterings, and introversion. Psychoanalysis needs new ideas. The world needs new ideas. New ideas arise out of conflict, conflict within one's own group, with other groups, and within oneself when old patterns have ceased to function well. New ideas arise also when theories, hypotheses, and experiences are communicated and shared in an atmosphere of cooperation and harmony, with the privilege to criticize and disagree. Discord and harmony coexist in nature. They are part of the reality of man. And it is with the complexity of that reality—intrapsychic, interpersonal, and inter-active—with which psychoanalysis has chosen to deal as a science and as an art. By its very nature, psychoanalysis must deal with the basic themes of human life, love and hate, money and power, birth and death, and sex. This calls on all the resources of the patient and the analyst, as a human being as well as a scientist.

This is why the training of the future analyst in groups will be much broader in scope than it is today and will include many disciplines only skimmed through in training today. With this background, the analyst in groups of the future will listen carefully to the experience of his elders but be less fearful himself of trying the new and the different. He will be less apt to stick rigidly to prescribed schools of thought, more tolerant of the right to dissent, less afraid of the danger of taking calculated risks, of examining the skeptical and heretical position. He will, in the future, value more and more his freedom to explore the prescribed, even as his knowledge and experience increase. He will learn with his patients that none of us is absolutely unique, but is, at the same time, homogeneous and heterogeneous; that we do not live alone or apart, a fact that makes it impossible to conceive of a one-person psychology, that not only authorities but peers are important and that help can come from them, that even his patients being together without him in alternate meetings can be reconstructive. In this future time, "socialization" will no longer be a dirty word in analysis whose only meaning is resistance. It will be acknowledged that socialization can be, at times, therapeutic. If it takes two to tango and at least two to tangle, just think of the possibilities that are opened up when there are eight or ten people in a therapeutic group!

This method of expanding boundaries of communication will also call for expanding boundaries of training for the group analyst himself, who will not only be a psychiatrist, a psychologist, or psychiatric social worker. He may also come from other ranks: sociologists, anthropologists, and other humanistic disciplines, just so long as he has demonstrated a genuine will to train further along group analytic lines.

It will not be demanded that he be a scholar; rather he should be endowed with horse sense, reasonableness, and a combination of common sense, intuition, training, and wisdom. And he will retain that essence of childhood, so dearly clung to by creative scientists and artists, the sense of wonder, which enables one to see freshly again and again, to question, to accept, and to renew.

The group analyst of the future will have a certain kind of knowledge and a love of that knowledge, not confined to neurology or statistics or research but including as much as possible history, philosophy, education, anthropology, comparative literature, mythology, and the arts and the sciences as they pertain to as many facets of human relatedness as possible.

And he will be a doer. He will have demonstrated in his own life that his creative impulses and powers have areas in which to breathe outside his chosen profession. Can he sculpt, paint, write, garden, or have a family? Each will find his own room and way of expression, but, in order to help his patients find their way, he needs to know about the creative experience; he needs to function as a total person, with a combination of head, hand, and heart. The kind of person he is will rank high in the table of standards for selection, because, above all, we would wish the group analyst of the future to be a humanizing force, and for that he himself needs to be a broad human being who has given up his own isolation even as he strives to bring his patients out of theirs. He lets himself see and be seen outside his office hours. And he finds the community and the outside world eager to meet him, eager to implement and expand their own boundaries on the community level as well as the personal.

This does not mean that we are advocating or recommending analysis in groups for everyone. That would be impractical and unnecessary. There are, however, good grounds for supposing that psychoanalysis in groups will not only be a setting for the treatment of neurotic illness or the training of the well-rounded analyst. One day, surely, group psychotherapy or some version of it will be exploited for its preventive possibilities and will be made available to adolescents in high school and even to children in elementary school. A school psychologist, trained in group therapy techniques, for example, would be in a position to counsel and guide teachers in dealing with less serious problems in day-to-day contact with students. It may be possible to catch some neurotic tendencies in children before they get too firm a foothold in the personality, and we may be able to uncover the secret, positive yearnings of the child and help to encourage them. I hope that more and more teachers and parents will elect to have a subjective experience in a therapeutic group, not only to stabilize themselves in their chosen professional work and in their social lives, but also to enable them to apply preventive mental health hygiene principles in their dealings with students and children.

With these innovations, public interest in group therapy is likely to grow, if only for the opportunity it offers for escape from isolation, the plague of modern man, into a kind of communication that is encouraged to be free and honest. All of us have disturbances and gripes on one level or another, and an opportunity to ventilate them can be beneficial, especially if, at the same time, the other fellow is encouraged to communicate his response. Trade unions, parent–teacher associations, and other professional groups, sharing common interests, may approach (some have already done so) insurance companies with a view of making psychoanalytic group therapy available at a lesser cost. And these companies, finding that analysis in groups is just as effective as individual analysis and less costly besides, may well take the initiative in supporting psychoanalytic treatment in a group.

In group, the patient is asked to give up his isolation in therapy, the analyst is asked to give up his omnipotent position that puts him into a kind of isolation. We hope the increasing ability of the individual to control his relationship one with another and one with the group will spread to the community and from the community to the state, the nation, and the world, although we know that to this end analysis itself can play only a small part.

A sign in a subway some months ago read: "PEACE." Underneath someone had written: "With or without people?" The answer to that question must, somewhere or other, lie in our individual hands. We have to be the first to realize that analysis, individual or group, is not the be-all and end-all of the problems of human existence. Some people of the world are hungry and medically uncared for and need life first. Some have life and need liberty. Some have life and liberty and need happiness. In some societies, children do not have much chance to live beyond 5. Life, liberty, and the pursuit of happiness are, in that order, as much our concern as anyone else's. What is more, as we have often seen in groups and as we are witnessing in the world today, sometimes all these three are being fought for at one and the same time.

How are we to meet these chaotic emergencies? By remembering that the search is greater than any one given answer and that, if an answer is found, it proves itself true by opening the way to a greater search. It is a truism that the revolutionist of today is the arch-conservative of tomorrow. That need not be if we resolve never to abandon the search.

Let us, in the future, find the courage to be pliant, to accept authority without ever relinquishing the right to question and criticize that authority. To think of possible differences without fear of retaliation and then to try the different. We want the courage to be adventurous, to take chances without being foolhardy. Today's spaceman was, according to some psychiatric thought, yesterday's schizophrenic. It took courage to be the first man in space, but it also took careful planning. It is this courage of the consciously aware, objectively prepared, that psychoanalysis in groups of the future will strive to foster. For that we will need to work together. If we are to meet the future face to face, it is better done hand in hand. From now on let it be said that psychoanalysis in groups is still dedicated to treating the emotional and mental disturbances of the individual; the future trend will be in the direction of fostering his individuality while decreasing his separateness and bringing him more and more into contact with his fellow human beings, saving the individual from drowning in homogeneity by fostering cohesiveness through appreciation of differences as well as through love of similarity. Perhaps that way we will be able to answer partially the age-old questions propounded by the Talmudic scholar Rabbi Hillel, "If I am not for myself who will be? If I am not for others, what am I? If not now, when?"

References

Anthony, E. (1971). The history of group psychotherapy. In *Comprehensive Group Psychotherapy*, ed. H. I. Kaplan and B. J. Sadock, pp. 4–32. Baltimore, MD: Williams & Wilkins.

Bellak, L., and Faithorn, P. (1978). Ego function assessment. *Weekly Psychiatry Update Series* 2.

Bennis, W., and Shepard, H. (1956). A theory of group development. *Human Relations* 9:415–437.

Berman, L. (1950). Psychoanalysis and group psychotherapy. *Psychoanalytic Review* 37:150–163.

Bion, W. R. (1959). *Experiences in Groups*. New York: Basic Books.

Brombert, V. (1967). *The Novels of Flaubert: A Study of Themes and Technique*. Princeton, NJ: Princeton University Press.

Burrow, T. (1927). *The Social Basis of Consciousness*. New York: Harcourt, Brace and World.

Day, M. (1967). The natural history of training groups. *International Journal of Group Psychotherapy* 17:436–446.

Foulkes, S. H., and Anthony, E. J. (1957). *Group Psychotherapy: The Psychoanalytic Approach*. London: Penguin Books.

Freud, S. (1907). *The Collected Papers of Sigmund Freud*. New York: Basic Books, 1959.

Grotjahn, M. (1950). The process of maturation in group psychotherapy and in the group therapist. *Psychiatry* 13:62–67.

Kernberg, O. (1980). *Internal World and External Reality*. New York: Jason Aronson.

Kissen, M. (1976). Some dynamic processes observed during an unstructured group laboratory experience. In *From Group Dynamics to Group Psychoanalysis*, pp. 25–65. Washington, DC: Halsted.

Kutash, I. L. (1968). Group compositions. Paper presented to group training course at Central Islip State Hospital, Central Islip, New York, November.

_____ (1980). Prevention and equilibrium–disequilibrium theory. In *Handbook on Stress and Anxiety*, ed. I. L. Kutash and L. B. Schlesinger, pp. 463–473. San Francisco: Jossey-Bass.

_____ (1984). Comments on psychoanalysis in groups: creativity in diegophrenia. *Group* 8:23–26.

_____ (1988a). Group composition. *The Group Psychotherapist* 1:9–12.

_____ (1988b). A mini article on a mini group. *The Group Psychotherapist* 1:19–20.

Kutash, I. L., Kutash, S. B., and Schlesinger, L. B. (1978). *Violence: Perspectives on Murder and Aggression*. San Francisco: Jossey-Bass.

Kutash, I. L., and Schlesinger, L. B. (1980). *Handbook on Stress and Anxiety*. San Francisco: Jossey-Bass.

Kutash, I. L., and Wolf, A. (1982). Recent advances in psychoanalysis in groups. In *Comprehensive Group Psychotherapy*, vol. 2, ed. H. I. Kaplan and B. J. Sadock, pp. 132–138. Baltimore, MD: Williams & Wilkins.

_____ (1984). Psychoanalysis in groups: the primacy of the individual. In *Inhibitions in Work and Love*, ed. H. Strean, pp. 29–43. New York: Haworth.

_____ (1990). *Group Psychotherapist's Handbook*. New York: Columbia University Press.

Lazell, E. W. (1921). The group treatment of dementia praecox. *Psychoanalytic Review* 8:168.

Locke, N. (1963). *Group Psychoanalysis*. New York: New York University Press.

Martin, E. A. Jr., and Hill, W. F. (1957). Toward a theory of group development: six phases of therapy group development. *International Journal of Group Psychotherapy* 7:20–30.

Menninger, K. (1958). *Theory of Psychoanalytic Technique*. New York: Basic Books.

Moreno, J. L. (1953). *Who Shall Survive?* New York: Beacon House.

Mullan, H., and Rosenbaum, M. (1962). *Group Psychotherapy*. New York: Free Press of Glencoe.

Nattland, C. (1983). Unpublished paper for Introduction to Group

Psychotherapy course. Graduate School of Applied and Professional Psychology, Rutgers University, New Jersey.

_____ (1990). The individual in the group. *The Group Psychotherapist* 3:8–10.

Pasternak, B. (1958). *Doctor Zhivago*. London: William Collings.

Pratt, J. H. (1922). The principles of class treatment and their application to various chronic diseases. *Hospital Social Services* 6:401.

Scheidlinger, S. (1980). *Psychoanalytic Group Dynamics—Basic Readings* New York: International Universities Press.

Schilder, P. (1936). The analysis of ideologies as a psychotherapeutic method, especially in group treatment. *American Journal of Psychiatry* 93:601.

Schwartz, E. K., and Wolf, A. (1963). On countertransference in group psychotherapy. *Journal of Psychology* 57:131.

Symposium on Countertransference (1953). *International Journal of Group Psychotherapy*. New York: Postgraduate Center, October.

Wender, L. (1940). Psychotherapy: a study of its application. *Psychiatric Quarterly* 14:708.

Wolf, A. (1949). The psychoanalysis of groups. *American Journal of Psychotherapy* 3:525–558.

_____ (1950). The psychoanalysis of groups. *American Journal of Psychotherapy* 2:221–231.

_____ (1957). Discussion of "Psychic Structure and Therapy of Latent Schizophrenia" by Gustave Byschowski. In *Psychoanalytic Office Practice,* ed. A. H. Rifkin, pp. 135–239. New York: Grune & Stratton.

_____ (1967). Group psychotherapy. In *Comprehensive Textbook of Psychiatry,* ed. A. M. Freedman and H. I. Kaplan, pp. 1234–1241. Baltimore: Williams & Wilkins.

_____ (1968). The discriminating use of feelings in group psychotherapy. In *New Directions in Mental Health,* ed. B. F. Riess. New York: Grune & Stratton.

_____ (1972). Psychoanalysis in groups. In *Major Contributions to Modern Psychotherapy,* pp. 5–26. Nutley, NJ: Hoffman-LaRoche.

_____ (1980). Diegophrenia and genius. *The American Journal of Psychoanalysis* 40:213–226.

_____ (1982). Psychoanalysis in groups. In *Comprehensive Group Psychotherapy,* vol. 2, ed. H. I. Kaplan and B. J. Sadock, pp. 113–132. Baltimore, MD: Williams & Wilkins.

Wolf, A., and Kutash, I. L. (1980). Psychoanalysis in groups: dealing with the roots of aggression. *International Journal of Group Tensions* 10:86–93.

_____ (1982). Book review of psychoanalytic group dynamics, ed. S. Sheidlinger. *Journal of the American Academy of Psychoanalysis* 10:632–635.

_____ (1984). Psychoanalysis in groups: creativity in diegophrenia. *Group* 8:12–23.

_____ (1985). Psychoanalysis in groups: dealing with difficult patients. In *Psychoanalytic Approaches to the Resistant and Difficult Patient,* ed. H. Strean, New York: Haworth.

_____ (1986). Psychoanalysis in groups. In *Psychotherapist's Casebook,* ed. I. L. Kutash and A. Wolf, pp. 332–353. San Francisco: Jossey-Bass.

_____ (1990). Psychoanalysis in groups. In *Group Psychotherapist's Handbook,* ed. A. Wolf and I. L. Kutash, pp. 11–46. New York: Columbia University Press.

_____ (1991). *Psychotherapy of the Submerged Personality.* New York: Jason Aronson.

Wolf, A., and Schwartz, E. K. (1958). Irrational psychotherapy: an appeal to unreason. *American Journal of Psychotherapy* 12:300–315, 508–521, 744–759.

_____ (1962). *Psychoanalysis in Groups.* New York: Grune & Stratton.

_____ (1964). Psychoanalysis in groups: as creative process. *American Journal of Psychoanalysis* 24:46–57.

_____ (1969). The interpreter in group therapy: conflict resolution through negotiation. In *New Directions in Mental Health,* ed. B. F. Rice, pp. 33–40. New York: Grune & Stratton.

Index